THE
BRITISH
ISLES

Neil Punnett and Peter Webber
Kingsdown School, Swindon

Basil Blackwell

© 1984 Neil Punnett and Peter Webber
First published 1984
Reprinted 1984 with revisions

Published by
Basil Blackwell Publisher
108 Cowley Road
Oxford OX4 1JF
England

Phototypeset in Mallard
Printed in Great Britain

ISBN 0 631 91430 7

CONTENTS

ACKNOWLEDGEMENTS

The authors would like to thank Chris Claridge, Doreen Dart and Margaret Shipley for their assistance. They also wish to express their appreciation to Judy and Sue for their help and understanding.

The authors and publishers would like to acknowledge the following — the maps 7.4(A), (B) and (C) are reproduced with the kind permission of the Milton Keynes Development Corporation; Stuart Ransom for 10.2(G) and (H); Finbar Furey for the song 12.9(A).

The authors and publishers would like to acknowledge the following for permission to reproduce photographs:

Aerofilms Limited 1.1 (2), 4.4, 5.6, 6.2, 8.3, 8.9, 10.9, 12.1, cover; Amey Roadstone Corporation Limited 2.8; RTZ Services Limited/Anglesey Aluminium Limited 4.8; Austin and Pickersgill Shipyards/Turners Photography 4.11 (2); Austin Rover Group 4.8, 4.12; Barnabys Picture Library 1.5, 2.8, 5.1, 6.4, 8.1; Blue Circle Industries PLC/Handford Photography 2.13; Brighton Resort Services Department 5.6; British Aerospace 4.13; BP Oil Limited 4.7; British Railways Board 5.6, 6.1, 9.6; British Ship Builders/Northumbria Air Fotos 9.2; British Steel Corporation 4.5, 9.13; British Tourist Authority 8.1, 8.3, 9.12 (2), cover; British Waterways Board 6.4; British Wool Marketing Board 4.10; Carless Exploration Limited 2.11; Central Electricity Generating Board 3.1, 3.2; City of Manchester 1.5; City of Sheffield 9.13, 13.1 (2); Civic Trust 6.2; Construction News 9.9; Crown copyright, reproduced with the permission of the Controller of Her Majesty's Stationery Office cover; Cumbernauld Development Corporation/Stewart Winning Photography 10.7 (3); Department of Industry 5.2; Development Board for Rural Wales 12.6; Mr Domleo 2.4; Dover Harbour Board 6.4; East Anglia Tourist Board Collection 8.1; East Sussex County Council 5.5; Ford Motor Company Limited 9.8; Forestry Commission 2.4, 2.5, 12.1; General Electric Company 4.14 (2); Govan Shipbuilders Limited 10.5; Sally and Richard Greenhill 5.2; Greenpeace 3.2; Gwent County Council 9.9; Harland and Wolff Limited 12.8; Highlands and Islands Development Board 12.1, 12.2 (4), 12.3 (3), 12.4; Hull Daily Mail 2.7; ICI Plant Protection Division 9.3; International Computers Limited 4.15; International Shipping Release 5.4; John Laing Construction Limited 10.12; London Docklands Development Corporation 10.11 (3); Mary Evans Picture Library 7.1, 9.1; McDermott Limited/Marcus Taylor Offshore Photography 12.2; Midlands County Council Planning Department 10.3; Ministry of Agriculture, Fisheries and Food 2.7; Mullard Limited 4.15; National Coal Board 1.5, 2.9, 2.10 (5), 9.1; Natural Environment Research Council 9.10, 11.1; National Farmers Union 2.1 (2); National Gallery 8.1; Overseas Containers Limited 6.3; Occidental International Oil Inc 2.12 (2); Peterborough Development Corporation 7.3; Popperfoto 9.9, 10.12, 12.7 (3), 12.9 (2), 13.2; Port of Bristol Authority 6.4; Port of Felixstowe 8.5(2); Port of London Authority 10.10; Neil Punnett 1.4, 2.4, 2.8, 2.10, 2.13, 4.1, 8.7, 11.4, 12.6, cover; PYE/Art-Wood Photography 4.3; Ian Selby 7.5(2), 9.10; Severn Trent Water Authority 12.5; Scottish Development Agency/GEAR 10.6(6); Scottish Tourist Board 12.2; Shell UK Limited 2.11 (2), 6.3, 9.3; Short Brothers' Aircraft Factory 12.8; Telford Development Corporation 7.3; Terence Soames/Mike Woodward 4.4, 9.8, 9.9; Chris Sugden 12.1; Transport and Road Research Laboratory 4.3, 6.2; Tyne and Wear Transport 9.6; Malcolm Veitch 10.4(2); Washington Development Corporation/Turners Photography 9.5(2), 9.9; Wales Tourist Board 11.5(2); David Webber 4.9, 4.10; Peter Webber 2.5, 2.9, 4.1, 4.2, 5.1, 5.5(2), 6.2, 7.5(2), 8.6, 9.1, 9.4(2), 9.6(2), 10.2(6), 10.3(3), 10.4, 11.1, 11.2, 11.3(2), 12.1(2), 12.2, 12.3, 12.4, cover; Sue Webber 8.7.

PREFACE

Using this book

This book has two parts. The opening chapters use a *systematic* approach to the geography of the British Isles. They link up with the later chapters which concentrate on *regional studies*. Whichever part of the book you are using you should refer to other examples of the subject you are reading about. Use the *cross-reference* system in the top right hand corner of the double page spread. For instance, if you are studying shipbuilding on pages 72–73 you must also use pages 138–139 where the shipbuilding industry in north-east England is discussed. Cross-references are not only made between the regional and systematic parts of the book but also within the separate parts.

Only the major link-ups are given in the cross-reference box. It is also essential to use the *indexes*. Check the index now, pages 222 to 224. The *geographical theme* index gives examples of the main points covered and the *place* index includes those places which have been written about. The index operates as a further cross-reference system. Finally, always be ready to refer to an atlas when reading this book.

The questions

There are three types of questions included. **A** questions involve recall and the completion of straightforward skill-based tasks. These type of questions appear widely on CSE examination papers. **B** questions are more varied and include the use of *key ideas*. They ask you to interpret data, think through the issues under discussion and make comparisons with similar situations. They sometimes ask you to suggest possible answers; you will realise that there are not always single 'right' answers to questions. Finally some **B** questions will ask you to examine your *values and attitudes*. They will help you to appreciate and increase your awareness of the issues being discussed. The **C** questions consist of O-level, A/O and O-grade questions or part questions. To answer them you will need a full understanding of the subject which will involve you studying more than the double page spread.

What is a region?

A region is an area with similar characteristics throughout. They may be physical, economic or social. A large area of highland made up of similar rocks may be a distinctive region. A coalfield or an area of similar farming may be a region. An area dependent upon the services of a large city may be a region. Regions can be created for a particular use (function). Examples are television regions, electricity and water authority regions. In this book, the use of the word 'region' refers to large areas of the country with broadly similar characteristics. In the main, the regions we study are based upon the *economic planning regions* established by the government in 1965 and modified slightly in 1974 (Fig A). Many make geographical sense. However, we have split some regions where geographical differences are more important than economic similarities. For example, the Lake District is separated from north-east England in the Northern region.

Fig. A

INTRODUCTION
1.1 GEOLOGY AND RELIEF

The British Isles consists of England, Scotland, Wales and Northern Ireland, which make up the United Kingdom, and the Republic of Ireland (Eire). It is situated between latitudes 50°N and 61°N, and has a great variety of natural landscapes which have developed from different underlying rocks.

The youngest rocks are to the south and east of a line drawn from the mouth of the river Tees to the mouth of the river Exe.

Igneous rocks Igneous rocks are formed from hot, molten material or *magma* which is found deep beneath the Earth's crust. Magma is sometimes forced towards the surface. When it flows on the surface it is called *lava*. Basalt, an igneous lava, is dark in colour and solidifies in the form of hexagonal columns. The largest outcrop of basalt is the Antrim Plateau area of Northern Ireland. Granite is another igneous rock. It has cooled and solidified beneath the surface. Outcrops of granite exposed by erosion are found in Dartmoor and several areas of Scotland.

ERA	MILLIONS OF YEARS	PERIOD	IMPORTANT BEDS	KEY
QUATERNARY	1 million		Recent	
			Alluvium	
TERTIARY (CAINOZOIC)	A	PLIOCENE OLIGOCENE AND EOCENE	Bagshot Beds	
			London Clay	
SECONDARY (MESOZOIC)	100	CRETACEOUS	Chalk/Greensand	
			Wealden Beds	
		JURASSIC	Oolites-Limestone	
		TRIASSIC	Lias Clays	
PRIMARY (PALAEOZOIC)	200 H	PERMIAN	New Red Sandstone	nrs
		CARBONIFEROUS	Coal Measures	
			Millstone grit and carboniferous limestone	
	300 C	DEVONIAN	Old Red Sandstone	
		SILURIAN		
	400	ORDOVICIAN	Lower Palaeozoic Rocks	M
		CAMBRIAN		
MOUNTAIN BUILDING	500 2000	PRE-CAMBRIAN	Very Ancient Rocks	
A ALPINE			Other rocks	
H HERCYNIAN			Volcanic	
C CALEDONIAN			Mainly granite	

Fig. B A geological time scale

Sedimentary rocks Sedimentary rocks are made from eroded material which is compressed and hardened into layers or *strata*:

Coal Mostly formed in the Carboniferous period (about 300 million years ago). Carbon from remains of tropical swamps and forests. Found north and west of Tees–Exe line.

Sandstone Cemented sand: old red and new red sandstone deposited in times of a hot desert climate. ORS — Exmoor; NRS — Midland Plain; greensands — Weald.

Chalk Fine deposits from the remains of marine animals. Contains calcium carbonate. Bands of chalk across lowland England: Chilterns, Downs.

Limestone Mixed remains of marine animals or chemical deposits. Harder older limestone — carboniferous limestone makes up parts of Pennines. Younger Jurassic limestones outcrop from Cotswolds to North York Moors.

Clay Fine deposits of silt and mud. Found in vales of basins of southern and eastern England — London Basin, Vale of White Horse.

Metamorphic rocks 'Metamorphosis' means great change. This type of rock has been changed by heat and pressure. Shale is changed to slate (e.g. in North Wales). In northern Scotland, gneisses and schists are the changed forms of igneous rocks.

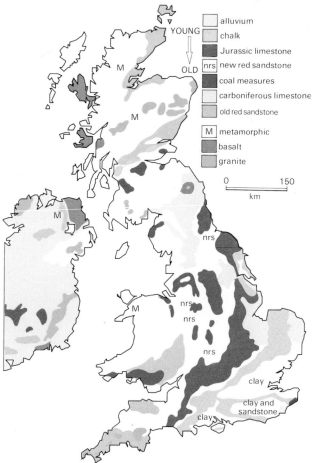

alluvium
chalk
Jurassic limestone
nrs new red sandstone
coal measures
carboniferous limestone
old red sandstone
M metamorphic
basalt
granite

YOUNG
OLD

0   150
km

Fig. A The geology of the British Isles

Other influences on the landscape Three *mountain-building periods* have affected the rocks and relief of the British Isles. The earliest, the Caledonian, produced the mountains of Wales, the Lake District and Scotland. A later period folded the rocks of south-west England, the Midlands and South Wales to form a lower, more hilly relief.

The most recent movements, about 35 million years ago, centred on Alpine Europe, but 'ripples' affected southern England. The rocks of the Cotswolds and Chilterns were tilted down to the south-east. The *synclines* or downfolds of the London and Hampshire Basins were formed. The *anticline* or upfold of the Weald of Sussex and Kent was a result of these ripples.

Weathering, erosion and *deposition* have added further variety to the physical geography of the British Isles.

The influences of the *Ice Age* can be seen in many parts of the country. Glacial *erosion* moulded the mountains of highland Britain. Glacial *deposits* (moraines, outwash material and boulder clay) have been left over much of lowland England. Only the south of England was untouched by ice.

The melting of the ice-sheets raised the sea-levels around Britain. Only 8000 years ago, England was finally separated from the continent of Europe. The rising sea-levels formed the inlets, creeks and natural harbours of the coast of southern and eastern England. The *rias* (drowned river valleys) of Devon and Cornwall and *sea-lochs* or *fiords* of western Scotland were the result of rising sea-levels.

Fig. D A Lowland scene

QUESTIONS

You should refer to your atlas to help you answer.

A1 (a) Make a large copy of Fig E.
   (b) In the spaces marked (a) and (b) write the correct description: highland Britain, lowland Britain, older rocks, younger rocks.

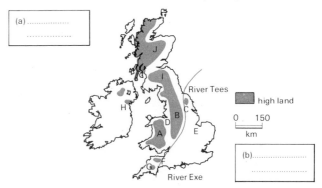
Fig. E

   (c) Name the highland and lowland areas labelled A to J.
   (d) Which area of lowland is west of the Tees–Exe line?
   (e) Which area of highland is east of the Tees–Exe line?
   (f) Draw in and name six major rivers.
   (g) Draw a line across southern England joining the Severn estuary with the Thames estuary. Label the line 'Limit of ice during Ice Age'.

B1 Look at a geology map in your atlas. Find the geological time scale. Make a note that the rocks of the Recent, Tertiary and Secondary *eras* make up lowland Britain. The primary and ancient rocks make up highland Britain.

  2 Each geological era is divided into *periods*. Note down the geological period for each rock shown on the geological map (A): for example, chalk — Cretaceous.

  3 Add to your sketch map the three major faults in Scotland — Great Glen Fault, Highland Boundary Fault, Southern Upland Fault.

Fig. C A Highland scene

INTRODUCTION
1.2 CLIMATE

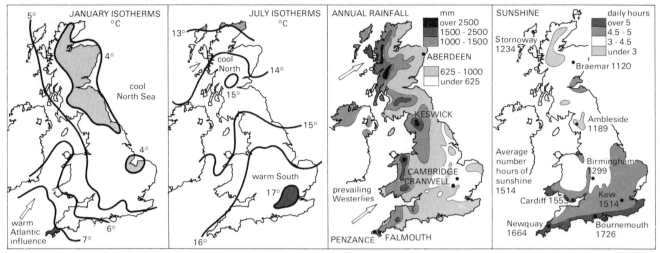

Fig. A January isotherms   Fig. B July isotherms   Fig. C Annual rainfall   Fig. D Sunshine

Variability is the most striking feature of the British weather. The weather can change daily and long settled periods are rare. Over a long period of time, the weather can be averaged out to give the *climate*. The climate of the British Isles is *temperate*; the summers are warm and the winters are mild. There is a lack of extremes and the climate is *equable*.

The location of the British Isles (on the north-west edge of the European continent where it meets the Atlantic Ocean) explains the climate. The *North Atlantic Drift* is a warm ocean current which starts as the Gulf Stream off the coast of Mexico. In winter, it keeps the temperatures higher than at many other places on the same latitude. Away from the influence of the current, winter temperatures are lower (Fig A). Eastern Britain is therefore cooler in January than western Britain. Further east in central Europe, January average temperatures are below freezing (0°C). Map A shows winter temperatures by using *isotherms*, which are lines joining places of equal temperature. The lines refer to average temperatures

reduced to sea-level. In summer (Fig B), the Atlantic Ocean has a cooling effect. Temperatures are higher away from the Atlantic. Figure B shows the influence of *latitude* on temperatures. It is warmer in the south where the sun is hotter in summer. In winter, latitude is not such an important influence.

The North Atlantic is the major influence on the climate. The warm air associated with the North Atlantic Drift is moist. The winds from the ocean, the *Westerlies*, affect the British Isles most of the time. These *prevailing winds* bring rain to the whole country, especially the west (Fig C). Much of the *precipitation* (rain, snow, hail) comes from *depressions* or *low pressures* (Fig E), the result of tropical air moving north. When it meets the colder air at the *polar front* it rises, forming a warm front. The rising air cools, clouds form and it rains. Another reason why the highlands of western Britain have a wetter climate is because the air is forced to rise in crossing the mountains. Temperatures fall by 1°C every 165 metres of height.

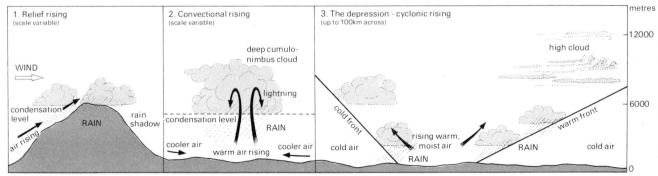

Fig. E When air rises, it cools, condensation occurs and clouds form

Before we look at the different climates in the country we need to look at other influences. When there is stable and descending air over the country, clouds do not form. It is usually dry and sunny. This weather system is called an *anticyclone* (high-pressure area). In winter, an anticyclone can bring long periods of frosty weather. In summer, the arrival of an anticyclone often means a 'heat wave'.

Eastern Britain is affected more by easterly airstreams from Europe and even Asia. In winter, these can be particularly cold. In summer, the continent is hotter than Britain and easterly and south-easterly winds can bring very warm weather. Sometimes, the British Isles are affected by hot tropical air from the dry Sahara. This 'heat-wave' airstream is rare and seldom reaches Scotland, which receives more Arctic air than southern England. Raw, cold winds from the polar regions can bring snow to the north coast of Scotland and the northern islands. The snow does not usually penetrate south but Arctic air often produces a 'cold snap'.

The four climatic graphs (Figs F, G, H, I) show how these influences affect regional climates. Cambridge (F) has a *temperature range* of 12°C (January 4°C, July 16°C). Its winter temperature is low because Cambridge is located in the east, away from the influence of the Atlantic Ocean. The rainfall is evenly spread through the year with a slight summer maximum. The higher rainfall in the months of June and July is partly because of *convectional rainfall*. The annual rainfall total of 553 millimetres is among the

lowest in Britain. Eastern Britain is drier because it is in the *rain shadow* of the western hills and mountains.

Summary of Keswick climatic graph (Fig I):

Temperature:	*January 4°C; July 15°C*
Temperature range 11°C	
Rainfall distribution	Autumn/winter maximum
Annual rainfall	1496 mm, west, mountains

QUESTIONS

A1 Complete the spaces below, using the following:
   cool summer, warm summer, warm winter, cool winter, high rainfall, low rainfall.

Areas of the British Isles

North-west: cool summer, warm winter, high rainfall.
South-west:
North-east:
South-east:

  2 Why is it cooler and wetter in the mountains of western Britain than in the east?

B1 Summarise the climate graphs for Cambridge, Aberdeen and Penzance.

  2 (a) Why is the annual rainfall so high at Keswick?
    (b) Why is the annual rainfall so low at Aberdeen?
    (c) Account for the January temperature of 7°C at Penzance and 2°C at Aberdeen.
    (d) Why are July temperatures slightly higher in Cambridge than in Penzance?

  3 Below are climate statistics for Falmouth in Cornwall and Cranwell in Bedfordshire:
    (a) Construct graphs of these statistics similar to Figs F, G, H and I.
    (b) Calculate the total rainfall and the annual temperature range for Falmouth and Cranwell.
    (c) Describe and explain the monthly distribution of rainfall at both places.
    (d) Describe and explain the seasonal variation of temperature at both places.

  4 Briefly describe the main factors which influence the climate of the British Isles.

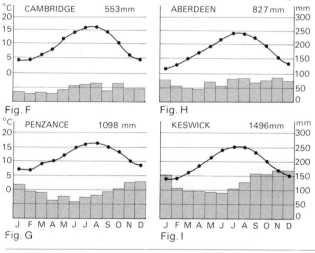

Fig. F · Fig. H · Fig. G · Fig. I

FALMOUTH	J	F	M	A	M	J	J	A	S	O	N	D
Rainfall (mm)	132	95	81	67	66	50	71	77	78	117	132	134
Temperature (°C)	4.9	4.8	5.1	6.3	8.6	11.3	13.1	13.2	12	9.4	6.6	5.1

CRANWELL	J	F	M	A	M	J	J	A	S	O	N	D
Rainfall (mm)	53	42	37	42	50	40	64	55	51	55	59	49
Temperature (°C)	3.4	3.8	5.6	8	10.9	14.2	16.3	15.9	13.7	10	6	3.9

1.3 WATER SUPPLY: THE PROBLEMS

Nature guarantees us a continuous supply of water through the *hydrological cycle*. Water evaporates from the sea, forms clouds, falls on the land as rain, runs back into the sea, and so on. It is a process that has no beginning and no end.

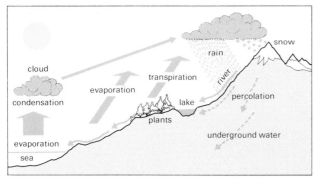

Fig. A The hydrological cycle

Each person in Britain uses 200 litres of water each day. Industry and agriculture need vast amounts. Rainfall in Britain is variable, and the driest areas are the south and the east where evaporation rates are highest. These regions have the greatest demand for water, but they do not have enough to satisfy their needs. The north and west have more than they need. The transfer of water from surplus areas to deficit areas is an expensive task. A network of pumphouses, treatment works, reservoirs and pipes is needed.

WATER CONSUMPTION PER DAY PER PERSON AT HOME	
Flushing lavatory	50 litres
Washing and bathing	50 litres
Washing clothes	20 litres
Washing up and cleaning	18 litres
Gardening	10 litres
Drinking and cooking	6 litres
Car washing	3 litres
Others	43 litres
TOTAL	200 litres

THE NEEDS OF INDUSTRY AND AGRICULTURE

An oil refinery uses *650 million litres* each day
A nuclear power station uses *4000 million litres* each day
2500 litres are needed to make 1 kg of synthetic rubber
250 litres are needed to make 1 kg of paper
4500 litres are needed to make a car
200000 litres are needed to make 1 tonne of steel
A dairy cow needs *130 litres* each day
A pig needs *14 litres* each day
A sheep needs *7 litres* a day

Fig. B Daily water consumption per person at home, and the needs of agriculture and industry

Clean water: Until this century, outbreaks of cholera and typhoid killed thousands of Britons. These diseases were caused by infected water. Now all the water supplied to homes can be drunk even though it may have been used many times before.

Ten regional water authorities manage the water cycle in England and Wales. They are responsible for:
1 Water treatment and supply
2 Sewage treatment and disposal
3 Land drainage
4 Flood prevention
5 Pollution control of rivers and lakes
6 Managing fishing, swimming and boating.

There are four main sources of water supply: from rivers, wells, springs and reservoirs.

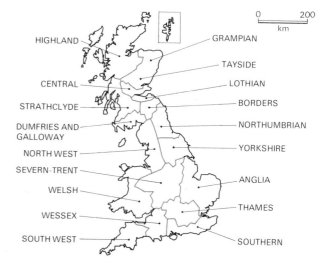

Fig. C The regional water authorities

Wells: Permeable rocks such as chalk, limestone and sandstone are called *aquifers* because they bear water. The water usually remains in the pores or cracks in the aquifer in much the same way as it will stay in a large sponge. It can be artificially pumped out through wells. When the aquifer is sandwiched between two impermeable rocks, pressure can build up at certain points. By drilling down to the aquifer, water will rise to the surface without any assistance. This is an *artesian well* (Fig D).

Springs: Springs occur where an aquifer overlies an impermeable rock. The water travels along the permeable rock and emerges as a spring, usually at the foot of a hill. Spring water contains dissolved minerals which have some medicinal value. It became fashionable to 'take the waters' of springs during the eighteenth century. A number of towns called spas grew up where there were large springs. Harrogate, Cheltenham, Bath and Droitwich are examples. Settlements have often developed along spring lines at the foot of chalk and limestone escarpments.

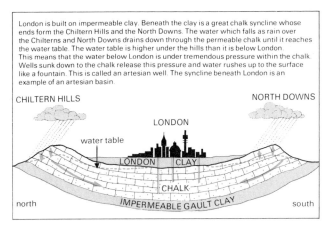

London is built on impermeable clay. Beneath the clay is a great chalk syncline whose ends form the Chiltern Hills and the North Downs. The water which falls as rain over the Chilterns and North Downs drains down through the permeable chalk until it reaches the water table. The water table is higher under the hills than it is below London. This means that the water below London is under tremendous pressure within the chalk. Wells sunk down to the chalk release this pressure and water rushes up to the surface like a fountain. This is called an artesian well. The syncline beneath London is an example of an artesian basin.

Fig. D The London basin

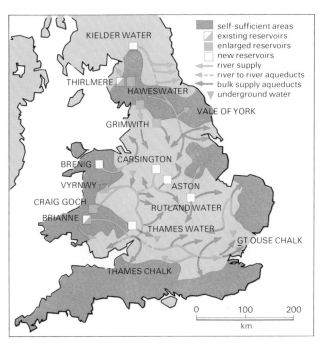

Fig. E A national water plan for England and Wales

Rivers: Rivers provide the main source of water supply throughout Britain. The water is usually pumped into open storage reservoirs before being treated and supplied to the water system. Water in the storage reservoirs is purified naturally and is readily available in times of shortage. The water is passed through filter beds before it can be used. Figure E shows the main river sources.

Reservoirs: Reservoirs have been built in the upland areas of Britain to store river water which would otherwise flow into the sea. The amount of water released into the river can then be controlled.

Reservoir schemes have faced tremendous criticism; you can read about the arguments concerning Welsh water on pages 208 and 210.

London's water supply: London stands on an artesian basin, and receives about one-tenth of its water from wells drilled down to the chalk aquifer. The water now has to be pumped to the surface because of over-use, and there are fears that the wells, used for centuries, may soon run dry.

Most of London's water is taken from the river Thames and its tributary the Lea. There are several large open storage reservoirs beside both rivers. At Staines and Walton-on-Thames there are eight reservoirs including the Queen Mary Reservoir which is over twice the size of Hyde Park. Water is pumped into the Thames from the ground water stored within the limestone of the Cotswold Hills and the chalk of the Marlborough Downs.

A water plan for Britain

The regional water authorities are working towards a plan to supply water by a grid system linking rivers by pipelines and tunnels (Fig E). Water is transferred from the wetter areas to the drier areas of the country, as far as possible by rivers. A number of large new reservoirs such as Kielder Water have been built to meet future demands. Schemes have been proposed to build barrages to store water in Morecambe Bay, the Wash, the Dee estuary and the Severn estuary. Such schemes could have serious effects upon wildlife and the environment. With the slower growth in water demand now forecast, it is possible that the barrage schemes will not progress beyond the drawing board for many years.

Sewage treatment

After use in the home and factory, water runs into the sewers and eventually to the local sewage works. Sewage works are located beside rivers in or near towns. The water discharged into the river has to be almost pure since it may be extracted as drinking water at the next town downstream.

QUESTIONS

A1 What are the regional water authorities responsible for?

 2 What is (a) an aquifer; (b) an artesian well? Name an example of each.

 3 Under what conditions do springs occur?

 4 List the four main sources of water supply.

B1 What geographical problem faces Britain's water supply industry?

 2 What are the main features of the National Water Plan?

 3 Which regional water authority do you live in? Find out where the water you drink comes from.

C 500 million litres of water are used in Greater London every day. Discuss the problems associated with supplying this great demand and say how they have been overcome.

1.4 WATER SUPPLY: KIELDER WATER

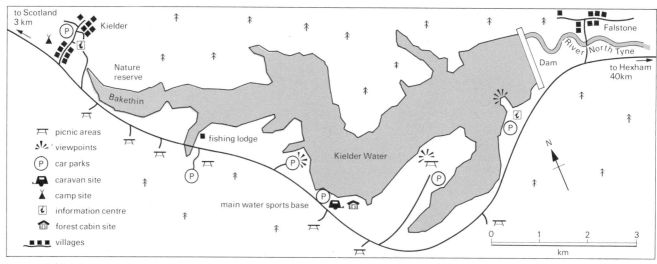

Fig. A Kielder Water

Britain's largest man-made lake is Kielder Water just south of the Scottish border. Covering 1086 hectares, Kielder Water is over three-quarters the area of Lake Windermere, England's largest natural lake. One and a half million trees were felled to make way for it, and a hamlet, several buildings and the main valley road were drowned by the rising water. Why was this remote Northumberland valley chosen?

The North-East England region has the same geographical problem as that which faces the country as a whole: the highest rainfall is in the north and west of the region while the highest demand for water is in the south and east. In 1981, the North-East used 1050 million litres of water a day, a 15 percent increase on 1971. The water resources of the region amounted to 1255 million litres a day. In order to meet likely increased demand, the Northumbrian Water Authority had to build more storage capacity. The best site for dam construction was a short distance upstream of the village of Falstone in the North Tyne Valley (see map A). This is one of the narrowest points in the valley and the gradient of the river North Tyne upstream of this point is fairly gentle. The site is close to large deposits of impermeable glacial boulder clay as well as sand, gravel and a hard igneous rock called whinstone which were suitable materials to build the dam.

It took four and a half years to build the giant dam, which is 1140 metres long and 52 metres high. The valley started to flood in December 1980 and the reservoir was complete and officially opened by the Queen in May 1982. The Kielder Water Scheme cost £170 million. The water authority had secured more

EEC money than any other British project. £60 million was given in the form of grants by the EEC Regional Development Fund and the British government. A further £43 million was loaned by the EEC at reduced rates of interest.

Kielder Water will supply up to 1130 million litres of water a day, enough for the current water demands of the whole region. Kielder is a regional scheme because its water will be available to almost all parts of the north-east. Water released from Kielder dam will flow for 58 kilometres down the rivers North Tyne and Tyne to Riding Mill, where a pumping station will transfer water from the Tyne to the Wear and Tees through a 38-kilometre-long aqueduct, most of which is in the form of a tunnel. The biggest consumers are the industrial conurbations on the coast.

Water supply is the most important function of Kielder Water but it was built with multipurpose use in mind.

Fig. B Kielder Water

Recreation

The Kielder area is being developed as one of the north-east's leading tourist attractions. Accommodation in the form of caravan and tent sites, forest cabins and outdoor activity centres have been built. People can walk freely around the 44 kilometres of shoreline and most of the surrounding forest. Car parks, picnic places and viewpoints have been provided along the southern shore beside the new C200 road.

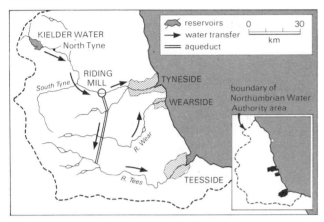

Fig. C The supply of water from Kielder

Figure D shows the Kielder Water Visitor Centre. There is an exhibition, and specialist information for tourists is available. There are also restaurant facilities. More organised recreational development has also taken place:

Fishing: Kielder Water has been stocked with over 250 000 brown trout. Fishing permits are sold direct to the public. Worm and fly fishing are permitted and motorboats are available for hire.

Water sports: Unlike older reservoirs there are few restrictions on water sport at Kielder because it simply regulates the flow of the North Tyne. Purification of the water takes place further downstream. The reservoir is used by small boats of all kinds, and water skiers.

Boat trips: Pleasure trips and ferry services are run.

Pony trekking: Riding schools take parties around the reservoir and through the surrounding forest.

Nature reserve: Bakethin reservoir has been set aside as a nature reserve. Heron, mallard, curlew and kestrel are amongst the birds to be seen here.

Two turbo-generators are being installed at the dam to produce hydro-electricity. Up to six megawatts of electricity will be supplied to the national grid, enough to cater for a town of 10 000 people.

Within the space of ten years, a remote and beautiful Northumberland valley has been transformed. Opportunities for employment have been improved for the local people. An important new tourist centre has been established and the demand for water in the north-east has been safeguarded into the next century.

Kielder Water has brought many benefits, but there is the possibility that it may be a white elephant. Demand for water in north-east England has begun to decline, mainly because the industries of the coastal areas have cut their demands; for example, the British Steel Corporation on Teesside reserved 160 million litres a day in 1974 but in 1982 it was using only 25 million litres. The North Tyne valley may have been drowned unnecessarily.

Fig. D Kielder Water visitors' centre

QUESTIONS

A1 Where is Kielder Water?
 2 Why was Kielder chosen as the site for the dam and reservoir?
 3 (a) Which areas use the water from Kielder?
   (b) How is the water supplied to those areas?
 4 List five uses of Kielder Water other than water supply.
B1 Explain fully why the Kielder Water Scheme was thought necessary.
 2 Design a publicity pamphlet for the Northumbrian Water Authority aimed at informing tourists of the facilities available at Kielder Water. It should include a brief summary of the purpose and development of the scheme.
C1 'The Kielder Water Scheme is unnecessary and has resulted in the loss of a valuable resource — solitude.' Discuss this statement and give your own views.
 2 You are a farmer in the Kielder Valley when the Kielder Water Scheme is announced. You learn that half your land is to be flooded. What arguments against the scheme will you present to the public enquiry?

1.5 CONTRASTS IN THE BRITISH ISLES

In the past, the life of the British people was closely linked with the physical environment. Today, that link has weakened and many aspects of human geography are similar throughout the country. Working conditions, education facilities, social security benefits and postal services are usually similar all over Britain, even though there are contrasts in the geography of the country. These photographs show different aspects of British life.

If you live in the north, you will have heard some unkind views about the south, and vice versa. Such observations about life in different parts of the country often arise from outdated ideas. For example, the television series 'Coronation Street' depicts some aspects of the northern way of life, but it is not typical of how all people in the region live.

The geographer needs to know that the contrasts are not just differences between the north and south.

Fig. A Many towns in southern England also have nineteenth-century terrace housing. Railway development throughout the country led to housing developments similar to 'Coronation Street'.

Fig. B Coal mines are found mainly in northern and western Britain, but coal was the foundation for the industrial development of the West and East Midlands. Coal has been mined in the Bristol/Somerset region and also in Kent.

Fig. C There are 'stockbroker belts' outside major northern urban areas such as Manchester, Glasgow and Newcastle-upon-Tyne.

Fig. D Over the past twenty years, redevelopment has taken place in many towns and cities. There are new shopping centres like this throughout the country.

Present-day contrasts are the result of the changing geography of Britain

Before 1800
Britain was a farming country. People worked on the land and travelling was very limited. There were few large towns.
Population 1801   10.5 million (excluding Ireland)
Urban population   20 per cent

Nineteenth century
Industrial growth mainly on the coalfields of the north and west. Transport improved, first with canals then railways. Villages grew into towns. Industrial cities developed, based on coalmining and heavy industry such as shipbuilding, iron and steel and textiles. Population growth was fastest in northern England. London, the capital, also developed quickly (1851 — 1 million).
Population 1861   24.5 million
Urban population   42 per cent

Twentieth century
Towns and cities continued to grow. Some towns joined up to make conurbations (Greater Manchester, Merseyside). Roads were greatly improved and urban growth spread along the main roads from the city centres. Some of the heavy industries began to decline. The 1930s Depression affected the northern industrial areas more than the southern regions.
Population 1921   44 million
Urban population   68 per cent

Twentieth century from 1945
After World War II the standard of living rose for the country as a whole. The demand for consumer goods increased. The new industrial growth was concentrated in the Midlands and south. In the older industrial areas (South Wales, north-west and north-east England), economic growth was slower. New problems arose, especially in the growth areas. Towns and cities became congested, noise pollution increased, road transport produced an unhealthy atmosphere for work and living.

The city centres suffered from rocketing land values. By the 1980s the inner city areas were problem areas.
Population 1961   52.6 million
Urban population   79 per cent
Population 1981   55.8 million
Urban population   76 per cent

Fig. E

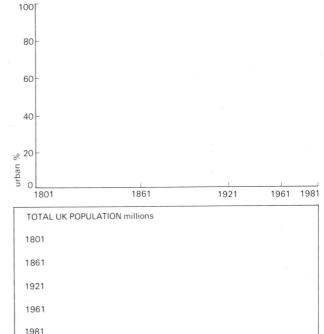

Fig. F Graph for Question A2

QUESTIONS
A1 Complete the conversation about the north and south. Are the comments true and accurate?

2 Use the urban population percentage figures to produce a line graph of urban population change from 1800 to 1981. Shade the area of the graph below the line and write URBAN POPULATION. Above the line write RURAL POPULATION. Fill in the total population figures from the text.

15

1.6 RICH AND POOR

The standard of living varies between the regions of the United Kingdom and within them. The geographer must discover how this happens and considers questions like: What is important to you in your area? How would you compare your quality of life with that of a person from another area?

Figure A shows some regional differences. The regions are those used for economic and social purposes. Only three aspects (variables) have been chosen to show differences. Compare Northern England with South-East England. You can see large variations between the two. The differences among the other regions are less. The statistics are the average for each region and hide great variations.

QUESTIONS

A1 Table B introduces more indicators of the quality of life. Follow these instructions and you will gain an understanding of social and economic contrasts in Britain today.

(a) Copy the table.

(b) For each column, find the highest value and write 1 in the rank order column. Carry on for all the regions so that you have a rank order from 1 to 11. The first column's rank order has been done for you.

Note: If two values are equal, give them the same rank, but make the next lowest two positions below, similarly, if three values are equal, make the next lowest three positions below.

(c) Copy the information about telephones from Fig A.

REGIONAL DIFFERENCES

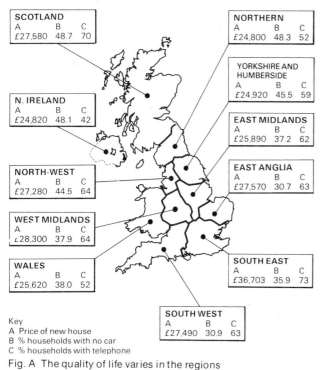

SCOTLAND
A £27,580 B 48.7 C 70

NORTHERN
A £24,800 B 48.3 C 52

YORKSHIRE AND HUMBERSIDE
A £24,920 B 45.5 C 59

N. IRELAND
A £24,820 B 48.1 C 42

EAST MIDLANDS
A £25,890 B 37.2 C 62

NORTH-WEST
A £27,280 B 44.5 C 64

EAST ANGLIA
A £27,570 B 30.7 C 63

WEST MIDLANDS
A £28,300 B 37.9 C 64

WALES
A £25,620 B 38.0 C 52

SOUTH EAST
A £36,703 B 35.9 C 73

SOUTH WEST
A £27,490 B 30.9 C 63

Key
A Price of new house
B % households with no car
C % households with telephone

Fig. A The quality of life varies in the regions

Regions of the UK	Household spending £ per week	RANK	Houses: % owner-occupied	RANK	Car: % homes with 1 or more	RANK	Central heating: % homes	RANK	Telephone: % homes	RANK	TOTAL RANK ORDER	FINAL RANK
UK average	87	—	55	—	58	—	54	—		—	—	—
South-east	96	1	56		61		59					
West Midlands	89	2	56		61		53					
East Midlands	84	6	57		60		61					
East Anglia	83	7	58		68		64					
South-west	80	10	63		65		57					
North-west	85	3	59		55		49					
Yorkshire and Humberside	79	11	55		49		48					
Northern	81	9	46		48		58					
Wales	85	3	59		61		53					
Scotland	85	3	35		52		45					
N. Ireland	83	7	49		51		37					

(Figures: 1979)

Fig. B The country's rich and poor regions

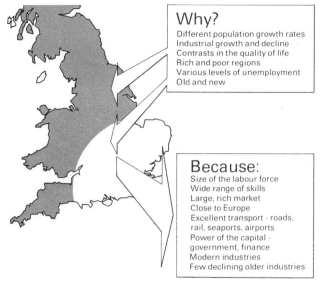

Fig. C

Why?
Different population growth rates
Industrial growth and decline
Contrasts in the quality of life
Rich and poor regions
Various levels of unemployment
Old and new

Because:
Size of the labour force
Wide range of skills
Large, rich market
Close to Europe
Excellent transport - roads,
rail, seaports, airports
Power of the capital -
government, finance
Modern industries
Few declining older industries

(d) When you have completed the rank orders of each column, add the six rank values for each region and write the total in the correct column.

(e) In the final column, write the rank order of the totals for each region.

Your rank order gives you a picture of rich and poor Britain. The following regions are usually considered more prosperous: South-East, East Anglia, West Midlands, East Midlands, South-West.

The less prosperous regions include: North-West, Yorkshire and Humberside, Northern, Wales, Scotland, Northern Ireland.

Was your rank order something like this? It depends how many variables you consider.

The conclusions fit in with the facts about how much people earn. At the beginning of the 1980s, people earned most in the South-East and West Midlands. They earned least in Northern England and Northern Ireland.

There are other ways to define rich and poor regions. Indicators that are sometimes used include *living space* (average number of persons per room), percentage of persons over 60 years of age, divorce rate, illegitimacy rate. Another regional indicator is *accessibility* (how easy is it to travel to and from places).

	% population over 65 years (1986 estimate)
UK average	14.8
South-east	15.2
West Midlands	14.0
East Midlands	14.3
East Anglia	14.8
South-west	16.9
North-west	14.5
Yorkshire and Humberside	14.9
Northern	14.4
Wales	15.6
Scotland	14.0
N. Ireland	11.4

Fig. E The distribution of old people

B Refer to Fig E.
   (a) Write out the list of the regions in rank order starting with the region having the highest percentage of old people.
   (d) Suggest reasons for the distribution of old people.
   (c) How do you think old people are distributed in your area?
   (d) Are some areas especially attractive to old people? What might happen if a lot of old people lived in a particular town or area?

C Look at Fig D. The darker shaded areas are those parts of Britain well served by Inter-City rail services.
   (a) Name the parts of Britain which are well served by Inter-City rail services.
   (b) Where are the most inaccessible parts of Britain for Inter-City rail services?
   (c) If we were to produce a similar map showing the parts of Britain which are well served by motorways, the result would be different.
      (i) Refer to Fig B, page 96, showing Britain's motorways, and suggest where the darker shaded areas well served by motorways would be.
      (ii) Which parts of Britain do you think are the least well served by motorways?

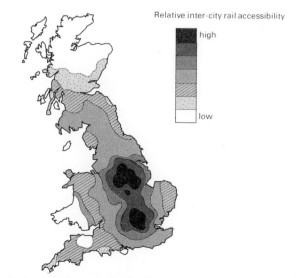

Relative inter-city rail accessibility

high

low

Fig. D Contrasts in transport facilities

17

1.7 GOVERNMENT AID

Regional development policy

One of the most important factors in the location of industry in the twentieth century has been the effect of government policy. The government has recognised that certain regions of Britain have problems such as serious unemployment which can be solved only through the introduction of new jobs. The table below summarises the history of regional development policy in Britain.

1928 The Industrial Transfer Act tried to persuade the unemployed to move to areas where work was available, mainly the south-east and Midlands of England. This met with only limited success, partly because people were unwilling to leave their homes.

1934 The Special Areas Act set up the special areas shown on Fig A. This had limited success because there was little money available.

1930s More success was achieved through the creation of trading estates such as Treforest in South Wales and Team Valley in the north-east.

1940 The Barlow Report is often called the foundation of regional policy in Britain. It recommended the movement of people and jobs out of the more prosperous areas into the special areas.

1945 The Distribution of Industry Act created the modern development area policy. Grants, loans and tax allowances were made available to industries bringing new employment to the areas.

1947 The Town and Country Planning Act forced firms to obtain an Industrial Development Certificate (IDC) if they wished to expand. IDCs were not

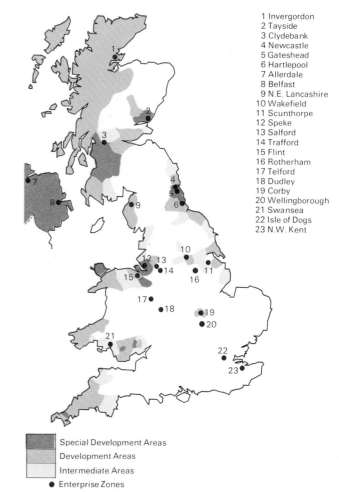

1 Invergordon
2 Tayside
3 Clydebank
4 Newcastle
5 Gateshead
6 Hartlepool
7 Allerdale
8 Belfast
9 N.E. Lancashire
10 Wakefield
11 Scunthorpe
12 Speke
13 Salford
14 Trafford
15 Flint
16 Rotherham
17 Telford
18 Dudley
19 Corby
20 Wellingborough
21 Swansea
22 Isle of Dogs
23 N.W. Kent

Special Development Areas
Development Areas
Intermediate Areas
● Enterprise Zones

Fig. E Assisted Areas and Enterprise Zones 1982

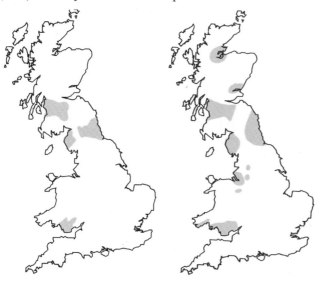

Fig. A Special Areas 1934   Fig. B Development Areas 1945–60

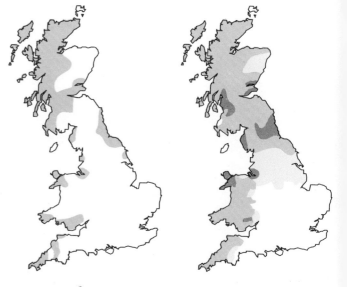

Fig. C Development Districts 1960   Fig. D Assisted Areas 1972

Incentive	Special Development Areas	Development Areas	Intermediate Areas
Building grants	22%	22%	20%
Plant and machinery grants	22%	20%	—
Factories for sale or rent	Up to 5 years rent free	Up to 2 years rent free	
Loans	On lower terms to provide additional jobs		
Grants for removal costs	Up to 80%	Up to 80%	Up to 80%
Help for transferred workers	Free fares, lodging allowances and help with removal costs		
Training	Free training at a Government Skill Centre		
Tax allowances	Tax reductions on buildings and machinery		

Fig. F Government aid for industry in the Assisted Areas

Fig. G Some views on regional development

normally granted outside development areas.

1960 The Local Employment Act replaced the development areas with the development districts shown on Fig C.

1972 The Industry Act established the three-tier system shown on Fig D.

1982 The three-tier system was retained but the size of the assisted areas was greatly reduced. Enterprise zones were established.

Figure F lists the incentives provided by the government in the assisted areas. In addition, the government has paid for improvements to the *infrastructure* of the regions (roads, electricity supply, docks and other services) and to improving the environment through the reclamation of derelict land, slum clearance and so on. Other policies associated with regional development included the establishment of new towns, expanded towns and, most recently, enterprise zones.

Since 1973, Britain has received regional assistance through the European Economic Community. In 1975, the European Regional Development Fund (ERDF) was set up to co-ordinate the EEC's regional policy. Each country receives a fixed quota of the fund. Britain received 24 per cent in 1981, second only to Italy's 35 per cent. The fund provides grants of up to 40 per cent of investment costs for industry in the assisted areas, which is used to top up national regional development grants. Between 1975 and 1981, Britain received £650 million from the ERDF. Loans are available through two other EEC bodies, the European Investment Bank and the European Coal and Steel Community.

Fifty years of government aid to the regions of Britain has not significantly reduced regional differences. There are still contrasts between rich and poor regions. It is difficult to say how much worse, or better, the situation would be today if there had been no regional aid, or aid of a different sort. It is probably true to say that conditions in the least prosperous parts of the assisted areas would have been worse. Some of the arguments for and against the regional development policy are shown on Fig G.

QUESTIONS

A1 When did government aid for the regions begin?

2 Study Figs A–E. List four regions which have received government aid continuously since 1934.

3 (a) Describe three kinds of government incentive for industry in the assisted areas (Fig F).

(b) List three ways in which the incentives for special development areas differ from those for intermediate areas.

4 What are Industrial Development Certificates (IDCs)?

B1 Why do you think the government regional policy has been called a 'carrot and stick' policy?

2 What may have happened to the United Kingdom if the government had never helped the problem regions?

PRIMARY INDUSTRIES
2.1 FARMING

Primary industry refers to the production of raw materials and food. No processing takes place. Primary industry includes agriculture, forestry, fishing, mining and quarrying. It is the basis of the manufacturing, or *secondary*, industry which creates much of Britain's wealth.

British farming has changed profoundly during this century. Farming now employs fewer people than ever before (only 2.5 per cent of the total workforce), yet farm production is the highest ever. This is possible because British farming is amongst the most efficient in the world.

British farms are amongst the most *mechanised* in the world. About 20 per cent of net farm income is spent on machinery. The number of tractors on British farms increased from 415 000 in 1963 to 580 000 in 1983. At the same time, the number of farmworkers has declined rapidly, from 480 000 in 1963 to only 210 000 in 1983.

Machines operate most efficiently on large farms. Farms have been enlarged through amalgamation. Farm sizes have also been increased by the removal of hedges. These actions have brought *economies of scale* (increased size and investment has resulted in increased profits).

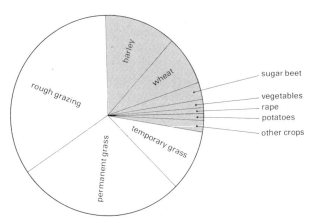

Fig. A Farming land use in the UK in the 1980s

British farmers have widely adopted scientific techniques. Artificial fertilisers, soil conditioners, insecticides and pesticides are the products of the chemical industry. Research in plant biology has developed higher-yielding and disease-resistant strains of familiar crops such as wheat and barley. Selective breeding and artificial insemination have increased the quality of livestock. The investment, mechanisation and use of scientific techniques makes British farming highly *intensive*.

Fig. B A broiler farm

Intensive farming: Intensive arable farming has caused the removal of hedges and enlargement of fields to allow more efficient use of machines. Artificial fertilisers and pesticides allow farmers to abandon traditional crop rotations. The soil now receives no rest as crops are continuously grown. Nutrients and minerals which were replaced by roots and fallow years are now replaced by soil conditioners. Although the cost of this intensive farming is high, the greater yields ensure higher profits.

The same is true of intensive livestock farming. For example, chickens were traditionally allowed to roam freely around the farmyard. Now such 'free range' chickens are rare. Most eggs and chicken meat are produced on *factory farms* like that illustrated. There are thousands of chickens inside the long, low buildings. This is a *broiler* farm. The buildings are kept at a constant temperature and the lighting is carefully controlled. The building is completely sterile so that no disease can enter. The chickens are fed on concentrated feed pellets and may be injected with drugs to increase their growth rate so that they are ready to be sold when they are eight weeks old. There may be twenty thousand chickens crowded into each building. About a hundred die each week, mostly from heart failure because they grow so quickly. Other chickens are kept inside buildings called *batteries*. Battery hens, contained within tiny cages, are egg producers. Each hen produces an average of 222 eggs a year.

Nearly all our eggs and chicken meat come from factory farms, and an increasing proportion of our beef and pig products. Dairy cows are kept indoors all year in some modern farms. These intensive methods mean that livestock can be reared over a much wider area of the country and production costs are greatly

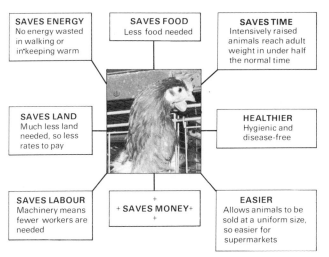

SAVES ENERGY No energy wasted in walking or in keeping warm	**SAVES FOOD** Less food needed	**SAVES TIME** Intensively raised animals reach adult weight in under half the normal time
SAVES LAND Much less land needed, so less rates to pay		**HEALTHIER** Hygienic and disease-free
SAVES LABOUR Machinery means fewer workers are needed	+ **+ SAVES MONEY+** +	**EASIER** Allows animals to be sold at a uniform size, so easier for supermarkets

Fig. C The advantages of intensive farming

reduced. Factory farming has been criticised by people who say it is cruel to treat animals in this way.

British farming and the EEC

Since entry into the EEC in 1973, British farming has been affected by the Common Agricultural Policy (CAP). The CAP has these aims:

1 To increase agricultural productivity
2 To ensure a fair standard of living for farmers and farmworkers
3 To safeguard supplies and prices
4 To make marketing easier.

Seventy per cent of the EEC's budget is spent on the CAP. The farmer is guaranteed a price which is fixed each year. An *intervention price* is set up for each product, and the EEC buys the surplus at that price if the EEC market price falls below it. The CAP also guarantees export prices for farmers through *export subsidies*. These protect the EEC farmer from world price changes. These policies mean that there is often surplus production within the EEC. The surplus products are stored (butter 'mountains' and wine 'lakes') or sold cheaply within the EEC or on the world market.

The CAP has affected British farming in many ways, but two effects have been especially important:

Oilseed rape: The rapid increase in production of oilseed rape has caused the spread of this bright yellow crop across the fields of eastern and southern England. Before Britain entered the EEC, only 10 000 hectares of rape were grown as a 'break' crop (one grown between a run of other crops to break the rotation). By 1983, 160 000 hectares were grown and the rape sold for cash. The black seeds are crushed to extract oil which is used for cooking oil, margarine and salad dressing. The residue of the crushing process contains proteins and is sold to animal feed

manufacturers. The EEC subsidises rape production because it wants to reduce vegetable oil imports.

Sheep: The 'sheepmeat regime' introduced in 1980 raised the guaranteed price for lamb by a quarter. This led to a rapid incease in the number of sheep in the UK, from 29.8 million in 1979 to 32.3 million by 1981.

QUESTIONS

A1 Name the two most important crops grown in Britain.
 2 What effects have intensive farming methods had on arable farms?
 3 Why has intensive livestock farming been introduced?
 4 Why do some people oppose intensive livestock farming?
B1 Study Fig A.
   (a) What percentage of farmland in the UK is used for (i) arable crops, (ii) temporary grass, (iii) permanent grass, (iv) rough grazing?
   (b) What are the three leading arable crops?

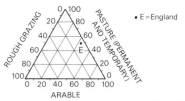

	Arable	**Pasture**	**Rough grazing**
England	43	45	12
Scotland	10	18	72
Wales	6	60	34
N. Ireland	8	72	20

Fig. D

 2 Study the triangular graph (Fig D). It plots agricultural land use in England.
   (a) Copy the graph. Using the figures in the table, plot the farmland for Wales, Scotland and Northern Ireland.
   (b) Explain the differences revealed by the completed graph.
 3 What effect has British membership of the EEC had upon British farming?
C 'Home Farm is in East Anglia. In 1960, the farm covered 720 hectares. It was a mixed farm with dairy cattle, cereals and fodder crops. Seventy people were employed. By 1984, the farm had taken over several neighbouring small farms and covered 1200 hectares. The livestock have gone and the farm now concentrates solely on wheat and barley which are grown in vast fields. Only fifteen people are employed on the farm in 1984.'
   Account for these changes.

2.2 ARABLE FARMING

Arable farming means growing crops. In Britain, the main crops are *cereals*, especially wheat and barley; *roots*, especially sugar beet and potatoes; *fodder* such as turnips and kale; and rape grown as an *oilseed* crop.

Area (million hectares)

Year	Barley	Wheat	Oats	Sugar Beet	Potatoes
1937	0.4	0.7	1.0	0.1	0.3
1967	2.4	0.9	0.6	0.2	0.3
1982	2.4	1.5	0.1	0.2	0.2

Yield (tonnes per hectare)

Year	Barley	Wheat	Oats	Sugar Beet	Potatoes
1937	2.1	2.2	2.0	3.1	16.8
1967	3.6	3.9	2.7	5.7	24.9
1982	5.1	6.1	4.8	6.2	34.9

Fig. A Agricultural production in Britain

Cereals

Figure A shows the changing nature of arable crop area and yield. Notice the following changes in area since 1937:

1 Barley has increased six times.
2 Wheat has doubled.
3 Oats has declined to one-tenth of its 1937 area.

The growth in the area under barley to almost half the total arable area is due to the demand for barley as an animal food. Another important factor is the development of new, high-yielding strains of barley. Wheat yields have increased even more. British wheat is a 'soft' variety because the moist climate does not let the grain ripen fully, even in eastern England. Soft wheat is not suitable for bread production; it is used in the making of cakes and biscuits. 'Hard' wheat for bread manufacture has to be imported from the USA and Canada.

The dramatic decline of oats is explained by its inferiority to barley: oats have a lower average yield, ripen later; and demand for human consumption has fallen. Most oats are now grown for fodder.

The geography of cereal production is shown on Fig B. Wheat is limited to the east of the country, barley and oats can be grown over more of Britain.

Cereal farming has become highly mechanised. The first combine harvesters were introduced on British farms in the early 1930s, but it was not until the 1950s that they became common. The combine

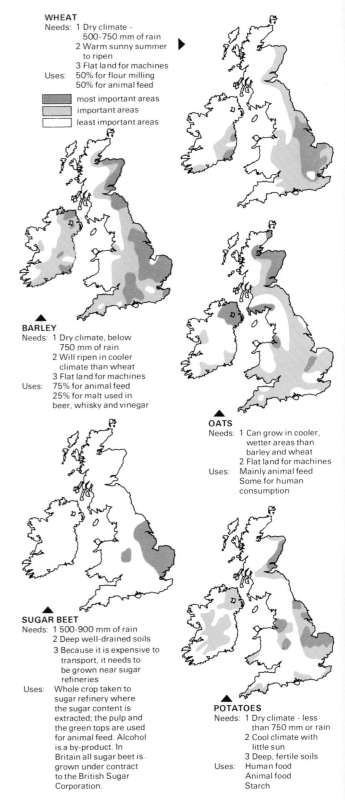

WHEAT
Needs: 1 Dry climate -
500-750 mm of rain
2 Warm sunny summer to ripen
3 Flat land for machines
Uses: 50% for flour milling
50% for animal feed

most important areas
important areas
least important areas

BARLEY
Needs: 1 Dry climate, below 750 mm of rain
2 Will ripen in cooler climate than wheat
3 Flat land for machines
Uses: 75% for animal feed
25% for malt used in beer, whisky and vinegar

OATS
Needs: 1 Can grow in cooler, wetter areas than barley and wheat
2 Flat land for machines
Uses: Mainly animal feed
Some for human consumption

SUGAR BEET
Needs: 1 500-900 mm of rain
2 Deep well-drained soils
3 Because it is expensive to transport, it needs to be grown near sugar refineries
Uses: Whole crop taken to sugar refinery where the sugar content is extracted; the pulp and the green tops are used for animal feed. Alcohol is a by-product. In Britain all sugar beet is grown under contract to the British Sugar Corporation.

POTATOES
Needs: 1 Dry climate - less than 750 mm or rain
2 Cool climate with little sun
3 Deep, fertile soils
Uses: Human food
Animal food
Starch

Fig. B The distribution and requirements of arable crops in Britain

cuts and threshes the grain as it moves through a field. Over half a hectare of grain can be cut and threshed in an hour. The introduction of the combine greatly reduced labour demands at harvest time on cereal farms. Farmers discovered that the combines worked most efficiently in large fields because less time was wasted in turning and manoeuvring, so cereal farmers have removed hedgerows and increased field sizes. The Fens and East Anglia have many huge cereal fields. The removal of hedges has drawbacks: soil erosion has occurred because the hedges sheltered the fields from strong winds, and the soil has been blown into drainage ditches causing flooding and contaminating the water with chemicals used on the fields.

Root crops

Potatoes are grown mainly for human consumption and are now harvested by machine. Potatoes are bulky and expensive to transport, but 'early' potatoes earn high prices in our supermarkets. Imports from Cyprus and Egypt provide Britain with 'new' potatoes soon after New Year's Day. The first British crop comes from the mild-winter areas of Cornwall, Pembrokeshire and the Channel Islands. Maincrop potatoes are grown in Lincolnshire and the Fens, Lancashire and Ireland. New potatoes from Egypt (mentioned above) are grown from seed potatoes flown from Scotland. Seed potatoes are grown in Fife and south of Ayr in Strathclyde. The cold climate reduces the danger of disease.

In Britain, all sugar beet is grown under contract to the British Sugar Corporation. The whole crop is sent to the sugar refinery where the sugar content (about 20 per cent by weight) is extracted; the pulp and the green tops are used for animal feed. Sugar beet has precise climatic requirements, but just as important is the economic requirement to be as close as possible to the sugar factory; sugar beet is bulky and 80 per cent of its bulk has little value.

Much of Britain's arable farming is now highly intensive. The use of machines and chemicals has increased, and the traditional crop rotations using roots to fix nitrogen and return the fertility to the soil have declined. Over much of the chalklands of southern England, arable farmers are practising a *monoculture* based on the continuous cropping, year after year, of wheat and barley. Such specialist cereal farming needs little labour and limited machine time. However, fertility has to be maintained by the liberal use of nitrogen fertilisers, and agrochemical sprays are needed to combat weeds and disease. The high yields possible each year justify the high input costs. The rising costs of chemicals and energy may affect the system in the future.

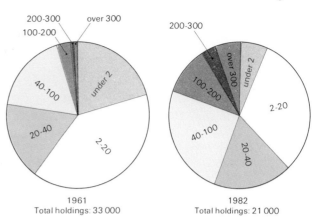

Fig. C Farm size in Britain (hectares)

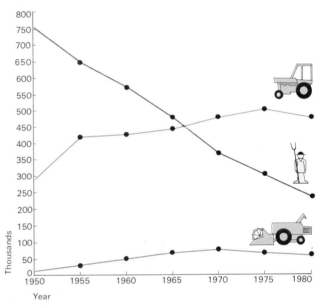

Fig. D The number of tractors and combine harvesters in Britain: the number of agricultural employees

QUESTIONS

A1 What areas of arable land were used for barley in 1937 and 1982? Explain the increase in area.
2 What is meant by 'soft' wheat?
3 Why has the growing of oats declined since 1937?
4 List the requirements of Britain's major arable crops (Fig B).
5 Study Fig C. Describe the changes which occurred between 1961 and 1982.
6 Study Fig D.
  (a) How many farmworkers were there in 1950?
  (b) How many were there in 1980?
  (c) Why has this decline occurred?
B1 Describe and account for the changes in British cereal farming since 1967.
2 Describe and account for changes in labour and machinery on British arable farms.
3 Explain why average farm sizes have increased and the total number of holdings has decreased.

2.3 FRUIT AND MARKET GARDENING

Fruit and vegetables are important crops in certain areas. The intensive growing of vegetables is called *market gardening*. Market gardens are usually less than ten hectares and often consist mainly of greenhouses. Heating, ventilation and humidity are controlled automatically and the greenhouse crop may be watered automatically by sprinklers. Ninety-five per cent of greenhouse production consists of tomatoes, lettuces and cucumbers.

Market gardening is expensive and hard work, but profits can be high. It has always been important in areas close to towns and cities, which provide a large demand. Cost of transport is kept low. Although land costs are high near cities, market gardens cover only a small area. As transport has improved, market gardening has been able to move further from the cities. The Fens have become Britain's most important fruit and vegetable growing area. In places with mild winters, crops can be harvested early to sell at high prices, e.g. Cornwall, Channel Islands.

Fruit

Soft fruits such as strawberries and raspberries grow best in the drier parts of the country such as south-east England, and in East Anglia and eastern

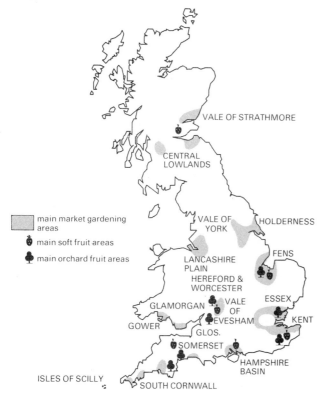

Fig. A The fruit and market gardening areas of Britain

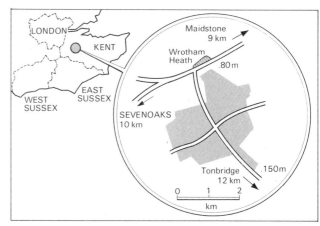

Fig. B The site of Orchard Place Farm

Scotland where the long summer days assist ripening despite the cooler temperatures.

Orchard fruits need rain during their growth. They are vulnerable to high winds and frost. The orchards have to be carefully sited. Planting orchards on slopes ensures free drainage of the soil and allows frosty air to flow downhill into the valley floors. South-facing slopes receive the most sunshine. Many of the apples grown in Somerset, Devon and Herefordshire are used in the production of cider.

Another important crop is the fruit of the hop vine. Kent and Herefordshire are the main hop-producing areas. Most are grown under contract for breweries.

A fruit farm in Kent

Orchard Place Farm lies on a ridge near the scarp foot of the North Downs 10 kilometres west of Maidstone. Figure C shows the crops grown. The underlying rock is lower greensand; the soil is a sandy loam ideal for fruit trees because it is well drained and warms up early in the year.

Apples and pears: Six types of cooking and eating (dessert) apples are grown, including Worcester, Spartan and Cox's Orange Pippin. Conference pears are grown. The trees are raised in a nursery and then planted at 5 m × 2 m intervals. They are pruned annually but it is four or five years before fruit can be harvested. The apples and pears are picked by local casual labour during August and September, and the fruit is stored in cool airtight chambers. During the winter, the fruit is graded and packed as required.

Strawberries: Strawberry plants are bought from certified growers. In the first year there is no crop, but they are then picked for three years before being ploughed in. Different varieties give a succession of

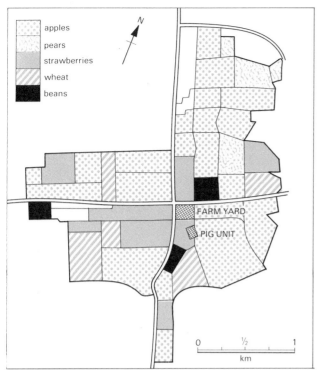

Fig. C Land use at Orchard Place Farm

picking in two seasons from mid-June to mid-July and from August until September.

Orchard Place Farm belongs to a co-operative marketing organisation. The strawberry co-operative involves forty growers from Kent and Sussex with a central marketing office in Paddock Wood. The strawberries are marketed throughout Britain and some exports are arranged. The apple co-operative consists of ten farmers combining to pack a variety of apples and pears for British supermarkets and wholesale markets. Other fruit growers have accepted contracts to supply canning or freezing factories. Some have invited members of the public to 'pick your own' at a reduced price.

Orchard Place Farm operates a pig unit with a herd of 1700 pigs. This is not typical of the region although several farmers keep some stock, mainly sheep. It is

Fig. D The advertising war

wise for a fruit farmer to have other activities because the fruit yields are dependent on the weather.

Machinery and labour: Fruit farming needs a lot of manual work. Orchard Place Farm employs one foreman, three tractor drivers and three general farmhands. There are fourteen women in the packhouse. Extra casual labour is employed for the fruit harvest from mid-June through to October. Up to 250 people, mainly housewives, are involved.

The farm has the following machinery and equipment:

8 tractors   2 forklift trucks
3 spraying machines   2 lorries for distribution
2 orchard mowers   2 general ploughs
1 pruning pulveriser   1 seed drill
1 strawberry planter   1 fertiliser spinner

The owner has to keep up with changing tastes and demands or he will suffer from competition. Britain's entry into the EEC has placed British farmers in competition with European growers. Yields of fruit in the south of France, Italy and Greece are often three times the yields obtained in Kent because of sunnier, hotter climates with less risk of frost. Many English orchards have been grubbed up because the farmers were unable to make a profit. English apple growers were overtaken by a sudden French sales drive in the late 1970s. By 1980, French Golden Delicious apples took 30 per cent of the British apple market. This cheap, high-quality apple was skilfully marketed. British apple growers had to improve quality and marketing. Advertisements such as that illustrated began to appear. The British claimed one big advantage: the better flavours of British varieties. Only time will tell whether our fruit farmers can compete with European growers.

QUESTIONS

A1 (a) What is meant by market gardening?
   (b) Where are the main market-gardening areas in Britain?
2 What physical and economic factors favour the growth of soft fruit; orchard fruit? Where are the main fruit-farming areas of Britain?
3 Where is Orchard Place Farm?
4 Describe the production of apples and pears at Orchard Place Farm.
5 Describe the different ways in which fruit can be marketed.
B1 Describe and account for the location of the major fruit- and market-gardening areas in Britain.
2 (a) What advantages do European fruit farmers have over English fruit farmers?
   (b) How have English apple growers responded to French competition?

2.4 DAIRYING

Each person in Britain drinks an average of 2.8 litres of milk each week. Add cheese, butter and other dairy products and it is not surprising to learn that milk is the most important product of Britain's farms. Over 20 per cent of farm sales are milk and milk products. Dairy farming is widespread throughout Britain, perhaps more so than any other type of farming.

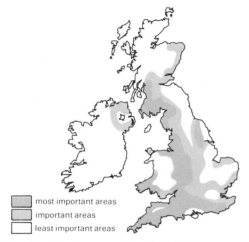

most important areas
important areas
least important areas

Fig. A The dairy farming areas of the British Isles

Dairy farming is most suited to the moister, milder areas of the country where grass is lush and juicy. A mild climate allows a long growing season. The west of Britain is thus particularly suitable for dairying. Elsewhere, demand from large urban areas has encouraged dairy farming despite the less-than-ideal climate, for example around London, the Midlands and the Vale of York. In such areas, dairying has to be on a more intensive basis: the cows have to be stall-fed throughout the winter and given fodder to supplement the grass. In some modern dairy farms, the cows are kept indoors all the time and fed on high-protein fodder. Such intensive methods use much less land. This is an important factor near major cities where land is expensive. However, very large herds are needed to ensure a profit. The cows are milked on a shift basis.

A Devon dairy farm

Ten kilometres south-east of Barnstaple in north Devon is the farm of Mr Robert Domleo, who moved into the area in 1960 and purchased the 70-hectare farm at Fishleigh Barton. It had been run as a beef cattle farm with some sheep and barley. By 1960, the farm was too small to be economic as a beef farm. Mr Domleo decided to change the farm into a dairy enterprise. He has since been able to expand by buying two neighbouring farms, Fisherton (40 ha) and Daffodil Farm (9 ha). Farms are not always simple organisations: this one is split up into three separate units but it is run as one farm, even though there are problems because of the split site.

The underlying rock is shale with ridges of sandstone. The soil is a sandy loam which is free-draining and easily ploughed. The farm lies in a rain-shadow area where rainfall averages 900 millimetres a year, lower than average for south-west England.

Mr Domleo owns 85 pedigree Friesian cows. The milking herd is kept at Fishleigh Barton. Each cow produces an average 6000 litres of milk per year (the national average is 4500 litres per year). From April to September, the cows graze outside on grass. During the winter, they are kept indoors and fed on barn-dried hay, which is cut when green and blown dry by a large fan in the barn. This method reduces the risk of spoiling by rain. The cows are let out at suitable times during the winter to graze on kale. A portable electric fence is used to prevent them treading the crop before they can eat it.

The cows are milked by machine in a herringbone milking parlour (Fig B). They have access to feeders which are controlled by computer to ensure that each receives the correct amount. The high-concentrate feed is prepared at the farm from its own barley. Up to 130 tonnes of grain is stored at the farm before being weighed and milled. Soya bean extract, fish meal and minerals are purchased and mixed with the barley to produce a high-protein concentrated feed.

The milk is collected by bulk road tankers belonging to the Milk Marketing Board. The tankers carry the milk to the board's creamery at Torrington.

The young cattle are fed on silage (grass stored

Fig. B The milking parlour

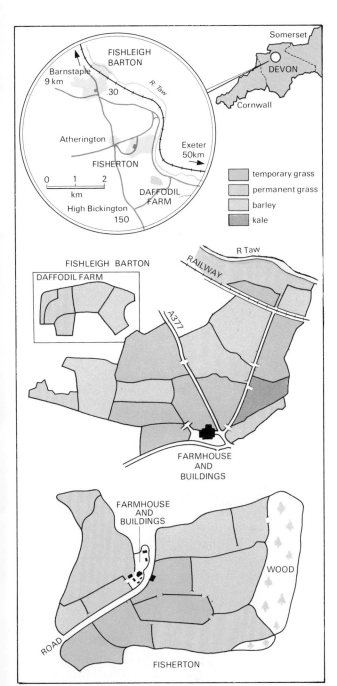

Fig. C Mr Domleo's farm

without drying) at Fisherton. During the summer, some of them graze at Daffodil Farm.

Sheep on the farm: The farm's main activity is dairying, but Mr Domleo has 150 ewes for early fat lamb meat production.

Machinery and labour: Like most modern farms, Mr Domleo's farm has a small workforce but many machines. There are two full-time farmworkers. One

part-time worker helps with general maintenance. Mr Domleo shares the work and looks after the sheep himself. The farm has the following machinery and equipment:

4 tractors	2 hay turners
1 corn drill	1 hay baler
1 muck spreader	2 grass cutters

Many ploughs, rollers, harrows and conveyors.

Contractors are employed for the combine harvesting and hedgecutting. It would be too expensive for Mr Domleo to have machines for these purposes.

Mr Domleo has received help from the EEC's Agricultural and Horticultural Development Scheme. Grants have been given for buildings and equipment including three new cattle buildings.

Financial aid will contribute to the success of any farm, but also needed are efficient management and the wise use of a range of modern technology.

QUESTIONS

A1 How much milk does each person in Britain drink each week, on average?

2 Why is the west of Britain most suited to dairy farming?

3 Why has dairy farming developed around London and in the Midlands?

4 Where is Mr Domleo's farm?

5 How are the cows on Mr Domleo's farm fed?

6 (a) What machinery does Mr Domleo have?

(b) Why does he hire contractors to harvest his barley and cut his hedges?

B1 What is meant by the term 'intensive dairying'?

2 Here is a list of the land-use at Mr Domleo's farm:

Land Use	Hectares	% of area
Temporary grass	33.6	?
Permanent grass	34.5	?
Barley	35.6	?
Kale	3.0	2.6
Woodland	?	9.1
Total	117.3	100%

(a) Complete the table and construct a pie graph of the statistics above.

(b) What percentage of the area is under grass?

(c) How are barley and kale used at the farm?

(d) Why is 9.1 per cent used for woodland?

3 Why does Mr Domleo keep sheep as well as cattle?

4 What effect do (i) relief, (ii) climate, (iii) soils have upon Mr Domleo's choice of farming?

C Select two of the following: market gardening; dairying; arable farming.

For both, explain how physical and economic factors influence its location and distribution within the British Isles.

2.5 FORESTRY

Only 9 per cent of Britain is forested. This is one of the lowest figures in Europe (EEC average 21 per cent), but forestry is an increasingly important activity. Timber is becoming a valuable and scarce resource.

Most of the broadleaved *deciduous* forests are in the lowland areas. The beech tree which grows well on the clay-covered chalklands of southern England was once widely used for furniture making. The oaks of the wetter vales and valleys once provided wood for houses, bridges and ships. The broadleaf trees grow slowly and reach maturity 100 to 200 years after planting.

Today, *coniferous* trees are being planted. The wood is used for pulp and paper, packaging, fencing and building. By far the most common tree is the *sitka spruce*. It grows to maturity in fifty years and thrives on infertile, wet soils in upland areas. Some coniferous forest plantations have been established in lowland areas such as Thetford in Norfolk, but the large-scale plantings are in upland areas of Scotland, Wales and northern England.

Over 90 per cent of Britain's timber needs are imported at a cost of about £3 billion per year, and planting or *afforestation* may increase towards the end of the century as we try to meet the ever-growing demand for timber.

1 Productive forest area (100 hectares)

	Forestry Commission	Private	Total
Coniferous (spruce, pine etc)	834	521	1355
Broadleaved (oak, beech etc)	50	344	394
	884	865	1749

100 hectares = 1 square kilometre

2 Wood production (100 m³)

	Forestry Commission	Private	Total
1973	1600	2100	3700
1982/86	2900	2500	5400
1987/91	3600	2800	6400

3 Employment

Forestry workers	19 000
Wood processing industries	14 000

Fig. A

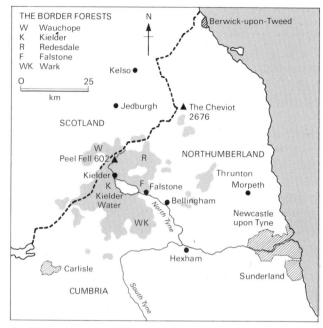

Fig. B The location of Kielder Forest

Fig. C Felling a mature tree

Fig. D Hauling timber

The Forestry Commission

The Forestry Commission was established in 1919 immediately after World War I. The country's timber supplies had been used at an alarming rate during the war and the government wanted to build up a strategic reserve of timber. Since then, the Forestry Commission has followed a wider range of objectives such as: producing wood for industry, providing employment in rural areas, conserving the natural beauty of the countryside and providing recreational facilities and working alongside agriculture.

Between 1945 and 1980, the Forestry Commission doubled its forest area. The amount of timber it produced in the same period increased more than five-fold, but employment did not increase because forestry work became more mechanised.

Kielder Forest

Kielder Forest is the biggest of the Border Forests (Fig B), the largest man-made forest area in Britain. Planting started in 1926, mature fifty-year-old trees are now being felled and production will continue to increase. Three times as much timber will be produced in 2000 than in 1980. Kielder was chosen for a number of reasons. Sheep and cattle farming was the only economic activity apart from some grouse shooting. Forestry was seen to be a more profitable activity, and the Forestry Commission gradually purchased land. The hills of the Kielder area range between 150 and 400 metres in height. The forests are most productive below 250 metres but planting has been done at higher levels. Rainfall is high in the west, about 1400 millimetres a year, but decreases to about 1000 millimetres in the east. Soils are leached (acidic) and consist of boulder clay and peat. The underlying rocks include carboniferous shales, sandstones, and some limestones.

Much of the early forest was planted by un-employed miners from Tyneside and Clydeside. In the post-war expansion, three forestry villages were built of which Kielder was the largest. At first, there were growth problems in areas of shallow soil as roots could not develop. Drainage was difficult and many areas remained too wet for growth. In 1947, a fire destroyed one year's planting in two hours. The problems have been largely overcome although there are still drainage difficulties.

The timber cycle: a wood crop in fifty years

1 Seeds grown in nurseries (in Scotland).
2 After two years, seedlings transplanted in nursery.
3 Hillsides are deep-ploughed and drained.
Trees are planted two metres apart when four years old on the ridges of the ploughed soil.
New forests are fenced to protect from deer.
Planting is sometimes under the shelter of older trees.
4 Early fertilising may be necessary. Pesticide spraying is sometimes carried out.
5 Successive thinnings made after 20 years — trees are then 9 to 12 metres high. Trees on land over 250 metres are not thinned.
6 Felling begins when trees are about 50 years old.
7 In 1982, wood was sent to a variety of processing plants: Washington New Town (boxes), Stockton (chipboard), Sweden (pulp and paper). Kielder wood

is also used for packaging, tunnel linings, fence posts and floor boards.

About 50 per cent of the trees are sitka spruce and 24 per cent Norway spruce (the Christmas tree). The remaining trees are Scots and lodgepole pines, larches and a variety of other broadleaved trees. The larches and other trees have been planted to give variety. The Forestry Commission are concerned to 'enhance the environment' and not to be accused of planting straight lines of conifers.

Fig. E The recreational facilities at Kielder Forest

QUESTIONS

A1 Look at Fig A.
  (a) Who owns most of Britain's forests?
  (b) What types of forests are most common in Britain?
  (c) What is the estimated wood production for the years 1987/91?
  (d) Who will produce the greatest amount of this wood?
  2 Why are conifers so popular as a tree crop?
  3 State simply how the Forestry Commission's objectives have changed since 1919.
  4 Why was Kielder suitable for planting the country's largest forest area?
  5 Using small, simple sketches, draw the 'timber cycle'.
B1 By the year 2025, Britain should be producing 15–20 per cent of its needs. Outline why this improvement will be important to the country.
  2 It was once forecast that 3000 people would work in the Kielder forests but only 210 people work there today. Suggest reasons for this.
  3 Two per cent of the Kielder area was flooded by building Kielder Water. In what ways has the new lake added to the attraction of Kielder?
C Based on a forest area you have studied (i) give an account of the physical environment, stating the difficulties it has presented to afforestation; (ii) state the extent to which the forest area has developed as a tourist attraction.

2.6 FISHING

Fish has a high food value and has supplemented the British diet for centuries. There are well over one hundred fishing ports in Britain and Northern Ireland. The largest ports (Fig A) account for over 60 per cent of the total weight of fish caught. Although the industry employed only 16 609 fishermen in 1981 (39 380 in 1938), it continues to provide food and export earnings.

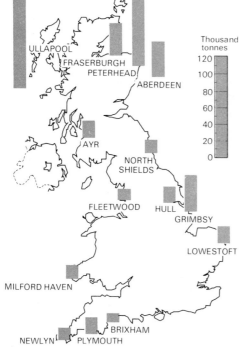

Fig. A The fishing ports of Britain, 1981

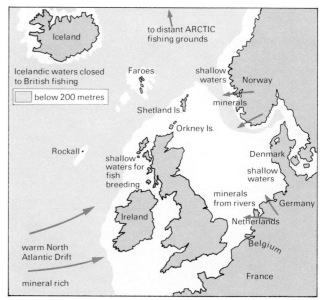

Fig. B Fishing in UK waters

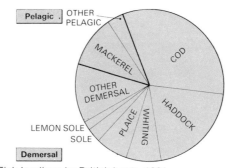

Fig. C Fish landings by British boats, 1981

The coastal waters: Britain has an indented coastline and several islands; fishing ports have developed in the many sheltered estuaries and inlets. Figure B shows other natural advantages for fishing. *Plankton* is the chief source of food for fish. These microscopic plants and animals thrive in the sea areas around Britain and Ireland. They grow quickly in the mineral-rich waters where ocean currents reach the *continental shelf* (the sea area up to 200 metres or 100 fathoms deep).

Figure C shows the main types of fish caught around Britain and in the distant Arctic fishing grounds. There are two types: *pelagic* fish such as mackerel and herring feed close to the surface of the sea; *demersal* fish such as cod, haddock and plaice feed near to the sea bed. Pelagic fish are more oily than demersal fish, which are also called *white fish*.

Certain coastal areas are important for certain types of fish. Cod tends to keep to the deeper and

more distant waters but mackerel are found in two specific areas. In the summer, mackerel shoals swim off western Scotland but by the autumn they are found off south-west England. Fishing fleets move with the shoals. Flat fish such as sole and plaice are taken in the shallow North Sea. If other types are to be caught for the dinner table, the British public must be persuaded to eat them. Coley is increasingly popular, and the blue whiting could become so.

Shellfish are of increasing importance to fishing communities. They have a high value and are now gathered in great numbers. Crabs and lobsters are plentiful around south-west England, oysters are collected in east and south-east England, and cockles and whelks are found in shallow inlets such as Morecambe Bay and the Wash.

The most important method of fishing, although now in decline, is *trawling*. Figure D explains how the trawlers scoop up bottom-feeding

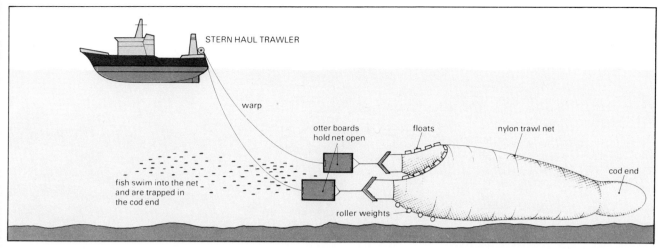

Fig. D Trawling

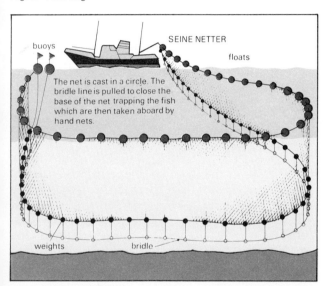

buoys

SEINE NETTER

floats

The net is cast in a circle. The bridle line is pulled to close the base of the net trapping the fish which are then taken aboard by hand nets.

weights   bridle

Fig. E Seine netting

demersal fish. Some trawlers are now being used to catch pelagic fish. *Seining* is another important fishing technique, explained in Fig E. With a recent increase in mackerel fishing around the western coasts, *lining* has grown in importance. Fishing lines with many baited hooks are used. Some fishing boats in Scotland have been converted to the *automatic long-lining* method, in which the line is on a continuous loop. It is winched in at one end of the vessel and passes through machinery which removes the fish and automatically baits the hooks. The line is passed out to sea at the other end of the boat.

In 1980 there were 3800 trawlers, seiners and liners in Britain's fishing fleet, but the number of large boats declined as distant-water fishing finished. Many of the largest trawlers have been laid up. The *freezer trawlers* which freeze the gutted fish on board, and the *factory trawlers* which process the fish into fillets, have little work to do.

There has been an increase in the smallest fishing boats. During the 1970s, over 1200 more small boats, under 27 metres in length, joined the fishing fleets. These privately owned boats illustrate the change in the fishing industry. The days of the long-distance trawlerman are over but fishing is still big business.

QUESTIONS

A1 Why are the seas around Britain so good for fish?

2 Complete the following table with some examples:

Type of fish	Species	Important sea area
demersal	?	?
pelagic	?	?
shellfish	?	?

3 Using the text and Figs D and E, describe trawling, seining and lining. To which type of fish is each method suited?

4 What is special about freezer trawlers and factory trawlers?

5 Comment on the following figures:
Fishermen in the United Kingdom

1938	39 380
1960	22 007
1975	17 061
1981	16 609

B1 Study the following figures:
England and Wales

Types of vessels	1975	1980
trawlers	1489	1573
liners	610	697
seiners	209	225

What types of fishing boats have increased the most? What trend do the figures not reveal?

2 Suggest how the public might be persuaded to eat 'new' types of fish such as the blue whiting.

2.7 FISHING: A CHANGING INDUSTRY

Fig. A Rusting trawlers in Hull Docks

There are several reasons for the decline of Britain's large-scale fishing industry which was based on distant-water trawling. In the mid-1970s, the rich Icelandic fishing grounds were closed to all except Icelandic vessels. The so-called 'cod war' showed the Icelanders' determination to protect their coastal water. Their fishing limit was extended from 19 to 80 kilometres in 1972 and to 320 kilometres in 1975. The effect on British and Irish trawling ports was disastrous. Figure C illustrates the decline of fish landings at Hull. Other ports such as Fleetwood and Aberdeen declined. In 1978, there were 130 trawlers operating from Hull; by 1981, there were only 36. The Icelanders extended their limits because of *overfishing*. Too many boats were taking fish around Iceland.

Overfishing is the reason for the decline of other types of fishing. The herring was overfished and several herring ports declined. Lowestoft and Great Yarmouth in the 1960s were in a similar situation to Hull today. Fishing in some areas has been affected by *pollution*: the North Sea is no longer rich in plankton because polluted rivers flow into it from all parts of Europe. Many of the shallow coastal breeding grounds are now 'dead'.

A further reason for the decline was the *competition* from foreign boats. Boats from the EEC, other parts of Europe and the USSR have fished successfully off the coasts of the British Isles, often operating at lower cost (perhaps by paying low wages). Visiting boats have sometimes competed unfairly by using small-meshed nets which take immature fish, thus reducing stocks.

Foreign boats unload their fish at British ports. Figure C refers only to British vessels. Fish landings at some ports are double the amounts shown: for example, in 1981 Grimsby received slightly more fish from foreign boats than from British boats and Hull received 50 per cent as much again from foreign vessels.

Coping with the changes

The British deep-water trawler fleets are out of work but the mackerel fleets are busy. Mackerel, one of the cheapest fish, has put Ullapool top in the rank order of tonnage caught. Only 25 per cent is actually landed, the rest being loaded direct on foreign processing ships. The practice of selling to foreign factory ships is known as 'klondyking'. By the early

Fish type	Tonnes (thousands)		
	1975	1980	1981
herring	107.2	3.1	36.3
cod	241.5	102.1	115.7
mackerel	48.3	353.4	197.2

Fig. B

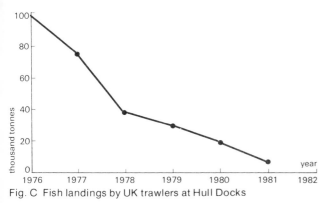

Fig. C Fish landings by UK trawlers at Hull Docks

Fig. D A Fisheries' patrol

1980s there was so much klondyking that foreign vessels were banned off the south-west coast of England. A similar ban has now been imposed off north-west Scotland. In 1982, factory ships from the USSR, Eastern Europe and Third World countries were working off Ullapool.

A ban is an important way of preserving declining fish stocks. A four-year ban on herring fishing proved this and herring are now increasing again. Another way of controlling fishing is to use *quotas*. Each boat or country is limited in the amount it can catch. All bans and quotas need careful policing: Fig D shows the fisheries patrol operating in the North Sea.

At the begining of the 1980s, there were discussions within the EEC about individual countries' coastal water limits. The agreements reached should protect the British fishing industry for years to come. From 1983, all large vessels fishing off northern Scotland need a licence, as do EEC boats wanting to fish in British waters. Only local inshore fishermen are able to fish inside a new 19-kilometre (12-mile) limit around the coasts of the British Isles. There is no foreign mackerel-fishing within a 320-kilometre (200-mile) limit of western coasts. The trend in Britain is a move away from distant-water fishing to more local fishing. Bearing in mind the high cost of fuel, this makes economic sense.

The old ports like Hull may never be important for fishing again, and ports such as Ullapool which have recently increased in importance may decline if mackerel fishing declines.

The fish-processing factories of Humberside receive fish from other ports of Britain by road, and the fishermen of Hull have started to move away. They are to be found mackerel-fishing in western waters or working on North Sea gas and oil supply vessels. The population of Hull has fallen since the mid 1970s.

Only 1.5 per cent of the world's fish catch is landed by the United Kingdom, which ranks eighteenth in the world. With modern fishing techniques, conservation and protection this position can be main-

tained, but there will be further changes in the types of fish caught and the relative importance of fishing ports. Fish farming could develop to include well-known sea-fish. Why hunt for fish when they could be farmed?

QUESTIONS

A1 Write about the decline of the fishing industry. Mention the following: overfishing, Icelandic fishing limits, pollution, foreign competition.

2 What is klondyking? Which types of fishing has this method involved?

3 What are quotas and fishing bans? Why have they been used?

4 Why do you think fish farming could eventually develop for sea-fish?

B1 Attempt to explain the figures in Fig B.

2 What have been the effects on Hull as long-distance trawling has declined?

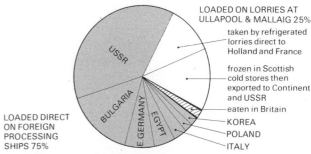

Fig. E The distribution of north – west Scotland's mackerel

3 Study Fig E.

(a) Attempt to explain the destination of north-west Scotland's mackerel.

(b) What methods of fishing and selling are used in this coastal area?

(c) What problems would have resulted if no mackerel ban had been imposed in 1983?

(d) Suggest possible ways of encouraging people to eat mackerel.

C Outline recent changes in the British fishing industry. Discuss the various ways of protecting the fishing industry for the future.

2.8 MINERALS

The growth of towns and cities, the expansion of industry and the building of roads and airports require building materials. For this purpose, rocks and minerals are extracted from the ground throughout Britain. The methods depend on the nature of the deposits. Surface deposits can be dug out or *quarried*, which may involve the stripping away of a top layer or *overburden* of soil or other rock which is not required. If the rocks are underwater, such as the gravels of the Thames Valley, they can be dredged.

Quarries and gravel pits close down when their profitable deposits have been exhausted. Do they remain as blots on the landscape or can the workings

Fig. B Killhope Wheel

be *restored*? Gravel pits can be restored for farming. In the Corby area of Northamptonshire, much of the former iron-ore workings have now been restored as farmland. If restoration is not possible, then workings can be screened by tree-planting. The waste heaps can be used for construction purposes such as road foundations, or levelled to improve the view.

Quarries and pits can be used for controlled dumping of domestic refuse and ash from power stations. Some of Greater London's refuse is taken by rail to an old gravel pit area at Sutton Courtenay in Oxfordshire. Ash from the West Burton power station on the River Trent in Nottinghamshire is taken to the old clay pits near Peterborough. Water-filled gravel pits can become centres for water sports, family recreation and the study of natural history.

South of Cirencester in Gloucestershire, thirty-five separate gravel pits have been designated the *Cotswold Water Park*. Conflicting recreational uses are separated so that water skiers do not get in the way of fishermen. Old quarries are used for leisure activities. The Morlais quarry near Merthyr Tydfil in South Wales is used by rock climbers. At Crickley Hill near Cheltenham in Gloucestershire, a disused quarry on an open hillside has been included in a country park.

Mining or *drilling* for rocks and minerals is necessary when they occur far underground. The depth of mining was once limited, but with modern technology coalmines can be up to 1000 metres deep. Drilling for oil often involves depths of 2000 metres.

Fig. A Batts Coombe

Some important rocks and minerals

Rock/mineral	Use	Examples of location
coal	fuel, chemicals	coalfields
oil/gas	fuel, chemicals	North Sea, Dorset
iron ore	iron and steel	Lincolnshire
chalk	cement, lime	south/east England
limestone	cement, chemicals	Pennines, Durham
clay	bricks, cement	lowland England
granite	building stone	Aberdeen area
china clay	pottery, paper	Devon/Cornwall
copper	plumbing, electricals	Cornwall
tin	tin plating	Cornwall
tungsten	drills and lathes	Devon
sands, gravel	building, concrete	lowland England

In the nineteenth century, *lead* was important in the Pennine areas of northern England. Figure B shows Killhope Wheel, once associated with lead mining in west Durham and now restored. The surrounding area has been designated a country park. Several old mining areas have become tourist attractions. Mining museums have been established and at Blaenavon in South Wales an old mine has been opened to the public.

Copper and tin were once mined extensively in Cornwall. Deposits of these minerals were always small compared to those in countries such as Malaysia and Bolivia. During the nineteenth century, metal mining in the south-west became less and less profitable as cheaper ores were imported. Because of recent rises in world metal prices there is an optimistic future for the mining industry in Cornwall. The major mining companies continue to prospect for new mineral supplies.

Fig. C Eyesore Quarry

QUESTIONS

A1 Name two minerals or rocks which are quarried and two that are mined.

2 In what ways can a gravel pit be restored?

3 Does a quarry have to be ugly?

Eyesore quarry (Fig C) is in a quiet area. Apart from the problems you can see in the sketch, the quarry is noisy and heavy trucks using the quarry often travel too fast and break up the road surface. The quarry owners have agreed to spend money improving the quarry environment. The local parish council has suggested planting trees and dredging the pond.

(a) Suggest what else could be done to improve the quarry surroundings.

(b) Suggest how the operations at the quarry could be made more acceptable to the local community.

(c) Re-draw the quarry after your improvements have been carried out.

4 Why are quarry owners not always interested in the environmental problems they cause?

Fig. D Edwin Richards Quarry, West Midlands

B1 Look at Fig D.

(a) Describe the methods of extraction used at the quarry.

(b) Suggest what operations are taking place in the buildings.

(c) What types of environmental nuisance do you think the quarry causes?

(d) What pollution-control methods could the owners use?

(e) Why is the hill site an advantage?

(f) What advantages might the quarry have brought to this densely populated area of the West Midlands?

2 (a) Name some minerals which Britain may produce in greater quantities in the future.

(b) Why should Britain want to produce its own minerals?

35

2.9 COAL

Coal was the fuel of the first Industrial Revolution in Britain. Coal is expensive to transport because it is bulky, so factories and mills were built on the coalfields. Country towns and villages became industrial cities. Throughout the nineteenth century, coal production and the number of miners steadily increased. Rows of terraced houses spread around the collieries and spoil heaps and winding towers dominated the skyline. Remote valleys in South Wales, Lancashire, Durham and other areas became centres of rapid growth in industry and population.

By 1913, almost 300 million tonnes of coal a year was produced by a million miners, and British coal was exported to many countries.

Since 1913, the British coal industry has suffered a decline. The coalfield regions, centres of economic growth in the nineteenth century, rapidly became areas of economic depression. Workpeople who remained in coalfield areas faced long years of unemployment and misery. The most important reasons for the downturn were:

1 Competition from imported oil which was cheaper, more efficient and cleaner than coal. Electricity and gas also became strong competitors.
2 Some important users of coal disappeared: steamships, steam railway engines, and coal-using gasworks.

Coalfield	Output per year (million tonnes)	Mines	Miners (thousands)
Yorkshire, Notts and Derby	65	98	132
North-east England	16	32	35
Scotland	9	20	23
South Wales	8	41	30
North Staffordshire	5	8	8
North-west England	4	8	9
Warwickshire	3	5	5
South Staffordshire	2	3	5
Kent	1	3	3
North Wales	1	2	1
Shropshire	1	1	1
Cumberland	1	1	1

	Output (million tonnes)	Mines	Miners
1913	299	?	1 000 000
1928	245	?	900 000
1955	211	850	699 000
1965	186	535	490 000
1975	117	245	246 000
1980	122	223	235 000
1982	126.6	198	218 500

Fig. B British coalfields — the facts

3 Important export markets were lost as coalmining began overseas. The opencast coalfields of the United States could produce coal much more cheaply than Britain's ageing expensive shaft mines.
4 Many coalmines closed because the most easily and cheaply mined coal was exhausted. There was a general movement from the *exposed* coalfields where the coal is found at the surface to the *concealed* coalfields where other rocks overlie the coal.
5 The introduction of mechanised coal-cutting caused unemployment. Many small pits had to be closed because the large machines were unable to operate in them.

Coalmining was a difficult and dangerous job. The miner worked in cramped tunnels which were always hot and dusty and often wet. They faced the constant threat of roof collapse, suffocation and explosion. The mining towns were no strangers to tragedy, and pit disasters happened frequently.

The decline in coalmining was a social problem because there were very few alternative jobs for the miners in the coalfield regions. Many coalfield settlements have declined or disappeared. Whole communities have lost their former way of life.

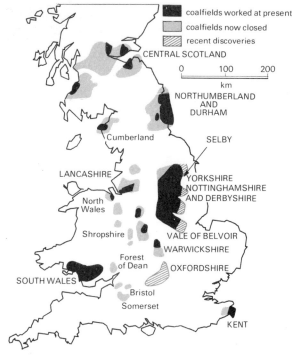

Fig. A The coalfields of Britain

Coal — The Once and Future King?

After years of decline, the coal industry now looks to better times due largely to uncertainties over oil and nuclear electricity. In 1973, the Middle East oil-producing nations raised the price of their crude oil by four times within the space of a few weeks. This oil crisis caused coal to be seen in a different light. It was once again as cheap as oil and it was to be found in Britain, not in the politically unstable Middle East. A search began for new coal deposits. Two coalfields were found and are being developed at Selby in North Yorkshire and in the Vale of Belvoir in Leicestershire. Further coal has been found beneath Oxfordshire, but there are no plans to develop this potential yet. There is thought to be enough coal in Britain to last over three hundred years. The world's oil reserves may not last another fifty years.

The most important use of coal is for electricity generation (Fig E). This will remain so, but research is taking place into new ways of processing coal to

Fig. D An old coal mine

produce synthetic oil and natural gas.

The closure of old mines will continue, until by the year 2000 a small number of large mechanised mines will produce around 150 million tonnes of coal a year. The showpiece of this revitalised industry will be the Selby field.

Fig. C A modern coal mine

QUESTIONS

A1 What effects did the Industrial Revolution have on the coalfield areas of Britain?

2 Why did the coal industry decline after 1913?

3 'After years of decline the coal industry now looks to better times ahead.' Why?

4 List (a) three coalfields which are no longer worked; (b) three areas where new coal deposits have been discovered.

B1 Study Fig B.

(a) Name the three coalfields with the highest annual coal production.

(b) What percentage of the total national output do the three leading coalfields produce?

(c) Construct a pie graph to illustrate the output statistics in the table.

2 Study Fig E.

(a) Construct two pie graphs illustrating how the use of coal has changed, one for 1928 and the other for 1980.

(b) Name two uses of coal in 1928 which had disappeared by 1982. Suggest reasons for these changes in demand for coal.

	Industry	Domestic	Electricity	Gasworks	Railway	Exports	Other uses
1928	36	17	8	7	6	22	4
1980	22	8	62	0	0	2	6
							(percentages)

Fig. E How the use of coal has changed

2.10 SELBY COALFIELD

In the 1960s, a new coalfield was discovered beneath the Vale of York, west of Selby. Surveys established it as the largest unexploited coalfield in Europe with reserves of over 600 million tonnes. After the oil crisis in 1973, it was decided to develop the Selby coalfield at a cost of over £1000 million.

In the past, the coal industry was a classic example of a *labour-intensive* industry. This means that a large part (up to 60 per cent) of the industry's costs consist of wages for the workforce. The Selby project shows the modern image of coal as a *capital-intensive* industry; only 20 per cent of the cost will be wages.

Five shaft mines will be sunk, and coal-cutting machines operated by push-button controls will load the coal on computer-controlled conveyors which will take the coal to the surface at one point, a sixth mine called Gascoigne Wood Drift. Due to the high level of mechanisation, only 4000 men will be employed compared with up to four times as many in old collieries of similar size. The miners employed at Selby will be from older Yorkshire collieries which are soon to close. Selby should achieve a productivity of 13 tonnes per manshift compared with the national average of 2.3 tonnes.

The coal will be taken away by trains carrying 1000 tonnes at 30-minute intervals throughout the day. The coal will be used to generate electricity in nearby power stations such as Eggborough, Ferrybridge C and Drax A and B.

The first coal from Selby was cut in 1983. All the mines will be operating by 1990, providing cheap, home-produced energy at the rate of ten million tonnes per year well into the twenty-first century.

The environmental impact

The development of a coalfield in a pleasant rural area such as Selby poses serious environmental problems. At the public enquiry, several local people were afraid that the coalmines would ruin the area and cause subsidence. However, although there will be problems, modern coalmining does not devastate the landscape in the way that earlier mining did. Tree-lined banks will be built around each mine. The major site, Gascoigne Wood, is being built on an already unattractive area of derelict railway sidings. Selby coal is so pure that no ugly spoil heaps will be needed. Winding towers 30 metres high will have to be built, but the winding gear will be enclosed.

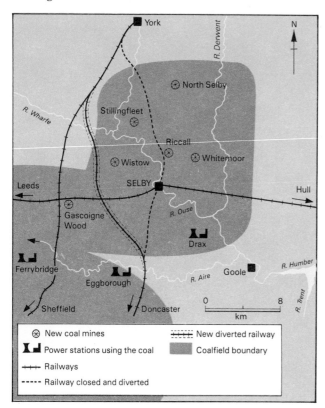

Fig. A Selby coalfield

Fig. B Operating hydraulic roof supports

Fig. C A Titan Tunneller

Fig. F Gascoigne Wood Drift mine under construction

Fig. D A shearer machine at work, cutting coal

Fig. G The surface control room at Gascoigne Wood Drift mine

Fig. E The Wistow Shaft mine

QUESTIONS

A1 What will be the annual output of Selby coalfield?

2 How many miners will be employed and where will they come from?

3 What will Selby's coal be used for?

B1 Explain the terms labour-intensive and capital-intensive.

2 Why will Selby have a much higher level of productivity than the national average for coal-mines?

3 What steps are being taken to reduce the environmental impact of the Selby coalfield?

4 A public enquiry was held into the plans to develop the Selby coalfield. You attended the enquiry as (a) a planning official of the National Coal Board, (b) a local farmer. Write the views which you would have presented to the enquiry in both cases.

39

2.11 NORTH SEA OIL AND GAS

Britain has discovered large reserves of oil and gas beneath the North Sea, and has been self-sufficient in oil and gas since 1980.

A huge natural gas field was discovered at Slochteren in the north-east Netherlands in 1959. The geological formation in which the gas was trapped was thought to continue under the North Sea. This created a problem: who owned the bed of the North Sea? International agreement was reached in 1964, and the sea bed was divided up according to the length of North Sea coastline that each country possessed. Britain received the largest sector.

Exploration

The rocks under the North Sea were surveyed using echo-sounders and seismic equipment. Geologists studied the results, searching for structures which would trap oil. Figure B shows what they were looking for. In each case, an impermeable layer of rock has prevented the oil escaping. Natural gas is often found above oil and water.

Geologists found possible oil traps, but the only way to be certain that oil existed was to test-drill. Drilling rigs were built, and the first area tested lay between the Netherlands and East Anglia. In October 1965, the West Sole gasfield was discovered. There are now nine gasfields off eastern England.

It was not until 1970 that the first major oilfield, Forties, was discovered.

Production

Development costs of North Sea fields are enormous, up to twenty times the cost of onshore fields. However, North Sea oil is light and low in sulphur so it is especially valuable.

Fig. A A North Sea oil rig

The oil is brought ashore by two methods:
1 Pipelines have been built to the most important fields. The oil is piped to shore terminals where it is treated to remove gas and water. Some terminals, such as Teesside, also have oil refineries; others, such as Flotta, pass the oil to refineries elsewhere.
2 Tankers bring oil ashore from smaller fields where the construction of a pipeline is not justified. Tankers of between 30 and 100 000 tonnes load oil from floating buoys moored above the oilfield and carry it to the shore.

The first North Sea oil came ashore in 1975. By 1980, Britain was producing enough to satisfy its own demands and export some as well. Self-sufficiency

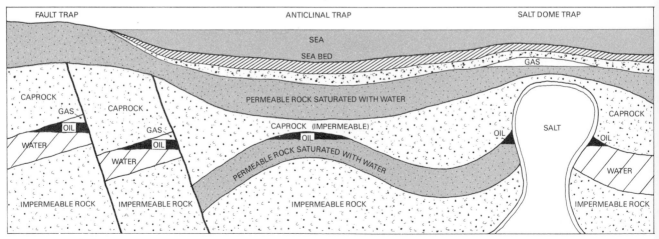

Fig. B Types of oil trap

Fig. C An oil tanker at an offshore loading buoy

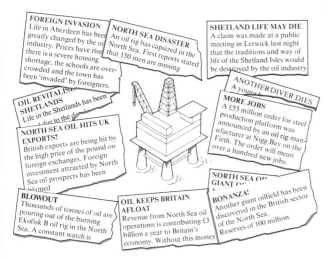

Fig. D Read all about it!

Fig. E Nodding donkey oil pumps in Hampshire

1973	1974	1975	1976	1977
0.1	0.1	1	12	38
1978	**1979**	**1980**	**1981**	**1982**
53	78	80	89	103

(a) Draw a line graph to illustrate these statistics.
(b) In which year did the largest percentage increase occur in the production?
(c) In which year did the largest absolute increase in the production occur?
(d) Why did these increases occur?

2 Study Fig D. Make a list of advantages and disadvantages which North Sea oil has brought to Great Britain. Design a newspaper article describing the discovery of oil near your home. Include forecasts of the likely effect on your area of oil development.

3 Suggest why oil finds have not had the same impact on settlement growth that coal did in the nineteenth century.

may last only for ten years or so, and Britain will have to depend upon imported oil once more unless new fields can be discovered. The answer may lie onshore. An onshore oilfield has been discovered at Wytch Farm in Dorset that sends over 1 million tonnes a year by train to the Llandarcy oil refinery in South Wales.

An extensive search has begun under southern England to find more onshore oil. A small field is being developed near Basingstoke in Hampshire. Oil rigs have drilled test wells in the English Channel, Celtic Sea and the Western Approaches. Natural gas has been discovered beneath Morecambe Bay.

QUESTIONS

A1 Why did the search for oil beneath the North Sea begin?
2 How is oil trapped underground?
B1 The following figures show oil production in the UK in millions of tonnes:

2.12 OIL AND GAS: PIPER FIELD

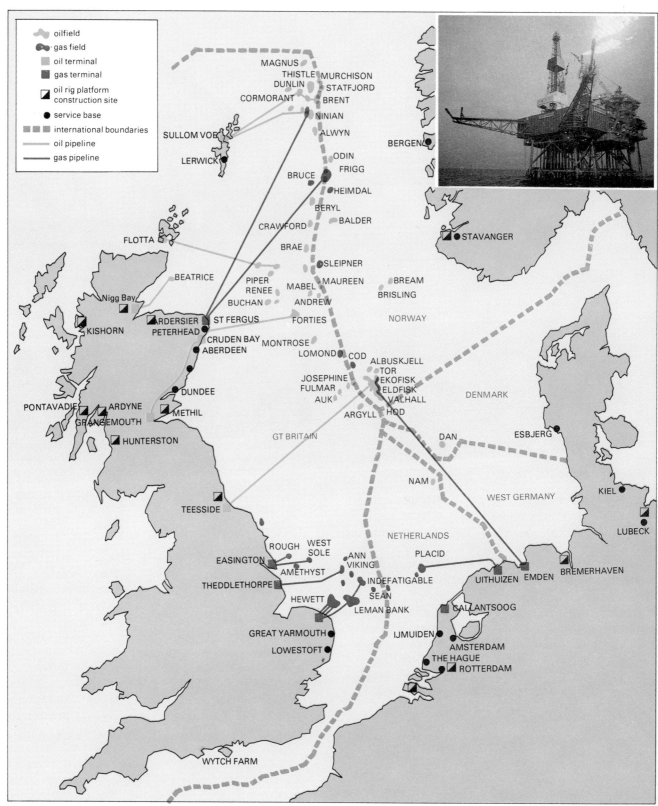

Legend:
- oilfield
- gas field
- oil terminal
- gas terminal
- oil rig platform construction site
- service base
- international boundaries
- oil pipeline
- gas pipeline

MAGNUS
THISTLE   MURCHISON
DUNLIN   STATFJORD
CORMORANT   BRENT
NINIAN
SULLOM VOE
LERWICK   ALWYN
BERGEN
ODIN
FRIGG
BRUCE
HEIMDAL
BERYL
CRAWFORD   BALDER
FLOTTA
BRAE
BEATRICE
SLEIPNER
PIPER   MAUREEN   BREAM
RENEE   MABEL   BRISLING
Nigg Bay   BUCHAN   ANDREW
ARDERSIER   ST FERGUS   FORTIES   NORWAY
KISHORN   PETERHEAD
CRUDEN BAY   MONTROSE
ABERDEEN
LOMOND   COD
STAVANGER
ALBUSKJELL
TOR
JOSEPHINE   EKOFISK
PONTAVADIE   FULMAR   ELDFISK
ARDYNE   AUK   VALHALL
GRANGEMOUTH   DUNDEE   DENMARK
METHIL   ARGYLL   HOD
HUNTERSTON
GT BRITAIN
DAN   ESBJERG
NAM
WEST GERMANY   KIEL
TEESSIDE
LUBECK
NETHERLANDS
ROUGH   WEST
SOLE   PLACID
EASINGTON   ANN
VIKING
AMETHYST   INDEFATIGABLE   UITHUIZEN   EMDEN   BREMERHAVEN
THEDDLETHORPE   SEAN
HEWETT   LEMAN BANK   CALLANTSOOG
GREAT YARMOUTH   IJMUIDEN
LOWESTOFT   AMSTERDAM
THE HAGUE
ROTTERDAM
WYTCH FARM

Fig. A North Sea oil and gas: inset of Piper platform

Piper is a medium-sized field 160 kilometres east of Wick in northern Scotland. It is operated by the Occidental group, an Anglo-American consortium.

Calendar of events
1972 North Sea 'blocks' awarded to the consortium
1973 Oil struck, field named Piper
    Planning permission obtained to build a land terminal on Flotta Island in Orkney
1974 Pipeline laid between Piper and Flotta, 220 km.
1976 Oil production platform completed and placed over the field. First oil piped ashore
1977 56-kilometre gas pipeline laid to link Piper to the Frigg gas pipeline system and thence to St Fergus gas terminal.

The steel production platform which sits above the Piper field was built at Ardersier near Inverness. It weighs over 14 000 tonnes and is over 150 metres high. It is home for 200 men, living and working in one of the harshest environments in the world.

The Flotta Oil Terminal: The oil from the Piper field and the neighbouring Claymore field, also operated by Occidental, is piped ashore to the Flotta terminal. Only eighty people lived on Flotta before the terminal was built. The island was quiet and the islanders lived a simple rural life. Occidental were aware of the need to keep disturbance to a minimum. Safeguards have to be taken against oil spillages, which kill wildlife, especially seabirds.

When the oil arrives at Flotta, it is treated to remove gas and water and stored to await loading on tankers of up to 100 000 tonnes. They carry the crude oil to refineries in Britain and Europe. Part of the gas is shipped out to be bottled as propane gas. The rest is used as fuel for the island's power station.

QUESTIONS

A1 Using Fig B, draw a bar graph to show the six main North Sea oilfields. The vertical scale

Major oilfields of the United Kingdom sector

Field name	Year of discovery	Year on stream	Peak annual production (in millions of tonnes)	Recoverable reserves (in millions of tonnes)
Brent	1971	1976	23	220
Claymore	1974	1977	7	55
Cormorant	1972	1979	12	70
Dunlin	1973	1978	7	70
Forties	1970	1975	24	240
Fulmar	1977	1982	9	55
Hutton	1979	1984	9	72
Murchison	1975	1980	7	51
Ninian	1974	1978	17	155
Piper	1973	1976	15	82
Statfjord UK	1974	1979	5	70
Tartan	1974	1980	4	35
Thistle	1973	1978	11	73

Fig. B

Fig. C The Occidental oil terminal at Flotta

should show recoverable reserves.
2 Where is the Piper oilfield?
3 (a) When was the Piper oilfield discovered?
  (b) What are its estimated recoverable reserves?
  (c) What is the annual production of oil from Piper?
4 Describe the Piper oil-production platform which is shown on Fig A.
5 (a) How is the oil and gas from Piper transported ashore?
  (b) Where is the oil and gas landed ashore?
B1 Draw a map showing (a) the position of the Piper and Claymore fields, (b) the pipelines from these fields, and (c) the onshore oil and gas terminal.
2 Suggest reasons why Occidental chose Flotta as the best site for their oil terminal.
3 Suggest how the construction of the oil terminal at Flotta may have affected the inhabitants of the island.
4 Study the table below showing consumption of energy in Britain:

Energy source	1950	1973	1980
coal	205	131	121
oil	25	160	121
natural gas	0	44	70
nuclear electricity	0	10	13
hydro-electricity	1	2	2

(Figures are in million tonnes of coal equivalent.)

(a) Draw a proportional bar chart to illustrate these statistics.
(b) Comment on the changes in energy consumption revealed by the statistics.

2.13 CHINA CLAY AND CEMENT

China clay

China clay (kaolin) is extracted from the granite areas of Hensbarrow Downs near St Austell, Cornwall, and Lee Moor near Plymouth, Devon. It is produced by chemical changes in granite and was formed when hot gases rose through the Earth's crust and broke down minerals in the rock. China clay is white.

The quarries are owned by English China Clays and employ over 1000 people. Much of the quarried material is waste sand, which is dumped in huge, steep-sided tips. Streams in the area run white because of the waste material.

The fine clay is purified, dried and transported to factories in Britain and Europe, especially Scandinavia and North America. A certain amount is shipped from the ports of Par and Plymouth, and from Fowey which can take larger boats of up to 10 000 tonnes. To reduce road congestion and nuisance, the owners have built a lorry road to Fowey on the course of an old railway line.

Uses	Percentage
paper manufacture	80
pottery and ceramics	10
paint, medicines, sweet fillings, rubber, fertilisers, cosmetics	10

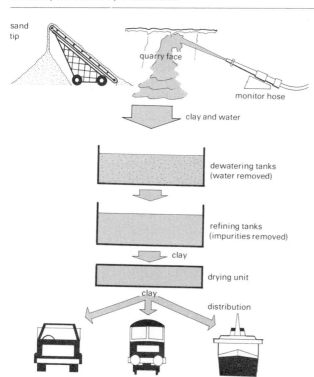

Fig. A China clay: from quarry face to distribution

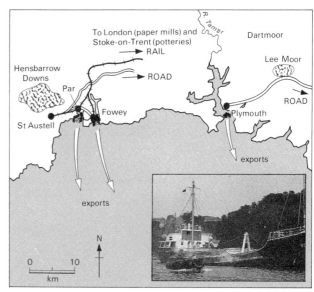

Fig. B The location of china clay quarries

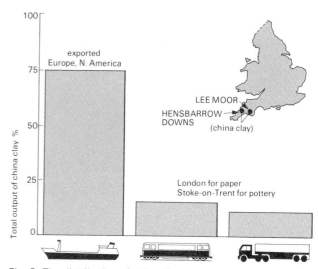

Fig. C The distribution of china clay

QUESTIONS

A1 What is china clay?

2 How is it extracted and processed?

3 What are the main uses of china clay?

4 How is the clay transported from south-west England?

B1 Most extractive industries involve some pollution. China clay waste affects the landscape and pollutes local streams. Do you think we should accept such pollution? What could be done to reduce it?

2 Britain exports few minerals. Which other minerals are exported from Britain?

Cement

Cement works are built close to supplies of chalk or limestone. Cement forms the basis of many modern building materials. When used with sands and gravels (aggregates), a wide range of concrete goods can be produced: building blocks, paving slabs, pipes, precast supports for bridges and buildings.

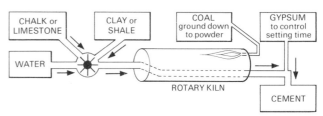

Fig. F Northfleet — how cement is made

Fig. D The Northfleet Cement Works, Kent

Key

A1 and A2   encircling railway; coal brought in, finished cement taken out

B   slurry tanks — receiving clay and chalk

C   rotary kilns (198 metres long)

D   gypsum intake

E   grinding mills

F   office block

G   exporting wharf

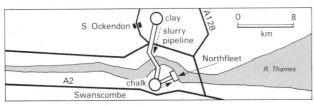

Fig. E The location of Northfleet

QUESTIONS

A1 Draw and label a simple line sketch of the Northfleet Works. Print the names of the raw materials in a different colour.

2 Using information given in this section, explain the process for making cement at Northfleet. State how each raw material is transported to the works.

3 Why is the Northfleet site so suitable for the production of cement?

B1 Energy accounts for about 40 per cent of cement-manufacturing costs. What are the other major costs?

2 Northfleet Works is situated in the middle of a built-up area. What problems do cement works present? What extra costs do you think have had to be met by the cement company?

ELECTRICITY

3.1 THE NATIONAL GRID

The first power station in Britain was opened in 1882. By the early decades of this century, each town had its own small power station. They had to be built close to their customers because electricity could not be transmitted far at that time. Today, electricity travels throughout Britain by a network of cables slung between steel pylons. The main cables are called the supergrid, and transmit electricity at 400 000 volts. Smaller cables carry electricity at lower voltages from the supergrid to the customer.

Fossil-fuel power stations

British power stations use three types of fossil fuel:

Coal-fired: Since coal is bulky and expensive to transport, coal-fired stations are on or near coalfields. The main locations are:
(a) The Trent Valley, where eleven power stations have been built including West Burton, Cottam and Ratcliffe-on-Soar, each of 2000 megawatt capacity (1 mw = 1 million watts). Low-cost coal is available from the nearby Yorkshire, Nottinghamshire and Derbyshire coalfields. The Trent provides cooling water and its valley provides suitable flat sites.
(b) The Lower Thames, where there are seven coal-fired power stations. The main locating factors are the great demand for electricity in the area, the large supplies of cooling water from the river Thames, and the easy shipment of coal down the east coast.

Oil-fired: They are located near oil refineries and away from coalfields. The largest, all 2000 mw, are at Fawley, Pembroke, Grain and Littlebrook, and use heavy fuel oil from nearby refineries. In Scotland, an oil-burning power station has been built at Peterhead. It uses North Sea oil brought ashore by pipeline. Peterhead is also equipped to use natural gas. There are small oil-fired stations on some of the islands off north-west Scotland.

Gas-fired: Most are small gas turbine units, using converted jet engines. Many are for standby use only. They are located mainly in areas remote from other power stations, eg, the Isle of Wight and East Anglia.

Figure B shows fossil fuels consumed by the Central Electricity Generating Board (CEGB), which controls the power stations in England and Wales. The proportions of the different fuels have varied considerably. Coal has increased from 69 per cent of the total in 1972/73 to 91 per cent in 1981/82, while oil has declined from 29 per cent to less than 9 per cent. As far as possible, the CEGB uses the cheapest fuel available. Figure C shows the generation costs estimated for three power stations currently under construction. The figures reveal why the CEGB and the government are in favour of nuclear and coal-fired power stations for the future.

Fig. A Major coal and oil fired power stations and the supergrid network

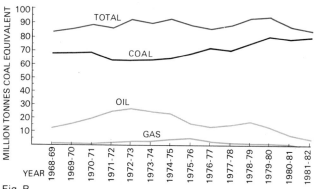

Fig. B

	Nuclear	**Coal-fired**	**Oil-fired**
	Dungeness B	Drax 2	Littlebrook D
Capital cost	1.03	0.77	2.00
Interest payments	0.74	0.46	1.13
Fuel costs	0.75	2.4	5.1
Others	0.25	0.21	0.25
Total cost	2.77	3.84	8.48
			pence per Kwh

Fig. C

A coal-fired power station

One of Britain's largest coal-fired power stations is Drax, 8 kilometres south-east of Selby in North Yorkshire. This location was chosen for three reasons:

1 It is close to the productive mines of the North Yorkshire coalfield.
2 There is ample flat land, with firm foundations.
3 Supplies of cooling water are available from the river Ouse which flows past the site.

Drax has three giant 660 mw generators. At maximum output, Drax generates 1980 mw, enough electricity to supply the needs of over two million people. Over 5 million tonnes of coal a year are brought from the Yorkshire coalfield by trains, each carrying 1000 tonnes of coal and operating on the 'merry-go-round' principle. Eighteen trains are needed each day.

A large power station needs a vast amount of cooling water. Over 200 million litres of water are

Fig. E Drax power station

needed at Drax every hour. The cooling water is used to turn steam back into water in the condenser. The cooling water is itself heated, and has to be cooled by piping it to ponds beneath the cooling towers. After being used several times, the cooling water is pumped back into the river Ouse and the temperature monitored to ensure that it does not rise above 30°C, which would be harmful to the fish.

Drax power station covers over 200 hectares. Filtering devices control air pollution, but some sulphur dioxide gas, dust and ash are released into the atmosphere. The waste ash, amounting to two million tonnes per year, is used mainly to cover a derelict ammunition dump nearby. The site is being landscaped.

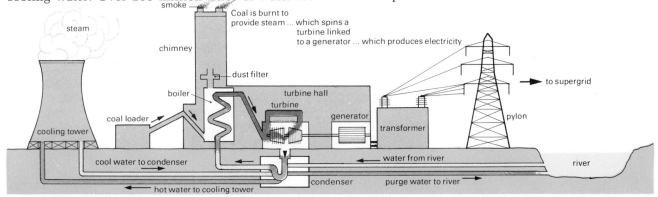

Fig. D How electricity is made

QUESTIONS

A1 What is the supergrid?
  2 Why is the Trent Valley a suitable location for coal-fired power stations?
  3 Where are most oil-fired power stations located?
  4 Why was Drax a suitable location for a coal-fired power station?
  5 How does a power station such as Drax affect the area around it?
B1 Why does the CEGB not favour oil-fired power stations?

  2 Study Fig B and explain the changes in the proportion of fuels consumed.
  3 What is meant by 'merry-go-round' train?
  4 Using Fig D, construct a flow chart showing how electricity is generated at a coal-fired power station.
C Discuss the factors affecting the location of fossil fuel-fired power stations in Britain. How has the distribution of power stations changed since the early decades of the twentieth century?

3.2 NUCLEAR POWER

The world's first commercial nuclear power station was opened in 1956 at Calder Hall in Cumbria. Today, seventeen such stations in Britain produce 10 per cent of our electricity. Since they use only small amounts of uranium as fuel, nuclear stations are not tied to their fuel source. The most important requirement is a large quantity of cooling water. All nuclear power stations except one are built on the coast. The exception, Trawsfynydd, has its own lake. The early nuclear power stations were built in fairly remote areas where less people were at risk in the event of an accident, and where other sources of energy were absent.

A nuclear power station is similar to fossil fuel-fired power stations in that it turns water into steam to drive a turbine linked to a generator. The heat needed to turn the water into steam is produced inside a nuclear reactor. Fuel rods of uranium are lowered into the reactor core. The uranium atoms are split in a controlled chain reaction called *nuclear fission*, which creates intense heat. The heat is then transferred to the boilers to create steam.

There are two types of nuclear power station in Britain, *magnox* and *advanced gas-cooled reactors* (AGRs). Nine magnox stations were built during the 1960s and have proved safe and reliable.

It was intended to have five AGR stations operating by 1976, but by 1983 only two were finished. Delays and cost increases were due to design and technical problems, poor industrial relations and the fact that each station had to be built on site rather than in a factory. AGRs produce more electricity than magnox stations (up to 1320 mw) and use enriched uranium fuel rather than the natural uranium used in the magnox stations.

Fig. A British nuclear power stations

As a result of high costs and delay to the AGR programme, the CEGB has turned to the American-designed *pressurised water reactor* (PWR) which should be cheaper and easier to build than the AGRs. Sizewell in Suffolk has been selected as the site for the first PWR in Britain. Named Sizewell B, the PWR will be built beside Sizewell A, a magnox station, if approved after a public enquiry.

The future

Research is continuing into the *fast breeder reactor*, which burns plutonium, a material created from uranium. Fast reactors can also 'breed' at least as much fuel as they use. Two experimental fast breeder reactors have been built at Dounreay in northern Scotland, but high costs and design problems have delayed further stations.

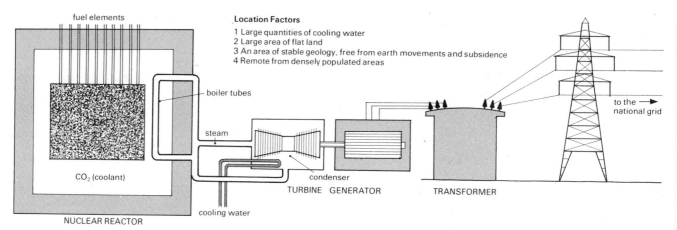

Fig. B Electricity from nuclear power — a magnox power station

Fig. C Greenpeace demonstrators

Fig. D Oldbury-on-Severn nuclear power station

Research is being carried out into the possibilities of generating electricity by *nuclear fusion* rather than fission (fission means splitting atoms; fusion means joining them). Nuclear fusion could solve our energy problems because it produces no dangerous radioactive waste and the fuel is simply water.

Opposition to nuclear power

Opposition to nuclear power has increased. Many people feel that it is too dangerous to proceed with. One of the greatest problems facing the nuclear industry is the disposal of the *radioactive waste*. Dangerously radioactive fuel rods are removed from the reactor core after seven years' use and stored in cooling ponds until their radiation levels have fallen below certain levels. They are then taken by rail to a reprocessing plant at Sellafield (Windscale), up to 2½ tonnes of spent fuel elements being carried in massive steel flasks weighing 50 tonnes. The flasks are designed to survive rail accident and fire, but their transport through built-up areas is opposed by anti-nuclear groups.

The waste parts of the fuel are converted into liquid and stored. There is at present no way of making the waste safe, and much will remain dangerous for centuries, some for thousands of years. The electricity boards point out that after twenty years of nuclear power the amount of stored radioactive waste would fill only one large house, but it is not satisfactory to store deadly material for centuries. Research is under way to discover permanent disposal methods. Firing the material into space or dumping it into the deep ocean trenches are two of the more fanciful ideas. The electricity boards' choice would be burial in deep shafts in remote ares of the country, but this has met with strong local opposition.

Medium- to low-level wastes are a problem also. Strictly controlled amounts of radioactive liquid and gas are discharged into the environment and other radioactive material is dumped at sea. Anti-nuclear groups have tried to disrupt the dumping.

The CEGB's plan to build a PWR nuclear power station at Sizewell in Suffolk has been attacked by anti-nuclear groups, who point to a near-disaster at the Three Mile Island PWR near Harrisburg, USA, in 1979. Opponents of nuclear power say that not enough is known of the long-term effects on the health of those who work in or live near nuclear power stations. They argue that Britain does not need more nuclear power stations because increased demand for electricity in the future can be met by new sources of power such as wind and tidal power.

QUESTIONS

A1 List the factors affecting the location of nuclear power stations.
 2 What is the fuel used in nuclear power stations?
 3 What do AGR and PWR stand for?
 4 List the problems of nuclear power.
B1 Why was the AGR programme delayed?
 2 What are the advantages of (a) nuclear fusion, (b) fast breeder reactors?
 3 What problems are posed by the disposal of radioactive nuclear waste? How far have they been overcome?
 4 Either (a) write a letter to a national newspaper supporting the construction of a PWR nuclear power station near your home, or (b) write a letter opposing it.
  Set out your reasons clearly and concisely.
C Describe and account for the location of nuclear power stations in Britain.

3.3 ENERGY ALTERNATIVES

Hydro-electricity

Only 2 per cent of Britain's electricity is generated by HEP stations because there is a lack of suitable sites. Most is generated in the Highlands of Scotland, but conditions are not ideal. Good sites for dams are rare because the valleys are usually wide. The major problem is that the water catchment areas are too small to support large schemes, and most HEP stations produce less than 50 mw of electricity. In some cases, catchment areas have been enlarged by building tunnels linking neighbouring drainage basins.

Dinorwic HEP station in North Wales is the largest in Britain. It operates on a *pumped-storage* principle, with two reservoirs at different levels. After driving the turbines, the water is pumped from the lower reservoir back to the upper reservoir to be used again. Dinorwic actually uses more electricity than it produces. Its six turbines produce 1800 mw; when operated in reverse they need over 2000 mw to pump water from Llyn Peris back up to Marchlyn Mawr. Why build a power station which uses more electricity than it generates? Dinorwic pumps water during the night when demand for electricity is low. During the day, it generates power cheaply which old, less efficient power stations would otherwise have to produce. Dinorwic therefore saves money.

A coal- or oil-fired power station takes several days

REQUIREMENTS OF AN HEP STATION

1 A constant supply of fast flowing water.
2 Deep valleys with narrow sections suitable for dam construction.
3 Impermeable rock beneath reservoirs.
4 A centre of population or industry nearby to use the electricity.

ADVANTAGES OF HEP	DISADVANTAGES OF HEP
1 It is cheap to produce	1 Very expensive to build
2 The fuel (water) cannot run out	2 There is a limited choice of suitable sites
3 It causes little pollution	3 Valleys may have to be flooded, destroying
4 Reservoirs can be used for recreation	farmland and disrupting local communities

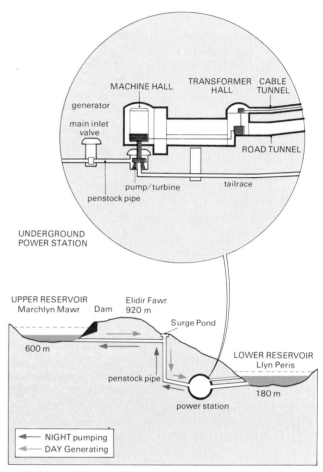

Fig. B Dinorwic pumped-storage power station

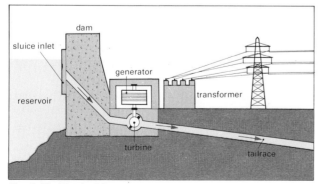

Fig. A Hydro-electric power

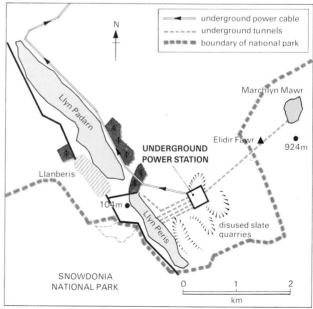

Fig. C The Dinorwic area

to reach full output after it is switched on, but Dinorwic takes only ten seconds to reach maximum output and can meet a sudden surge in demand. Some fossil-fuel stations are kept expensively ticking over as a reserve for surges in demand.

Electricity for the future

The rising cost of fossil fuels and fears over nuclear safety have led to research into alternative energy. Several forms of *renewable energy* have been studied.

Wind power: A new generation of windmills, called aero-generators, are being developed to produce electricity. Small experimental aero-generators have been installed in Wales and Scotland, but Britain's first large wind turbine is on the Orkney Islands. This 80 metre high giant produces 3 mw of electricity, enough to supply 15 per cent of the needs of Orkney. It has replaced two diesel power stations, which will be retained for use in conditions of calm or wind-speed over 100 kph.

The variability of wind power means it could never supply more than 10–20 per cent of Britain's electricity, but this would be a useful contribution.

Tidal power: A tidal power station exists on the river Rance, in France. The tidal current spins turbines linked to generators. In Britain, research has shown that power could be obtained from the tides of the Severn estuary, but a barrage would be expensive and would have serious effects on the environment.

Wave power: Tremendous energy is contained in the waves Britain receives from the Atlantic Ocean, but wave power would be difficult and expensive to generate on a large scale. A chain of machines up to 100 km long would be needed to produce 2000 mw of electricity, and only small-scale schemes seem practical in the near future.

Geothermal energy: Some areas of Britain, such as Bath, have natural hot water beneath them, and it may be possible to extract enough to provide heating, or to help produce steam to generate electricity. A large reservoir of geothermally heated water has been found beneath Marchwood, near Southampton. It is estimated that the water could produce about 4 mw of electricity.

Research is under way on 'renewable' geothermal heat, involving pumping water down a deep borehole into hot granite (the 'hot dry rocks' method). The granite will crack, the water will pass through the network of fractures and be heated to 150°C. The heated water would rise up a second shaft to the surface where its energy would be used to drive turbines. Tests have been carried out in Cornwall.

Solar power: Solar collectors to heat water have been used in Britain for several years. It would be difficult to apply this system to the production of hot water in the large amounts needed by power stations, in view of Britain's low sunshine amounts. The direct conversion of solar energy into electricity by the use of solar cells would be impracticable for a small country like Britain. A 2000 mw solar power station would cover 150 square kilometres and could generate only when the sun shone.

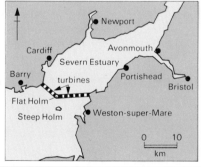

At Weston-super-Mare there is a tidal range of 11 m. A barrage could be built from Weston to the Welsh coast between Cardiff and Barry. Sluice gates would open on the rising tide and close at high tide, keeping the water trapped above the barrage. At low tide, the sluices would be opened and the water used to spin 9-metre diameter turbines. The electricity output of the barrage would be 5–6000 mw at its peak, but equal to 2000 mw throughout the year because the turbines would operate only for a few hours, twice a day. It would take over ten years to build the barrage.

ADVANTAGES OF THE BARRAGE
1 A reliable supply of cheap electricity.
2 The Bristol Channel could be used for recreation. At present it is too dangerous.
3 Jobs: 20 000 construction workers and 500 permanent staff, plus work for the engineering industry

PROBLEMS
1 Very expensive (£5 600 million).
2 The seaports of Cardiff, Bristol and Newport will lose trade because the reduced tidal range will limit the size of ships.
3 Sewage and industrial effluent is at present disposed of in the estuary. This would be stopped.
4 The salmon fisheries of the Usk and Wye would be threatened.
5 Loss of tidal mudflats would affect wading birds.

Fig. D The Severn Barrage

QUESTIONS

A1 What are the advantages and disadvantages of hydro-electric power stations?

2 Why is only 2 per cent of Britain's electricity generated by HEP stations?

3 How does a pumped-storage power station differ from an ordinary HEP station?

4 What is an aero-generator? Where in Britain have they been built?

5 (a) Where is Britain's best potential tidal power site? (b) How does a tidal power station work?

B1 A pumped-storage power station uses more electricity than it produces. Why are pumped-storage schemes built?

2 What would be the advantages and disadvantages of a Severn tidal barrage?

C Discuss and evaluate the various alternative sources of energy.

4.1 CHANGING INDUSTRY

By the end of the eighteenth century, Britain was becoming an industrial society. The rapid change from a rural agricultural society to an urban industrial society has been called the *Industrial Revolution*.

Fewer and fewer people were employed on the land because of enclosures and changing agricultural methods. More food could be produced by less people. Industry offered jobs, and migration of workers to the industrial areas began. Town growth was a result of industrial growth, and small towns and villages expanded. Britain became known as 'the workshop of the world'. In the nineteenth century, Belgium, West Germany and the USA began to compete with Britain's factories to supply the world's markets.

Figure B shows the different stages of economic growth. Countries may move from a traditional society to a highly industrialised one in a series of stages. At each stage, people's income and standard of living will increase. Since the 1920s, Britain has been at the high mass consumption level.

Types of industry

Primary industry refers to the production of raw materials and food, but not processing them. For example, forestry refers to growing and cutting down trees, but making wood into furniture or paper is a *secondary* or manufacturing industry. The other type of industry or employment is the *tertiary* or service sector. Although it does not produce goods, it does create wealth.

Fig. A

Changes in industry

Since the mid-1970s, changes have been taking place within Britain's industrial structure. The decline in manufacturing revealed by the pie graphs has greatly affected the geography of Britain. Much of the manufacturing industry grew up in specialised areas:

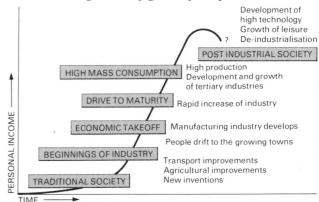

Fig. B Stages of economic growth

	Total employees (thousands)	Percentage of total
Total	20 068	100
Agriculture, forestry, fishing	345	1.7
Mining/quarrying	324	1.6
Total primary	669	3.3
Food, drink and tobacco	591	2.9
Chemicals, coal, petroleum products	410	2.0
Metal manufacture	298	1.5
Engineering, vehicles	2535	12.6
Textiles, clothing	644	3.2
Other manufacturing	1122	5.6
Total manufacturing	5600	27.8
Construction	999	5.0
Gas, electricity, water	320	1.6
Transport and communication	1357	6.8
Distributive trades	2514	12.5
Financial, professional	7105	35.4
Public administration, defence	1504	7.5
Total services	13 800	68.9

(Figures 1982; source, *Employment Gazette*)

Fig. C Employment in Britain

manufacturing decline 82   unemployment 84
urban Britain 106   NW England 156

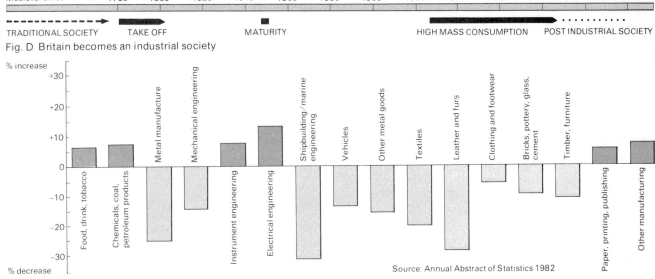

Fig. D Britain becomes an industrial society

Fig. E Changing manufacturing production 1975-80

Source: Annual Abstract of Statistics 1982

for example, the steel industry developed on the coal and iron-ore fields. As manufacturing has declined, certain areas have suffered badly from unemployment and economic depression.

Figure E shows growth industries and those that are declining. Most of the growth industries are *light* rather than *heavy*. They are usually concerned with making *consumer goods* or *high-technology* products. Examples are domestic machines, quality food and drinks, electronics and computers. An exception is the rapid growth of employment in North Sea oil and gas industries.

The traditional heavy industries which developed on the coalfields in the nineteenth century have declined. Many of these activities are termed *basic* industries. They make the products required to make manufactured goods. Basic industries like steel, metalworking and heavy engineering have all declined as total manufacturing production has fallen.

Although manufacturing has declined there has been growth in hi-tech industry, but this most recent 'technical revolution' has not brought many new jobs. The industrial processes need machines and equipment rather than people.

The changing industrial structure has brought large-scale unemployment; in 1976, 5 per cent of the British workforce were unemployed; by 1983, unemployment had reached 15 per cent. We may be experiencing a further stage in Britain's economic development, the coming of post-industrial society.

QUESTIONS

A1 What was the Industrial Revolution and how did it affect Britain?

2 What do the terms primary, secondary and tertiary industry mean?

3 (a) Give two examples of primary, secondary and tertiary industry.

(b) What percentage of Britain's workforce is employed in each of the three sectors of industry?

4 Give examples of industries making consumer goods and high-technology products.

B1 Study the table below, which shows the population of Britain between 1700 and 2000:

	Population (in millions)
1700	7
1750	9
1800	12
1850	22
1900	38
1950	50
2000 (estimated)	58

(a) Construct a line graph to illustrate the growth in population between 1700 and 2000.

(b) In which 50-year period did the greatest absolute increase occur?

(c) In which 50-year period did the greatest percentage increase occur?

(d) Attempt to explain the appearance of the line graph.

2 Explain why some regions of Britain have suffered greater industrial decline than others.

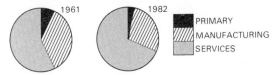

Fig. F Britain's changing levels of employment 1961-82

4.2 DISTRIBUTION OF INDUSTRY

All industries have special needs. They will try to locate carefully to make most profit and to keep costs as low as possible. Large areas of the country such as the Highlands of Scotland, Central Wales and Cornwall have little manufacturing industry, but may not be suitable as locations. Other areas are more favourable for industrial growth (Fig A).

Fig. A

Example 1 This assumes that the cost of transporting the raw materials to the factory is higher than the cost of transporting the product to the market. The factory is pulled to the raw materials.

Example 2 If much more of one raw material is used in the manufacturing process it will have a greater pull on location.

Fig. B

The influence of raw materials: The major industrial cities and the main industrial areas shown on Fig A were well established by the turn of the twentieth century. Early industries had to be close to sources of raw materials because inland transport was inadequate and expensive.

Iron-making was the foundation of the Industrial Revolution. The raw materials are iron-ore, coking coal and limestone, which are bulky and heavy. Nineteenth-century ironworks grew up on coalfields where deposits of iron-ore occurred. Figure B shows the pull of raw materials on the location of an industry such as iron-making.

An essential ingredient of all industry was fuel or energy. Coal was the energy source for raising steam and heating furnaces. It was, in fact, a raw material, and had a strong influence on the location of industry. Modern forms of energy such as oil, gas and electricity have a much weaker effect on industry because they can be distributed efficiently.

The influence of the ports: Industries requiring large amounts of imported raw materials are best located at ports. Ports provide *break-of-bulk* points: large quantities of bulky raw materials are unloaded and cannot be economically carried further. Thus, *port industries* using and processing raw materials grow up at seaports. Most of the country's largest industrial cities are also ports. Industrial cities inland quickly developed efficient links with coastal ports. Manchester was linked to the Mersey by the Manchester Ship Canal. The towns and cities of the Midlands and Yorkshire were linked by a network of canals and, later, railways. Roads and motorways are part of the modern system of links with ports.

Any transport route will provide suitable break-of-bulk points for industrial location. At the beginning of the Industrial Revolution, canals attracted industry. Later, factories developed along the railway routes. Figure C shows the Horlicks factory at Slough. The factory, built early this century, no longer uses rail transport and the former sidings are now the premises of a road transport company.

Market location: Some industries, particularly those providing raw materials for others, need to be near their customers. Bakeries are usually near their markets because fresh bread is perishable; motor car component factories are usually near the car assembly plants.

Labour supply: Factories need workers. Industry that uses a lot of labour is called *labour intensive*, and

Fig. C The Horlicks factory at Slough (railway location)

where a greater proportion of capital and machines are used it is *capital intensive*. Large towns and cities are sources of workers and managers, and new industry is often pulled towards urban areas where pools of labour are available.

Many of the old-established industrial centres still exist, although the original reasons for their location have disappeared. An example is Sheffield, where there is no longer any iron-ore but iron and steel goods are still made. *Inertia* is the term used to explain the continuing existence of the iron and steel industry in the Sheffield area.

More recently, the pull of the older industrial areas has declined and new attractions have emerged. Industry is more *footloose*. The new light industries are not dependent on fuels and raw materials. They do not have to be near their markets because transport does not account for a high proportion of their costs. *Government and EEC incentives* and local authority persuasion may attract industry today.

A satisfactory location for workers and staff does not always have to be one where costs are lowest and profits are highest. A factory location may be influenced by local amenities; schools, housing and leisure facilities are all important in helping to decide where to start a firm or business.

The location quotient: If we have employment statistics for a particular region or town it is possible to work out the degree of industrial *localisation*. The *location quotient* helps us to see the relative importance of various occupations in an area. The fact that the West Midlands is an important region for engineering and vehicles can be seen by comparing its location quotient with other regions.

$$\text{location quotient} = \frac{\begin{array}{c}\text{\% of West Midlands}\\ \text{employment in engineering and vehicles}\end{array}}{\begin{array}{c}\text{\% of Great Britain's}\\ \text{employment in engineering and vehicles}\end{array}}$$

$$= \frac{22\%}{12.6\%} \quad \text{or} \quad 1.75$$

A location quotient above 1.0 means that the percentage for the particular area is higher than that for the whole country.

We can compare the West Midlands location quotient of 1.75 with other regions. You can work out the last two.

$$\text{north-west} = \frac{13.2\%}{12.6\%} = 1.04 \qquad \text{south-east} = \frac{11.5\%}{12.6\%} = 0.91$$

$$\text{London} = \frac{8.6\%}{12.6\%} = \ldots\ldots \qquad \text{north} = \frac{13.1\%}{12.6\%} = \ldots\ldots$$

QUESTIONS

A1 Why did large industrial areas develop around (a) the coalfields, (b) the ports?

2 Look at Fig A.
  (a) Some new industrial areas depend on new types of fuel and raw materials. Suggest reasons for the growth of industrial centres at Teesside, Aberdeen and on the Moray Firth.
  (b) Some new industrial areas depend on new markets. Suggest reasons for the development of new industry in the London area and south-east England.

3 Many new industries are footloose. What do you understand by this term? Where in the country would such industries be found?

B1 Figure B gives examples of two different factory locations. Both are influenced by raw materials. Now look at the following two examples. For each example state which factors are influencing the location of the factory.

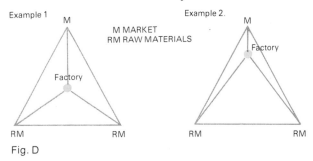

Fig. D

2 In question B1, the only locating influences are raw materials, the market and transport. What other factors influence industrial location?

3 Define the terms port industries, labour-intensive and capital-intensive industries, linkages, inertia.

4 (a) What is a location quotient?
  (b) Calculate the following quotients:

	Percentage employed	
	East Anglia	Great Britain
food, drink, tobacco	6.1	2.9
metal manufacture	0.3	1.5

  (c) What do the two location quotients for East Anglia tell us?

MANUFACTURING INDUSTRIES
4.3 LOCATING A FACTORY

A television manufacturer wants to open a new factory to make components for televisions. The company has already carried out a national survey of possible sites and the choice has been narrowed down to ten. You must carry out a detailed survey of each location with the aim of choosing the location with the *lowest total* costs.

The costs involved in manufacturing are made up of *fixed costs* and *variable costs*. In this exercise, the only fixed costs are labour and raw materials. The others vary according to the possible location. The table gives details of the costs involved. The map shows the ten possible locations, and the costs for Location 2 have been done for you. Follow the example and then calculate the costs for the other nine possible locations.

The location with the lowest total costs is the most suitable site.

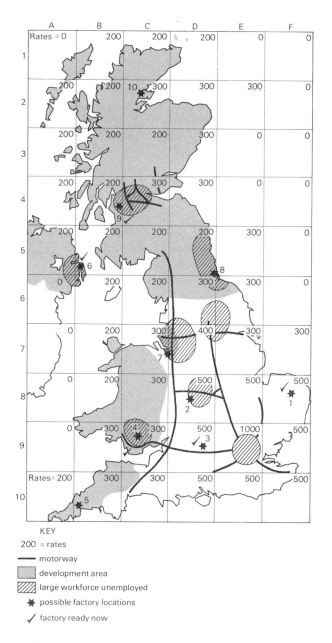

KEY

200 = rates

— motorway

▨ development area

▨ large workforce unemployed

✶ possible factory locations

✓ factory ready now

Fig. A

Fig. B

Costs	£	Location one	Location two	Location three
Labour costs (fixed)	+ 500		500	
Raw material costs (fixed)	+ 500		500	
Rates (variable — see map)			500	
Transport costs:				
(a) Number of squares to London *without motorways*	× £10		0	
(b) Number of squares to London *with motorways*	× £5		15	
Sea crossing	+ 100		0	
Development Area grants	− 500		0	
Large workforce unemployed	− 100		− 100	
Factory available now	− 500		0	
Total			£1415	

Fig. C

Fig. D

QUESTIONS

A1 (a) Which location do you suggest for the new components factory?

(b) Give reasons for your choice.

2 Which locations are a possible alternative if the company decides not to accept your first choice?

3 Which locations are high-cost? What disadvantages do these locations face?

4 What are the possible disadvantages of choosing the lowest-cost locations?

5 The exercise has stressed the importance of costs in industrial location. (a) Have any important costs been left out of the exercise? (b) Other factors besides costs are becoming increasingly important in industrial location. Suggest some other factors which might influence a company's choice of a new location.

B1 Study Fig D and answer the following questions.

(a) Briefly describe the industrial landscape.

(b) Suggest likely reasons for the location of industry here.

(c) What are the advantages for the local population of a modern industrial area such as this?

(d) What problems might be experienced in the local area if a new industrial estate was located there? (The evidence may not be clear from a photograph.)

4.4 IRON AND STEEL

The British iron and steel industry has gone through several changes of location over the last three centuries.

Stage A: Small beginnings: From the sixteenth century, small ironworks were built with waterwheels to power the bellows and hammers. The iron was smelted in a furnace heated by charcoal. The best sites were therefore in forested areas beside rivers. Early ironmaking areas were the Forest of Dean in Gloucestershire and the Weald of Kent and Sussex.

By the late seventeenth century, Britain was facing an energy crisis because timber was running out. The British iron industry began to decline and foreign iron had to be imported.

Stage B: The move to the coalfields: The energy crisis was solved by a Shropshire ironmaster named Abraham Darby, who perfected the use of coke instead of charcoal to smelt iron at Coalbrookdale. Darby's son, also called Abraham, invented the blast furnace which made the coke burn fiercely. Limestone was added to the blast furnace to remove impurities from the iron. These technological changes in the process of ironmaking were accompanied by a change in the power source. The waterwheel was replaced by the steam engine.

During the eighteenth century, the old ironmaking areas began to decline and new ironworks were built on the coalfields.

Stage C: Steelmaking: In 1856, Henry Bessemer invented a reliable method of making steel using his 'Bessemer converter' which meant that existing ironworks had to be modified. Many older coalfield-based ironworks were closed because they were unsuitable.

Stage D: The move to the coast: Reductions in the amount of coal needed to produce a tonne of steel meant that steelworks were increasingly freed from their coalfield location. New steelworks were built on iron-ore fields at Corby and Scunthorpe, but the best location in the twentieth century was on the coast beside deep water such as Port Talbot (Fig C). This was because the British ore, always low in iron content, was becoming more expensive to mine as the best deposits were exhausted.

Today, only 20 per cent of the ore used in British steelworks is home-produced. The old coalfield-based steelworks closed as large coastal works opened. The economics behind this are simple: carrying iron-ore by rail for 100 kilometres costs as much as transporting it over 6000 kilometres by sea.

Stage E: Rationalisation: The closure of the coalfield-based steelworks has meant the disappearance of many famous towns from the steelmaking map.

The collapse of an industry
In 1967, leading privately-owned steel companies were nationalised (taken over by the government). The British Steel Corporation (BSC) was formed. It

Fig. A The Ebbw Vale steelworks: coalfield location

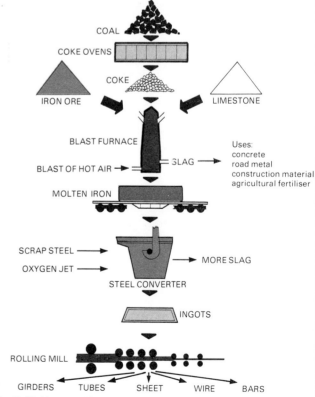

COAL

COKE OVENS

COKE

IRON ORE

LIMESTONE

BLAST FURNACE

BLAST OF HOT AIR → ← SLAG →

Uses:
concrete
road metal
construction material
agricultural fertiliser

MOLTEN IRON

SCRAP STEEL →

OXYGEN JET →

→ MORE SLAG

STEEL CONVERTER

INGOTS

ROLLING MILL

GIRDERS   TUBES   SHEET   WIRE   BARS

Fig. B Making steel in an integrated steelworks

Fig. C The Port Talbot steelworks: tidewater location

was clear to BSC that the cheapest way to produce steel was in large, modern *integrated* steelworks using imported iron-ore and the basic oxygen process of steelmaking.

In 1972, a £3000 million scheme was announced to raise steel production. This ambitious scheme was dependent upon the forecast increase in steel production. Far from increasing, British steel production declined dramatically from 27 million tonnes in 1968 to only 11 million tonnes by 1980, and BSC was losing over £1 million a day. Unable to sell the steel they produced, the corporation rapidly closed its old plants, causing severe unemployment. Even the sites chosen for development in 1967 were affected: the workforces at Llanwern, Port Talbot and Scunthorpe were halved. Total BSC workforce fell from 180 000 to under 100 000.

The reasons for the collapse include:

1 Over-investment, and high interest charges.
2 Demand for steel dropped because of the economic recession, resulting in overcapacity.
3 Increased competition from cheap foreign steel.
4 Poor industrial relations and a thirteen-week strike in 1980 caused customers to lose confidence and reduced the morale of workforce and management.

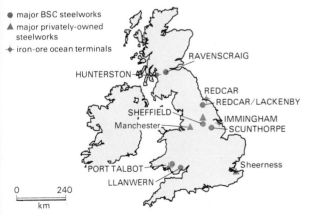

Fig. D The British steel industry

QUESTIONS

A1 Study Fig E and make a large copy.

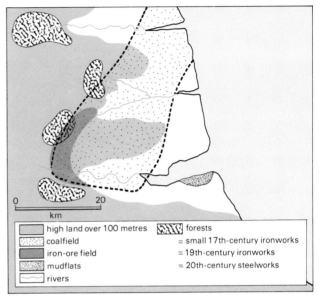

Fig. E

(a) Choose three suitable sites for small seventeenth-century ironworks and mark them on the map. Make a key to show the raw materials and power source.
(b) Choose two suitable sites for early nineteenth-century ironworks. Make a key to show the raw materials and power source.
(c) Choose the best site for a twentieth-century steelworks. Make a key to show the raw materials.
(d) Explain briefly your choice for each site.

B1 The table shows the sources of iron ore for the British steel industry today:

Source	% of total
Domestic (UK)	22
Brazil	19
Canada	16
Sweden	9
Australia	8
South Africa	8
Others	18

(a) Construct a pie graph to illustrate these statistics.
(b) The average iron content of British ore is 25 per cent; the foreign ores average 60 per cent iron content. What effect does this have on the transport costs of foreign ore compared to British ore?

2 Why did the British steel industry decline during the 1970s?

C Describe and account for the present-day location of the iron and steel industry in Britain.

4.5 IRON AND STEEL: NEW AND OLD

Figure A shows the Redcar/Lackenby iron and steelworks on Teesside. The Lackenby steel plant was supplied with iron from three blast furnaces at the neighbouring Cleveland works. In 1979, a new blast furnace was opened at Redcar and the three Cleveland furnaces were closed. The Redcar site was chosen because it was close to a new deepwater ore terminal. Imported coking coal and iron-ore are unloaded from bulk carriers of up to 150 000 tonnes.

Fig. A Redcar/Lackenby steelworks

Steelmaking at Teesside

Stage 1: The coal is sent to the coke ovens and the iron-ore to the sinter or pellet plants.

Stage 2: The coke and iron-ore pellets are loaded into the blast furnace which produces 10 000 tonnes of iron daily. The furnace gases are used to fuel a 71-megawatt power station which provides the blast of hot air for the furnace, and the electricity used on the site.

Stage 3: The liquid metal from the blast furnace is carried by a special train to the steelmaking plant at the Lackenby works seven kilometres south-west of Redcar. The original plan for Redcar included three blast furnaces and a steelworks on the same site but these plans were cancelled in 1978.

Stage 4: At Lackenby, the molten iron is turned into steel by the basic oxygen process, in which a blast of oxygen is blown through the iron by an oxygen lance. Each 260-tonne batch of iron is turned into steel

within fifty minutes. The old open-hearth furnaces took between eight and twelve hours to produce 360 tonnes of steel.

Stage 5: The steel is sent to the casting mills to be cast into slabs and ingots.

Stage 6: The rolling mills turn the cast steel into coil, plates or beams which are sent to customers in Britain and abroad.

Redcar/Lackenby produces 4.5 million tonnes of

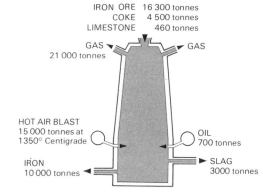

Fig. B An aerial view of BSC Teesside

steel per year, 30 per cent of total British production, and employs 10 000.

The site covers seven square kilometres, most of which is not yet used. However, if it is developed as originally planned, Redcar may become one of the world's major steel centres.

IRON ORE 16 300 tonnes
COKE 4 500 tonnes
LIMESTONE 460 tonnes

GAS 21 000 tonnes
GAS

HOT AIR BLAST 15 000 tonnes at 1350° Centigrade
OIL 700 tonnes

IRON 10 000 tonnes
SLAG 3000 tonnes

Fig. C The raw materials

Corby

Corby in Northamptonshire is a town founded on iron and steel. In 1934, only 1200 people lived there, but in that year an iron and steelworks was opened. Corby was chosen because it was at the centre of a large iron-ore field. Within two years, the workforce of the steelworks was double that of Corby's original population. A thousand of the men had been recruited from the depressed steel districts of central Scotland to work in the new plant. Over half of Corby's population today is of Scottish descent. The 1983 population was 47 500.

By 1950, Corby had a population of 16 000. It was designated as a new town to control its rapid growth and attract alternative employment. Despite this, by the mid-seventies over half the town's workforce was still employed at the steelworks. The town's economy was closely linked with the works; the steelmen and their families spent their money in local shops, cafés and pubs. There were few other industries. When BSC closed the iron and steelmaking part of the plant in 1980, 6000 men lost their jobs. The tube-steel plant remains open, employing 5000.

Following the closure, Corby was declared a development area and an enterprise zone, the first in the Midlands. Aid from the government, local authorities, the European Regional Developent Fund and the European Coal and Steel Community has been intended to bring new jobs. Industrial estates have been laid out, warehouses and factories built. BSC has set up a subsidiary, BSC (Industry), to help create jobs in areas affected by steel closures.

Corby is seriously affected by closure of the steel-works. The unemployment rate is over 20 per cent. The town has the highest crime rate in Northamptonshire. There is no hospital or railway station. The technical college has closed and shops are closing. Hundreds of council houses stand empty. Some new firms have been attracted, but other companies also have made men redundant. Corby faces strong competition from two nearby new towns, Northampton and Milton Keynes, but its situation is more encouraging than that of steel-closure areas such as Consett in north-east England and Ebbw Vale in South Wales.

QUESTIONS

A1 List the main source of raw materials for the Redcar/Lackenby works (Fig D).

2 (a) How much steel does Redcar/Lackenby produce in a year?

(b) How many people are employed there?

3 Why was Corby chosen as the site for a steel-works in the 1930s?

4 Why was Corby steelworks closed?

5 The table below shows the population of Corby between 1931 and 1983:

year	1931	1951	1961	1971	1976	1981	1983
population (in thousands)	1.2	16	36	51	54	52.7	47.5

Draw a line graph to illustrate these statistics.

B1 The table below shows the production of steel in four countries between 1960 and 1980, in millions of tonnes:

Country	1960	1965	1970	1975	1980
UK	25	27	28	20	11
Japan	22	41	93	102	111
West Germany	34	37	45	40	44
Brazil	2	3	5	9	15

(a) Draw a line graph to illustrate these statistics.

(b) Suggest why Brazil has expanded its steel production rapidly since 1970.

2 The figures below show the amount of coal required in tonnes to produce one tonne of iron in Britain:

year	1840	1875	1935	1980
tonnes of coal	3.5	2.3	1.7	1.0

How do these figures help explain the locational changes in the British steel industry between 1840 and 1980?

3 Why did the closure of the steelworks have such a dramatic effect upon the community of Corby?

4 Design an advertisement to attract industrialists to build factories in Corby. You should make the advertisement as informative as possible and list the incentives available.

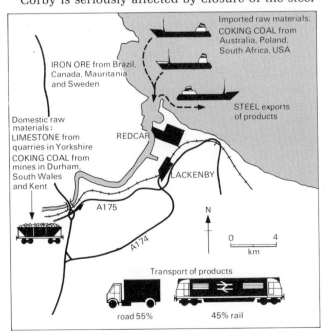

Fig. D The material input and output of the Redcar blast furnace

4.6 OIL-REFINING

Crude oil is a mixture of liquids and gases. The oil has to be processed to separate the various products. The processing is carried out at an *oil refinery*.

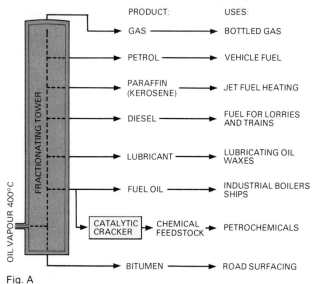

Fig. A

Fig. C

1 The crude oil arrives by ship or pipeline and is stored in tanks.

2 The crude oil is piped to the *fractionating tower* (Fig A) and heated to 400°C so that it evaporates. The oil vapour rises up the tower and cools. As it cools, condensation takes place. Each product condenses at a different temperature and height up the tower. The heavy oils such as bitumen condense first and petrol condenses last, leaving gas at the top of the tower.

3 Fractionation produces too much heavy oil, so some is sent to the *catalytic cracker* where lighter oils are obtained.

Until World War II most of Britain's oil was imported from refineries near the oilfields overseas. After the war, many refineries were built in Britain. It was much cheaper to import crude oil and refine it than to import the expensive products.

Figure C shows the location of these oil refineries. They are all on the coast, due to the following factors:

1 Deep water is needed for the crude-oil tankers.

2 Large amounts of cooling water are used, up to 24 million litres per hour.

3 A large area of flat land is needed, up to 500 hectares.

4 The distribution of the wide range of refined products is expensive, so the refinery has to be as close as possible to its markets.

Oil refining in South Wales

South Wales is the major oil-refining centre in the UK. The first large oil refinery was opened at Llandarcy near Swansea in 1921. Crude oil was imported through Swansea Docks. After World War II, oil tankers were built larger and larger in order to carry more oil at a cheaper rate. Swansea Docks was too small for them. In 1961, a new deepwater terminal was opened at Milford Haven, 100 kilometres west of Llandarcy. Milford Haven is a ria, or drowned river valley. Tankers of up to 250 000 tonnes dock at the BP terminal and the crude oil is sent by pipeline to Llandarcy. Llandarcy is an example of *industrial inertia*. It was cheaper for BP to keep the Llandarcy refinery open than to build a new one at Milford Haven. Coastal tankers still operate from Swansea Docks to distribute oil products.

The deep water at Milford Haven has attracted other oil companies. There are now three oil refineries here (Fig D).

	1938	1950	1955	1965	1975	1982	1983
Number of refineries	8	13	15	18	22	18	16
Annual capacity (million tonnes)	2	11	30	72	150	112	102

Fig. B The development of oil refining in the UK

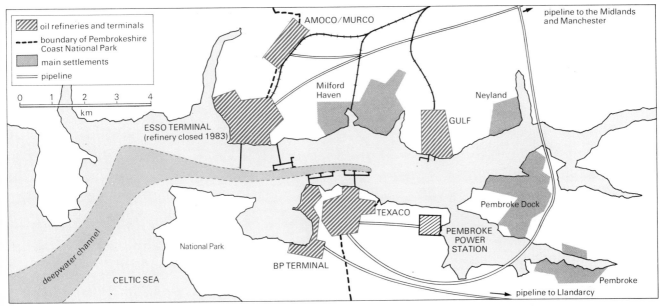

Fig. D Milford Haven

Amoco/Murco refinery at Milford Haven: This refinery was built by the American-based multi-national company Amoco. It was opened in 1973 on a 300-hectare site (Fig D). The refinery was expanded in 1981 by the construction of a catalytic cracker built in association with Murco Petroleum, another US multinational.

Crude oil from the North Sea, north and west Africa and the Middle East arrives in tankers of up to 275 000 tonnes. The refinery has its own deepwater jetty with three berths for crude and product tankers. This is a medium-sized refinery with an annual capacity of 5.4 million tonnes (the largest refinery in Britain is Fawley with an annual capacity of 15.6 million tonnes).

The products of the refinery include petrol, propane, butane, diesel, naphtha and fuel oil, which are distributed as follows:
1 By sea, in coastal tankers of up to 30 000 tonnes.
2 By rail, via the refinery's own rail sidings. Four or five trains leave the refinery every day.
3 By road, in tankers carrying petrol and diesel to petrol stations throughout the area.
4 To the Midlands and Manchester by a 400-kilometre pipeline owned jointly by all the refinery companies at Milford Haven.

Despite the great size and cost of the refinery, only 345 people are employed, 80 per cent recruited locally. The refinery contributes to the local economy through rates, harbour dues and local services.

Since the mid-1970s, demand for oil has decreased because of rising prices and the economic recession. Six oil refineries have closed.

Refining area	Number of refineries	Annual capacity (million tonnes)
South Wales	4	24.9
Humber	2	15.9
Southampton Water	1	15.6
Thames Estuary	2	13.2
Mersey Estuary	2	13.0
Tees Estuary	2	10.2
Firth of Forth	1	8.8
Firth of Tay	1	0.35
Firth of Clyde	1	0.3
Total	16	102.25

Fig. E The annual capacity of oil refining areas

QUESTIONS

A1 What processes take place at an oil refinery?
2 Describe the location of Britain's oil refineries.
3 What changes have occurred in the British oil-refining industry since the mid-1970s?

B1 Figure E shows the capacity of Britain's oil-refining areas. On a map of the UK, locate each area and draw circles proportional to the refinery capacity of each area, to a scale of 10 mm diameter: 10 million tonnes. Mark areas with a capacity of less than 5 million tonnes with a dot.
2 Account for the growth and recent decline of the oil-refining industry in the UK.
3 Why does Llandarcy oil refinery provide an example of industrial inertia?
4 (a) Draw a sketch map showing the location of the Amoco/Murco oil refinery.
   (b) Explain the siting of the oil refinery.
   (c) List the products of the refinery and describe the distribution of these products to market.

4.7 CHEMICALS

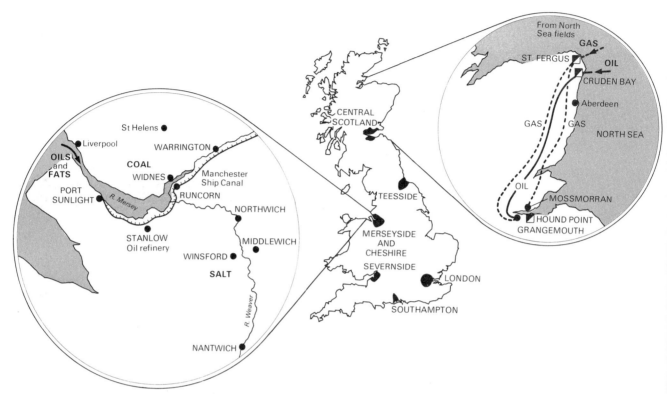

Fig. A The location of chemicals in Britain

The chemical industry is one of Britain's most important industries. Half a million people work in the industry and chemicals account for 15 per cent by value of British exports.

Heavy chemicals

These are basic to the whole structure of the industry. They have been called the chemical 'building blocks'. Heavy chemical works are located at the source of the raw materials or at tidewater sites for imports. Works have concentrated at these sites; they share the same port facilities and transport systems. Often, there are *linkages* in the manufacturing processes.

One of the major heavy chemical areas is north-west England. Beneath the valley of the river Weaver in Cheshire lie deposits of rock salt, which is extracted by pumping water into the rock layers to dissolve the salt and form brine which is pumped up to the surface. The water is evaporated from the brine, leaving the salt. The heat was obtained originally by burning coal from the south Lancashire coalfield, but today electricity is used.

The brine is piped from the saltfield to the chemical-producing towns of Runcorn and Widnes. Here, it is electrolysed to yield caustic soda, hydrogen and

chlorine, which are used to produce a range of chemicals including fertilisers, phosphorus and ammonia. Soap-making became established at Widnes, Warrington and Port Sunlight based on imported fats and vegetable oils from West Africa plus salt and caustic soda. Petrochemical industries have developed in the area using materials from Stanlow oil refinery. Other industries associated with chemicals in this area include margarine and detergent at Port Sunlight and glass at St Helens.

Another important heavy chemical area is Teesside. The Billingham works was located here during World War I using local salt and coal. Billingham now produces a range of heavy chemicals including sulphuric acid, nitric acid and ammonia.

Light chemicals

Light chemicals such as dyes, disinfectants, detergents and pharmaceuticals depend upon heavy chemical products. Many light chemical works are located near heavy chemical plants. Others have been built in development areas where government incentives are available, or near to markets, especially in and around London. Bristol and Swindon have attracted several light chemical firms

North Sea oil 40–43   Teesside 140
South Wales 151   NW England 156

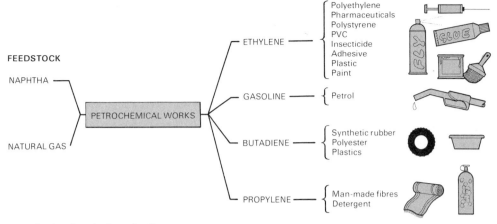

Fig. B Flow-diagram of petrochemical production

with easily available large sites, low rent and the M4 motorway link with London. As with heavy chemicals, there are linkages within the industry which result in concentration of plants.

Petrochemicals

The petrochemical industry uses *naphtha* from the oil-refining process and natural gas as raw materials. Most petrochemical works are located near oil refineries such as on Teesside and Southampton Water. An important exception is Severnside, where an ICI plant at Avonmouth makes plastics from ethylene piped from Fawley.

At Mossmorran in Fife, a new petrochemical complex uses North Sea natural gas piped ashore from the Brent and Frigg Fields to a land terminal at St Fergus near Peterhead. Here, a separation plant removes methane and transfers it to the natural gas grid. Natural gas liquids which remain are piped south to Mossmorran. Work on the Mossmorran site began in 1979 and the plant should be fully operational by 1985. It was originally intended to be built at Peterhead where the natural gas comes ashore, but local protests led to the project being re-sited to central Scotland where unemployment rates were higher. Mossmorran forms a part of a much larger petrochemical industry in eastern central Scotland. There is a large refinery at Grangemouth. The main pipeline from the Forties North Sea oilfield terminates at the refinery. The refinery provides feedstock (raw materials) for several neighbouring petrochemical plants producing synthetic rubber, plastics, man-made fibres and chemicals.

Petrochemicals has been a growth industry since World War II, but since the late 1970s demand has fallen. The resulting overcapacity has caused job losses and plant closures.

QUESTIONS

A1 How important is the chemical industry for Britain?

 2 What is meant by 'building block' chemicals?

 3 Why are heavy chemical works located at the source of the raw material or at tidewater sites?

 4 How is salt extracted from the Cheshire saltfield?

 5 List the chemical products of north-west England.

 6 What does the term 'feedstock' mean?

B1 Describe and explain the location of the chemical industry in Britain.

 2 'Petrochemicals has been a growth industry since World War II, but since the late 1970s demand has fallen.' Explain the growth and recent decline of the petrochemical industry.

C (a) With the aid of a sketch map, locate the major areas of one advanced industrial nation which are concerned with the production of *either* heavy chemicals *or* petrochemicals.

 (b) Select one of the areas you have located and account for its production and importance.

Fig. C BP Grangemouth

4.8 ALUMINIUM

Fig. A

Kitchen foil, a drink can, an airliner . . . what do these have in common? They all use aluminium.

Aluminium has several advantages over other metals. It is strong but light in weight. It does not rust. It is a good conductor of electricity and transmitter of heat. It is non-magnetic and easy to recycle. It can be rolled into wafer-thin foil or drawn into fine wire.

The process of producing aluminium was perfected in the 1880s. The raw material is a rock called bauxite which is found in several countries including Australia, Jamaica, Guinea and the Soviet Union. There is none in Britain. The bauxite is crushed and refined to a white powder called alumina, from which molten aluminium is produced.

The major requirement for an aluminium smelter is large amounts of cheap electricity. Often this means hydro-electricity. Three small plants had been built in Britain by 1930, all in the Highlands of Scotland and all with their own hydro-electric power stations. They produced about 30 000 tonnes of aluminium per year.

By 1965, Britain was using over 300 000 tonnes of aluminium, most of which had to be imported. During the late 1960s, three large smelters were built. No suitable hydro-electric sites were available so cheap electricity had to be obtained elsewhere. The Invergordon and Holyhead smelters obtained their electrical supplies from the national grid, but the Lynemouth smelter has its own power station using coal from a modern colliery nearby.

The smelters, built in development areas, were hailed as a major triumph for the government's regional development policy. Unfortunately, none found it easy to compete with foreign imports. The Invergordon smelter closed in 1981, a victim of the economic recession. The smelter's owners, British Aluminium, blamed the high cost of electricity.

Anglesey aluminium smelter

A smelter started production at Holyhead, North Wales, in 1971. It is jointly owned by an American company, Kaiser Aluminium, and a British company, Rio Tinto Zinc. Holyhead was chosen for the following reasons:

1 Access to electricity from the national grid via Wylfa nuclear power station. The smelter requires 230 megawatts.

2 Deep water available for berthing alumina bulk carriers of up to 55 000 tonnes.

3 Road and rail links for distribution of products. Exports are shipped out through Holyhead Harbour.

4 A large area of available land; the smelter covers over 100 hectares.

5 Availability of labour.

6 Government grants and other assistance (Holyhead is within a development area).

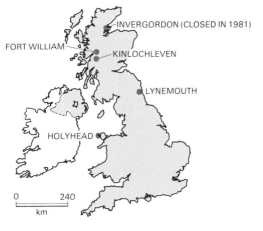

Fig. B (i) Aluminium smelters in Britain

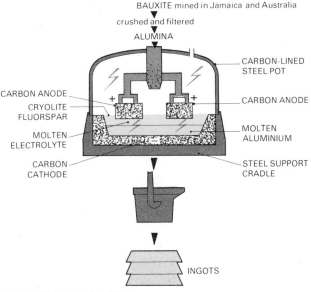

Fig. B (ii) Making aluminium

Fig. C The Angelsey aluminium smelter

1 Deepwater terminal
2 Offices and laboratories
3 Alumina storage
4 Carbon area buildings
5 Aluminium potrooms
6 & 7 Maintenance and storage
8 Air filtration equipment and chimney
9(a) Electricity input
  (b) Liquefied petroleum gas
10 Conveyor
11 Rail link

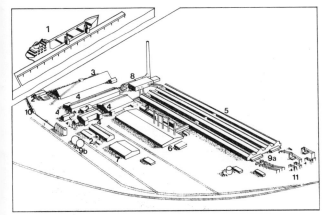

Fig. D The Angelsey aluminium smelter

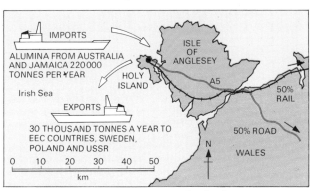

Fig. E Material assembly and product distribution

The smelter produces up to 112 000 tonnes of aluminium per year and employs 1300 people, which makes it one of the largest single employers in North Wales. The layout of the smelter is shown in Fig D. The four pot-rooms are each over half a kilometre long. This is a large and expensive plant, and care has been taken in the design of the buildings to minimise its impact on the beautiful scenery of Holy Island. Air filters prevent harmful air pollution.

QUESTIONS

A1 What advantages does aluminium have over other metals?

2 Where are Britain's four aluminium smelters?

3 How is aluminium produced?

B1 Explain why Holyhead was chosen as a site for an aluminium smelter. Use these headings in your explanation: (a) Power, (b) Transport, (c) Labour, (d) Government policy.

2 Here is a list of the market areas for aluminium produced at Holyhead for a recent period of three months:

Market area	Amount in tonnes
Aluminium Powder Company (next to the smelter)	1003
rest of Wales	2250
north-west England	4300
Midlands	2184
Scotland	162
south-east England	1708
north-east England	385
East Anglia	10
exports	8998

This is 'raw data' printed in the form in which the authors obtained it.

Present this data more usefully by doing the following:

(a) Place the market areas into rank order.

(b) Calculate the total tonnage.

(c) Calculate the percentage of the total sent to each market area.

(d) Construct a pie graph to illustrate the percentages.

4.9 TEXTILES

Wool cloth has been spun and woven for 12 000 years. *Spinning* involves twisting individual strands to make yarn which is then woven to make cloth. *Weaving* takes place on a loom. The first looms consisted of lengths of yarn (*warps*) hung on a beam and weighted with stones. The *weft* yarn was then threaded across the warps. The two basic processes have been greatly improved and today are highly mechanised.

Alongside clothmaking a chemical industry grew up, making bleaches, soaps and dyes. The raw materials were salt from Cheshire and imported fats and oils. Machines were made in the engineering factories of several towns, especially Manchester. A distinct urban landscape developed, in which tall mills with chimneys rose above densely-packed terraced houses. Living and working conditions were often hard.

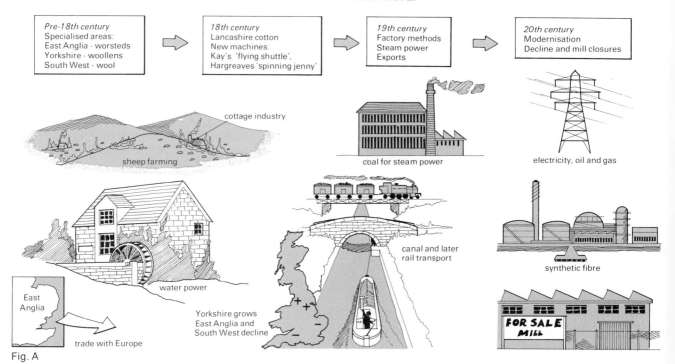

Fig. A

England had become a major wool and cloth-making country by the twelfth century. Four areas of the country became important: the West Country, West Yorkshire, Lancashire and East Anglia. Lancashire and West Yorkshire had soft water for washing the yarns, and fast-flowing streams which could be used for water power.

Cotton

During the Industrial Revolution, the coalfields attracted large-scale factory development. Lancashire became the world's most important cotton goods area. Liverpool developed as its major importing and exporting port. Later, Manchester became a port with the opening of the Manchester Ship Canal. Towns specialised in the clothmaking processes but in some towns there were mills which combined spinning and weaving.

Wool

Across the Pennines in West Yorkshire, the textile industry specialised in wool. Like Lancashire, there had been a *domestic* or *cottage industry* making wool cloth. Sheep-farmers combined farming with making yarns and cloth. Large-scale factory methods were possible with steam-powered machinery. The coal came from the Yorkshire coalfield. Many aspects of the woollen industry are similar to the cotton areas.

Yorkshire benefited from being near the Lancashire cotton industry because many new textile machines were invented and first used in Lancashire. Yorkshire mill-owners modified the cotton machines for the woollen industry. East Anglia and south-west England took several decades to follow suit and lost trade as a result. They were at a disadvantage because of their remoteness from coalfields.

Yorkshire, unlike Lancashire, specialised in

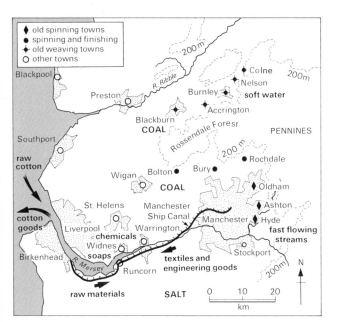

Fig. B Textiles in Lancashire

Fig. C A canal-side woollen mill in Huddersfield

products, not in processes:

woollens: Huddersfield and south-eastern towns such as Dewsbury and Batley

worsted (a tightly woven woollen cloth): north-western towns such as Bradford, Halifax and Keighley

shoddy (a textile made up from old knitted goods): Dewsbury and Batley

carpets: Halifax and Dewsbury

marketing: Bradford

clothing: Leeds

textile machinery: Bradford, Leeds, Huddersfield, Keighley and other towns.

Decline

The cotton and the woollen industries have declined since World War I. Figure D shows the changes in employment and output in the two major textile-producing areas. The decline in employment in Lancashire between 1950 and 1981 was 86 per cent. In Yorkshire, the decline was 70 per cent.

The reasons for the decline include:

1 Out-dated machinery.
2 Old fashioned processes.
3 High production costs.
4 Competition from man-made fibres.
5 Competition from producers overseas — the Far East, India, Korea, Portugal, Greece and Italy.
6 Loss of overseas markets as developing countries started their own textile industries.
7 Slowness to adapt to changing market demands.

QUESTIONS

A1 Explain briefly the meaning of the following: spinning, weaving, loom, warp, weft.
 2 Make a list of the changes in the English textile industry from medieval times to the present day.
 3 What type of urban landscape grew up in the textile areas in the nineteenth century?

B1 Look at the statistics in Fig D.
   (a) Calculate the decline in numbers employed between 1950 and 1981 for Lancashire and Yorkshire.
   (b) In 1981, which area was the most productive (produced more cloth per employee)?
 2 Use your atlas to draw a map of West Yorkshire. Locate the Yorkshire towns listed on this page. Design a key for the specialised products.
 3 Why has the textile industry suffered such a great decline since 1920?

Lancashire cotton area

	Employed	Cloth woven (million metres²)
1950	330 000	2266
1960	214 000	1750
1970	109 000	1220
1975	80 000	910
1981	44 000	490

Yorkshire woollen area

	Employed	Cloth woven (million metres²)
1950	170 000	377
1960	153 000	343
1970	94 000	215
1976	55 000	142
1981	45 000	105

Fig. D Textiles in Lancashire and Yorkshire 1950-81

4.10 TEXTILES TODAY

You will probably find that your blouse or shirt is made of polyester and cotton and your skirt or trousers contain polyester and wool. What looks and feels like a woollen jumper will probably contain acrylic fibre and it is almost certain that you will have some nylon in your hosiery or underwear.

Britain is an important manufacturer of *synthetic fibres*, made in petrochemical centres such as Teesside and the Mersey area. The *cellulosic* fibres are derived from cellulose and have been produced in Britain since the 1920s.

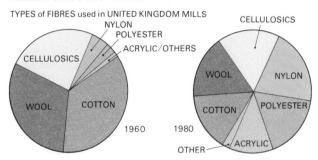

Fig. A

The introduction of man-made or artificial fibres (Fig A) has been one of many changes in the British textile industry. The textile areas had to adapt to decline, and mills had to become more efficient if they were not to fall out of use. Many small firms were taken over, and today a few large combines control the textile industry. They have introduced new systems of management and provided finance for modernisation. Government grants were given to help improve efficiency and firms were paid to keep workers in employment. The textile industry has been protected from some overseas competition by *quotas*, which limit the amount of cloth imported.

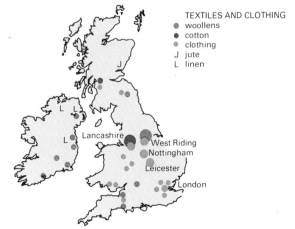

Fig. B Textiles and clothing

Tariffs have been introduced, which means that foreign cloth is subject to an import tax. The imported cloth becomes more expensive, which makes British cloth more competitive.

Cloth manufacture is still carried out in the traditional centres of Lancashire and West Yorkshire, but factories making clothes are now widespread. Hundreds of thousands of employees have left the textile industries. Many looked for jobs elsewhere, and others found new jobs locally. Long-distance commuting (daily travelling) has been another answer. Former mill-workers now commute to the Manchester area from many parts of the former Lancashire textile region. In West Yorkshire, commuting to new employment centres is common.

There are many Asians working in textile mills. Immigrants were attracted to textile manufacturing during the 1960s and 1970s and were ready to work shifts. Night-work is generally unpopular, but Asian workers were willing to take it on. The survival of textiles owes a lot to this change in the labour source.

The British textile industry has made a determined effort to improve the quality of its output. British wool competes successfully on quality. Man-made fibre producers such as ICI are increasing their range of synthetic fibres. The emphasis is on quality.

Fig. C

Washpit Mills, Huddersfield

Washpit Mills occupy a valley-bottom site to the south of Huddersfield. The oldest building dates back to 1842, when it was described as a 'fine new mill'. The site was chosen because of the water supply, and Washpit has first call on the water, which has always been essential to textile manufacture. In the case of

Fig. D Washpit Mills, Huddersfield

Washpit, water was needed to provide steam as well as for washing the wool and preparing the dyes. Later, local mill owners joined together to construct Holme Styes reservoir upstream from Washpit. This ensured a year-round supply of water.

The mills were extended as orders for cloth increased. In 1899, Washpit Mills made the first khaki serge material for the government armed forces. Khaki was sold throughout the British empire in the early years of this century. Cloths for sports jackets, overcoats and skirts were made for countries all over the world.

Today, several firms operate in Washpit Mills, producing skirt cloths, sports jacket and trouser cloth. Much of the output is exported. Washpit is one of many mills in the Huddersfield area of West Yorkshire, and the competition for orders is severe. There must be strict quality control, the most modern types of yarn must be used and order deadlines met. To survive in the woollen trade, the workforce must be productive and management must continually seek new orders.

QUESTIONS

A Look at Fig C.
1 Why is it necessary to advertise British wool in magazines and on television?
   (a) Name some man-made fibres.
   (b) What are the raw materials used to make (i) cellulosic fibre, (ii) synthetic fibre?
2 Write down the types of cloth you are wearing today. Which of your clothes are made of natural fibres and which of man-made yarns?

Find Huddersfield (location of Washpit Mills) on Fig A (page 158). List the site advantages for woollen mills in this area.
4 List the types of cloth Washpit Mills have produced in the past and produce now.
5 What synthetic yarn do you think is used with wool to make trouser and skirt cloths at Washpit Mills?
6 How do Washpit Mills keep new orders coming in?
B1 How has the textile industry adapted to its decline?
2 Discuss reasons for changes at Washpit Mills since World War II.
3 'The clothing industry is footloose and is characterised by small firms.' Suggest why the clothing industry is more dispersed than the clothmaking industry (Fig B).
4 Look at the following statistics of wool production:

	Sheep including lambs (million)	Total wool production (million kg)
England	14.7	—
Wales	8.0	—
Scotland	7.7	—
Northern Ireland	1.1	—
UNITED KINGDOM	31.5	52
rest of EEC	26.5	62
TOTAL EEC	58.0	114
Australia	133.4	700
Soviet Union	141.6	461
New Zealand	70.6	381
Argentina	35.2	170
South Africa	24.5	105
rest of world	526.8	911
WORLD TOTAL	990.0	2842

   (a) Draw a bar graph to show total wool production.
   (b) What percentage of EEC wool is produced in the United Kingdom?
   (c) Compare wool production per sheep in the United Kingdom with that in Australia and New Zealand.
   (d) Suggest reasons for these differences.
C1 Account for the growth of the textile industry in either Lancashire or West Yorkshire.
2 Suggest reasons for the decline of the industry since World War I. What problems has the region had to face?

4.11 SHIPBUILDING

The United Kingdom produced more than one-third of the world's ships annually until the middle of the 1950s. By 1956, Japan had established a lead which it has never lost.

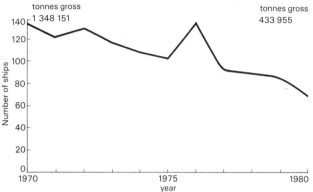

Gross Tonnage is the measurement of the cubic capacity of a ship's closed spaces — holds, decks.

	% world's ships built in UK	position of UK among shipbuilding nations
1913	58	1st
1936	36	1st
1950	38	1st
1955	27	1st
1961	15	2nd
1971	5	4th
1981	3	10th

Fig. A

Shipbuilding remains important on some of Britain's largest estuaries. About 70 000 people are employed in the industry, and for every ten shipbuilders there are twelve other workers in the supply industry. Eighty-five per cent of all output is now concentrated in British Shipbuilders. Thirteen per cent is held by Harland and Wolff in Belfast and about 2 per cent by private yards. More than half the ships built in Britain are exported.

Shipbuilding has experienced one of the greatest declines of any large industry in Britain. In 1955, 300 000 people were employed. By the time the industry was nationalised in 1977 and British Shipbuilders came into existence, only 86 000 were left. Each year since has seen a further decline in the workforce, for these reasons:

1 British shipyards have been faced with foreign competition, notably from Japan. More recently, Third World countries such as South Korea and Brazil have established their own shipbuilding industries.

2 British yards were slow to modernise and build undercover yards which proved to be much more efficient. They were slow to adapt to changing demands for new ships.

3 British shipyards often failed to meet order deadlines.

4 Since the late 1970s, there has been overcapacity in world shipping. Many perfectly good ships, especially oil tankers, are laid up because there is no demand for them.

5 The industry has suffered from under-investment, a lack of forward planning and many industrial disputes.

Fig. B SD14 cargo ship

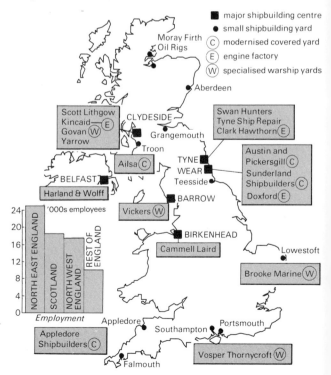

Fig. C Shipbuilding in the UK

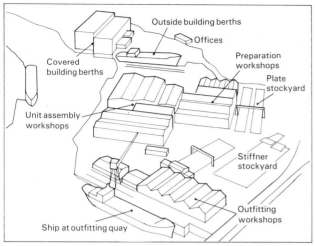

Fig. D The Southwick Shipyard

Overcoming the problem of decline: Large amounts of government money have gone to the shipbuilding industry. The major shipbuilding areas are in the development areas, which receive help for new industrial development. The nationalisation of most of the industry in 1977 brought it under the single overall management of British Shipbuilders, who have concentrated investment in a few profitable yards.

Siting a shipyard

Britain's main shipyards have grown up on *deep sheltered river estuaries* such as the Tyne, Clyde and Mersey. Shipyards need a supply of *steel plate* and a range of other building materials. The older yards are close to coalfields, but the newer yards have never been dependent on coal for fuel. Associated with the major shipbuilding centres are marine engineering, engine-building, electrical and instrument equipment firms, furniture and fitting manufacturers. As many as 300 firms may contribute to the building of a ship.

One of Europe's most modern shipyards is Southwick in Sunderland, on the Wear estuary. Austin & Pickersgill, part of British Shipbuilders, have built undercover shipbuilding units since 1975. No longer do employees work outside on the slipways. Today, ships are built in factory units. Production is more efficient and more ships can be built. Austin & Pickersgill have successfully built standard ships since they introduced their SD14 (15 000 tonnes) in 1966. This is a cargo ship, of which 200 have now been sold. Larger standard ships have been developed.

The history of the present company can be traced back to 1826. Teesside iron and steel was used and coal supplies came from nearby Durham pits. Today's company is the amalgamation of three separate Sunderland firms which grew up building colliers (coal-carriers) at several sites along the Wear. Southwick shipyard is large and flat, and launching is easy although 50 000 tonnes is the size limit. It is an example of a successful shipyard.

QUESTIONS

A1 Give two examples of each of the following, with locations: a major shipbuilding estuary; a shipyard specialising in warships; a covered shipyard; a ship's engine company.

2 List the methods used to halt the decline of shipbuilding in Britain.

3 Locate the labelled areas on Fig D on the photograph of Southwick shipyard. Draw a map of the area shown in the photograph. Label the map and use a key.

B1 'If shipbuilding declines, the economy of the surrounding area suffers severely.' Explain why this has been true of the major shipbuilding estuaries.

2 Suggest reasons for the recent success of Austin & Pickersgill.

3 Construct a pie chart to illustrate the following statistics:

Shipbuilding area	% of British total tonnage launched 1981
Clydeside	23
Wearside	21
Tyneside	15
Belfast	10
Teesside	9
Birkenhead	9
Barrow in Furness	2
Appledore	1
others	10

C Account for the decline of the British shipbuilding industry since World War II. What solutions have been tried to halt the decline?

4.12 MOTOR VEHICLES

The motor vehicle industry is one of the most important in Britain today. Over a million people work in jobs connected with vehicle manufacture.

The earliest car factories grew up in the West Midlands and south-east England. Important factors in this early growth were the engineering skills of the West Midlands and the prosperous market of the south-east. By the 1930s, over 90 per cent of all the jobs in the vehicle industry were in these two regions.

During the 1960s, the large car manufacturers were refused permission to expand their factories in the Midlands and the south-east. The government insisted on new assembly plants being built in the development areas, and three plants were opened on Merseyside and two in Central Scotland.

The 1970s were unhappy years for the British car industry. Exports fell whilst foreign imports rose from only 8 per cent of the British market in 1970 to 60 per cent in 1980. Production from British factories dropped, workforces were reduced and three assembly plants were closed (Linwood in Scotland, Speke on Merseyside and Abingdon in Oxfordshire). Competition from Japan, France, West Germany and Italy was particularly fierce, and British cars were not matching foreign vehicles for quality or price. British factories were often overmanned and slow to introduce modern technology. Many plants were hindered by poor labour relations.

It was not until the 1980s that the British industry was in a position to fight back against foreign competition. An important product of the early 1980s was the Austin Metro.

The Austin Metro

Some of the most famous British cars have been built at Longbridge, Birmingham, including the Austin Seven, Mini, Maxi and now the Metro.

The Metro project shows the great investment and advanced technology which modern industry requires. It cost only £23 000 to buy and equip the first Austin factory at Longbridge in 1906. By contrast, £285 million has been spent on the Metro, for which a new 70 000 m² factory has been built at Longbridge. Many of the operations are controlled by computer and the early stages of assembly are performed by robot welding machines individually controlled by microprocessors. Figure D shows Metros moving along a completely automated assembly line; there are no humans in sight.

The automated process has several advantages:
1 Many monotonous and tough tasks are handled by machines rather than by men. This makes working in a car factory more pleasant than it used to be.
2 The Metro can be produced more quickly and efficiently. For example, sample checks used to take several men up to four days. Now, one man using a

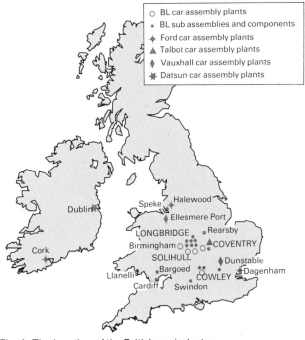

Fig. A The location of the British car industry

Fig. B Assembling a Metro

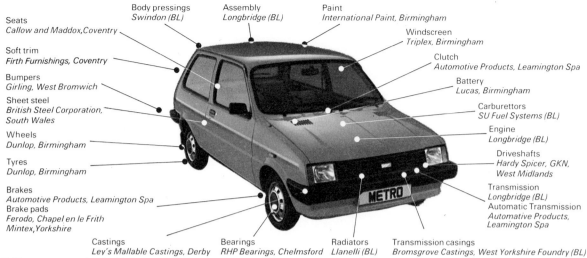

Seats
Callow and Maddox, Coventry

Soft trim
Firth Furnishings, Coventry

Bumpers
Girling, West Bromwich

Sheet steel
British Steel Corporation, South Wales

Wheels
Dunlop, Birmingham

Tyres
Dunlop, Birmingham

Brakes
Automotive Products, Leamington Spa
Brake pads
Ferodo, Chapel en le Frith
Mintex, Yorkshire

Body pressings
Swindon (BL)

Assembly
Longbridge (BL)

Paint
International Paint, Birmingham

Windscreen
Triplex, Birmingham

Clutch
Automotive Products, Leamington Spa

Battery
Lucas, Birmingham

Carburettors
SU Fuel Systems (BL)

Engine
Longbridge (BL)

Driveshafts
Hardy Spicer, GKN, West Midlands

Transmission
Longbridge (BL)
Automatic Transmission
Automative Products, Leamington Spa

Castings
Ley's Mallable Castings, Derby

Bearings
RHP Bearings, Chelmsford

Radiators
Llanelli (BL)

Transmission casings
Bromsgrove Castings, West Yorkshire Foundry (BL)

Fig. C The components of a Metro

laser probe can completely check a sample car within five hours.

3 A smaller workforce is needed. For example, the underbody assembly of the Metro is done by multi-welder machines controlled by ten men. On a conventional assembly line, the same task would be performed at a slower rate by eighteen men.

The Metro was launched in October 1980 amid a blaze of publicity. Immediately, the car took 10 per cent of the British new car market. Six thousand Metros are produced at Longbridge every week and a third are exported.

The massive investment needed for the Metro could not have been achieved without help from the government. British Leyland, the maker, was on the verge of collapse in 1975 when the government granted financial aid. Between 1975 and 1981, £1000 million was given. The government did this because BL was the last British-owned mass-production car firm. It provided work not only for its own employees but for hundreds of thousands more in component factories, steelworks and glassworks throughout Britain. Half of the components used in the Metro

come from firms outside the BL organisation. There are thought to be as many as 7000 separate firms contributing to the Metro. If BL was to close, the British industrial economy might face disaster.

British Leyland's future is not assured by the success of the Metro alone. The company needs a range of successful cars if it is to survive. BL adopted a different policy with its second new car of the 1980s, when it joined with the Japanese company Honda to assemble under licence a Honda car which BL named the Triumph Acclaim. Attention is now directed towards two all-new British cars, the Maestro and the Montego.

BL's survival has cost a great deal of money and many jobs have been lost. In 1978, 170 000 people worked for BL; by 1982, less than 100 000 were left.

QUESTIONS

A1 Why was the car industry concentrated in the West Midlands and south-east England until the 1960s?

2 Where were new assembly plants opened during the 1960s, and why?

3 What advantages does the highly-automated Metro assembly line have?

4 Why is the British government willing to give BL such great financial aid?

B1 Explain the present-day location of the car assembly industry.

2 The table below shows British car production from 1972 to 1980:

Thousands of cars produced								
1972	1973	1974	1975	1976	1977	1978	1979	1980
1.92	1.71	1.54	1.27	1.33	1.32	1.18	1.07	0.92

(a) Draw a line graph to illustrate these statistics.
(b) Why did British car production decline during the 1970s?

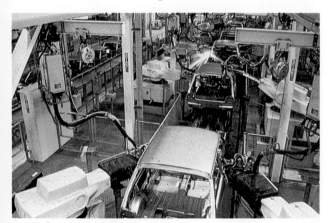

Fig. D Built by robots!

MANUFACTURING INDUSTRIES
4.13 AEROSPACE

Over 220 000 people work in Britain's aerospace factories and exports of aerospace products earned over £2000 million in 1981, over 4 per cent of total British exports.

Fig. A Aerospace factories in Britain

Figure A reflects the early dominance of aviation by the south of England. Before and during World War II, aircraft factories were dispersed for strategic reasons. After the war, several famous names disappeared as companies merged. Rationalisation caused the closure of many factories. Today, one company dominates the industry: British Aerospace. There is one major engine manufacturer, Rolls-Royce, and one helicopter manufacturer, Westland. There are also several smaller companies such as Short's of Belfast, building specialised aircraft, and hundreds of component manufacturers.

The largest single centre of the UK aerospace industry is Bristol. At Filton, to the north-east of the city, are three huge factories employing 22 000 people:

1 The aircraft group of British Aerospace at Filton; this factory has produced many famous aircraft including Concorde. It no longer builds complete aircraft but manufactures centre fuselages for the BAe 146 airliner and wing boxes for the A310 Airbus. Components are made for other aircraft and there are also extensive research facilities.

2 A second British Aerospace factory at Filton is part of the Dynamics Group. This factory manufactures guided missiles and missile guidance systems. There

is also a large space-engineering facility assembling satellites and solar arrays.

3 The third factory at Filton belongs to Rolls-Royce. Here, jet engines are made for military aircraft including the Harrier and the Tornado.

International collaboration

The cost of developing new aircraft is so high that small countries such as Britain can no longer afford to build large, expensive machines by themselves. This is especially true of airliners. Since 1945, most of the world's airliners have been built in the USA. Three US firms, Boeing, Lockheed and McDonnell Douglas, dominated the world market, and large British airliners such as the VC-10 and Trident sold only in small numbers. In the 1960s, European countries began to co-operate in the investment, design and production of aircraft, of which the most famous is the Concorde, produced jointly by Britain and France. A more successful example of international co-operation is provided by the Airbus project.

Fig. B How the airbus industry is financed

Airbus: Six companies in five European countries joined to form Airbus Industrie in 1970. The cost of the Airbus is shared between four countries (Fig B). The Dutch company, Fokker, became an associated member, financing only its own share of the work. Since 1970, Belgium and Italy have become associated with Airbus Industrie.

The first product was the A300 Airbus. Britain makes sub-assemblies and components for the A300 but the aircraft is assembled in France. About 2000 people are directly employed on the A300 in Britain, mainly at Chester where the wings are built. The location of factories involved in the Airbus construction (Fig C) shows that this is truly an international programme.

The A300 first flew in 1972, but the project seemed doomed to fail. While its American competitors picked up hundreds of orders, only thirty-five A300s

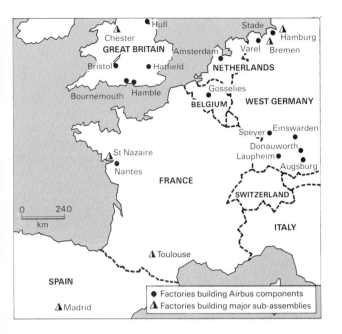

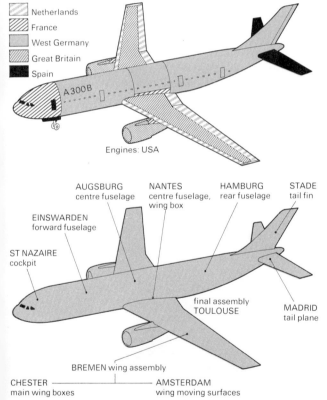

Fig. C The location of factories building the A300 airbus

Spurred on by the success of the A300, Airbus Industrie is now building a second airliner, the A310, which flew for the first time in 1982. Over 100 have been ordered. A third type, the A320, is under development.

Civil aircraft make up 20 per cent of British Aerospace's sales, and 70 per cent comes from military equipment. There is international collaboration in military products: the Tornado is built with Germany and Italy, the Harrier with the USA, the Jaguar with France. Because of this high dependence upon military sales, the aerospace industry is vulnerable to changes in defence policy.

Few British industries involve such high technology and great expense. Few are so closely affected by government policy. The risks are great, but the rewards for success are high: the A300 will provide employment and profit for its makers well into the 1990s.

QUESTIONS

A1 Why is the aerospace industry important to Britain?

2 Why was it necessary for several countries to co-operate in the production of aircraft?

3 Using Fig C, answer the following:
   (a) Which factories build major sub-assemblies?
   (b) What are the sub-assemblies built at each factory?

4 Why has the A300 Airbus proved so successful?

5 Why is the aerospace industry vulnerable to government defence policy?

B1 Describe and explain the location of the British aerospace industry. Name one important centre of the industry and describe the activities at that location.

2 On an outline map of the world, draw proportional circles to represent the following statistics (you will have to calculate a suitable radius for your circles):

Geographical distribution of British Aerospace's export sales	
Region	**£million sales**
Africa	53.3
Australia and Pacific	6.1
Central and South America	29.0
Europe	464.8
Far East	170.3
Middle East	183.4
North America	120.4
Total	1027.3

Comment upon what your map reveals.

had been sold by 1976. However, the rising cost of fuel made the A300 seem more attractive to airlines. It is cheaper to operate than the American airliners, which have three or four engines compared to A300's two. Sales rapidly increased after 1976. By 1982, 250 A300s had been sold throughout the world. It sold even in the USA, and Lockheed had to halt production of its Tristar because of the competition.

4.14 ENGINEERING

Fig. A The turbines at Peterhead power station

Fig. B A turbine generator being exported to the USA

Heavy engineering

Heavy engineering requires land and money in large quantities. Raw materials are expensive to transport, as are the finished products. The machine in Fig B is 40 metres long and weighs 400 tonnes. It was built by GEC Turbine Generators Ltd, who have factories at Rugby, Manchester, Stafford and Larne (Northern Ireland).

Heavy engineering includes the manufacture of a wide range of bulky products such as boilers, bridges, engines and turbines. Terms like *marine, railway* and *textile* engineering refer to specialist manufacturing. Heavy engineering is scattered throughout the British Isles but the most important areas are the coalfield conurbations. The presence of coal and iron were important in the early years of the industry. Ships' boilers and engines are made on Clydeside and Tyneside. Textile machinery is concentrated in Lancashire and west Yorkshire and railway engineering is important in Derby.

Electrical engineering

Heavy engineering has declined in recent years, but *electrical engineering* has grown. In 1900, it was new, and enjoyed constant growth as technology advanced. Today, its products include domestic goods, washing machines, television sets and video equipment. It is often impossible to distinguish between electrical and mechanical engineering, and sometimes equally difficult to separate electrical engineering from *electronics*.

London and the south-east were the early centres for this branch of engineering. They offered a large skilled labour force, a large and wealthy market, access to information (university and government departments) and entrepreneurs who were willing to take risks.

The industry is much more footloose than the heavy mechanical engineering, and has dispersed from the south-east to other parts of Britain. Many development areas have attracted electrical engineering companies: for example, Hoover located in Merthyr Tydfil in South Wales. The company has its original factory in Perivale, London, but expanded to the old iron-making and coalmining town. New towns and expanded towns have attracted many engineering firms.

Fig. C Engineering in Britain

Emerson Electrics, Swindon: Emerson Electrics is one of several electrical engineering companies in Swindon. The firm makes electrical drives and power supplies for a range of industries and employs about 200 people.

The company moved to Swindon because '. . . we have an ideal building, ample room for expansion and the cost is only half what we would have to pay for the best alternative in London'. Swindon is not in a development area and no government incentives are offered, but there are several reasons why companies are attracted there. A firm's location decision is based on cost, and a Swindon location can cut costs:

1 The local authority has provided industrial estates.
2 The town has skilled labour as it was formerly a railway engineering centre.
3 It is an accessible town, on the M4 motorway and inter-city railway line. It is only one hour from Heathrow Airport.

4 Rates are lower than London.
5 There is little time-wasting traffic congestion.
6 Much of the town is new. It has grown fast as a London overspill town.

In the United Kingdom, engineering is the most important type of manufacturing industry in terms of output and numbers employed. Almost every town in the country has some engineering manufacture. The region with the highest location quotient (see page 55) for engineering and vehicle manufacture is the West Midlands, with 22 per cent of the workforce employed in these industries compared to 12.6 per cent in Britain as a whole:

$$\frac{22}{12.6} = \text{location quotient } 1.7.$$

Vehicle engineering: is particularly important in the West Midlands, and component factories are spread throughout the region: for example, Lucas (electrical) and GKN-Sankey (wheels).

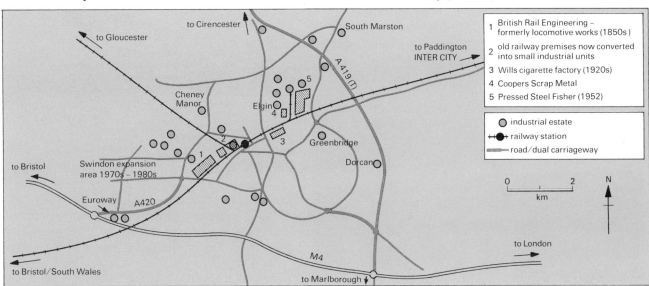

Fig. D Swindon's changing industry

1 British Rail Engineering – formerly locomotive works (1850s)
2 old railway premises now converted into small industrial units
3 Wills cigarette factory (1920s)
4 Coopers Scrap Metal
5 Pressed Steel Fisher (1952)

QUESTIONS

A1 How would you describe the following engineering products: bridges, washing machines, car headlights, turbines, ships' boilers, toasters? (Use descriptions such as heavy, electrical, marine.)

2 Where are the heavy engineering centres of the British Isles?

3 What particular factors of production are needed to build turbine generators such as those shown in Fig A?

4 What types of engineering can be found in the following locations? Clydeside; Rugby; Derby; Merthyr Tydfil.

5 Why did London and the south-east develop as the early centre for electrical engineering?

B1 The movement of electrical engineering companies from south-east England to development areas is an example of industrial relocation. Outline the reasons why these companies relocate in development areas.

2 Emerson Electrics did not move to a development area but to Swindon. Why did this company choose Swindon? Number your reasons and indicate which ones are similar to your answer to B1.

3 Figure D shows the location of old industry in Swindon, and the modern industrial estates. How do the locations of the industrial estates differ from those of the older engineering industry in Swindon?

4.15 ELECTRONICS

A typical British home has many machines such as televisions, refrigerators, vacuum cleaners, cookers and deep freezes. The last few years have seen many more new machines enter our homes: video-recorders, pocket calculators, personal computers, stereo hi-fi systems. All are products of the electronics industry.

The electronics industry is able to choose its location freely because neither the raw materials nor the products are bulky. Their high value makes transport costs only a small fraction of the total. As a result, electronics firms can be found in most British towns. However, despite its footloose nature, there are factors which have encouraged the concentration of the industry in certain areas:

1 Many of the earliest developments in electronics took place in London due to the concentration of research workers and money. The first radio and television broadcasts (1922 and 1936) were made from London, and it was several years before broadcasts were made from elsewhere. There is still a concentration of electronics firms in the London area.

2 Electronics firms have traditionally sought female labour because the work is light and intricate and female wages have been lower than male wages. Certain areas such as coal and steel-producing districts have large numbers of women seeking work. South Wales and Central Scotland were two areas which benefited from electronics development.

Fig. B The location of Plessey electronics factories

3 Electronics firms responded quickly to government regional development policy. New factories were built in the development areas to take advantage of the grants and loans available.

4 Linkages between the various sections of the electronics industry are important. Once established, electronics areas tend to attract more firms. Pools of skilled labour are soon available. Certain universities such as Cambridge, Stirling and Edinburgh have become famous as electronics research and development centres. The reputation of an area is important for the electronics industry. The western corridor along the M4 has been called 'Silicon Valley' and Central Scotland 'Silicon Glen'.

Silicon chips

One of the cheapest yet most important products of the electronics industry is the semiconductor integrated circuit microprocessor, otherwise known as the silicon chip. Silicon chips are at the heart of the microelectronics revolution. Twenty-five years ago, microelectronics did not exist. Now it is one of the fastest growing industries in the world. Microelectronics can cram the power of a major computer into devices so small, and at a cost so low, as to have been unthinkable a few years ago.

From computer games and pocket calculators to robot welders and computerised offices, the British economy is being influenced by the silicon chip. The efficiency and cheapness of the new machines is

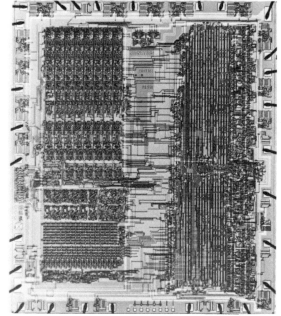
Fig. A The complexities of a silicon chip

Telecommunications	Electronic systems
Telephone exchanges	Radar
Transmission systems	Radio
Public address systems	Missile guidance systems
	Air traffic control
	Navigation instruments

⦿ PLESSEY

Engineering and components	Peripheral systems
Microprocessors	Minicomputers
Transistors	Microcomputers
Integrated circuits	Visual Display Units
Pneumatic equipment	Printers
Electrical equipment	Add-on Memory

Fig. C Plessey's electronics activities

threatening to cause unemployment on a vast scale in offices and factories.

Two British companies provide examples of the varying scale within the electronics industry: Plessey employs 32 000 people within Britain, Sinclair Research employs fifty.

Figure B shows the location of Plessey factories and emphasises the importance of the south of England in the electronics industry.

Sinclair Research was set up by Sir Clive Sinclair, one of Britain's most famous inventors of recent years, to invent, research and develop electronic equipment which will then be mass-produced by subcontractors. Sinclair made his name in the early 1970s with the production of the first cheap pocket calculators. He founded Sinclair Research in 1979 at Cambridge, where he lived, to retain the links he had established earlier with Cambridge University. Sinclair recruited a small team of research workers and soon introduced the ZX-80, a microcomputer which cost less than £100. In March 1981, he produced the cheaper and better ZX-81 which rapidly became the best-selling computer in Britain. In 1982, the Spectrum microcomputer was launched as the world's cheapest computer with sound and a colour display. Sinclair's computers were soon for sale in High Street shops. Almost single-handedly, Sinclair created a new mass-market industry: personal computing. By 1983, over one million of his computers had been sold throughout the world. The computers

Fig. D Electronics in the office

are built by Timex at Dundee and by Thorn-EMI at Feltham in Middlesex, providing employment for 2000 people. Sinclair Research is involved in other projects including larger computers and flat-screen televisions.

Sinclair's success has been based upon his inventive genius and his ability to keep one step ahead of his competitors. Britain's electronic industry faces serious competition from overseas. Many of the electronic consumer goods in British homes have been made in Japan, Hong Kong, South Korea, Singapore and Taiwan. Companies based in those countries can take advantage of the low production and labour costs and are able to sell their products cheaper than British-based companies. The British electronics industry has to concentrate on quality and new ideas. The research and development part of the industry is vital.

QUESTIONS

A1 Make a list of all the electronic and electrical equipment in your home. Try to discover the country in which each was made. What percentage of the products were made in Britain?

2 Why is the electronics industry 'footloose' in its location?

3 Why does the silicon chip threaten to cause unemployment?

4 Describe the location of Plessey's UK factories.

5 Why is Sinclair Research based at Cambridge?

B1 What factors affect the concentration of the British electronics industry in certain areas.

2 The following table shows the countries from which Britain imports and to which it exports electronic products:

Imports %		Exports %	
USA	27	West Germany	12
West Germany	15	France	10
Japan	13	USA	7
France	8	Italy	6
Netherlands	6	Netherlands	6
Italy	6	Irish Republic	5
Irish Republic	5	Sweden	3
Belgium	3	Belgium	3
Hong Kong	2	Denmark	2
Singapore	2	Switzerland	2
Total £3740 million		Total: £3860 million	

(a) Construct two pie graphs to illustrate the statistics.

(b) Comment on the differences revealed by the two tables.

3 Why does Britain face competition from far-eastern countries in electronic goods?

81

5.1 MANUFACTURING IN DECLINE

BP to close Belfast oil refinery

427 jobs still have to go at BSC Motherwell

Ford to axe 1,300 jobs at Halewood

Timex plant at risk after 2,000 sacked

Fig. A The recession hits the headlines

Fig. B

In the early 1980s, many companies shed jobs and huge numbers of workpeople became unemployed. The reasons are complicated, but the main ones can be understood:

1 *Competition* from countries where production is cheaper than in Britain (Brazil, Korea and Taiwan can produce steel more cheaply than BSC; many household goods are made in Japan, Singapore and Hong Kong; over 95 per cent of computer equipment bought in Britain is made abroad).

2 *High cost of production:* labour costs are high (there has been overmanning in several major industries) so are the costs of old and inefficient equipment. Britain has been slow to modernise and invest in new technology.

3 The *wrong products*: in many cases, Britain was slow to adapt. Old-style watches and cash registers were made in Dundee when the silicon chip was being introduced into these items in other countries.

4 Britain's *management / labour relations* need improvement: problems stem from a long history of inadequate industrial co-operation and sense of purpose.

5 The *increasing importance of tertiary or service industry:* while manufacturing has been declining, there has been growing employment in service industries.

Figure C shows the stages of development for western economies. Britain was an *agricultural economy* before the Industrial Revolution but between the mid-nineteenth and mid-twentieth century it was an *industrial economy*. In the 1960s, more than one-third of all workers were employed in the secondary or manufacturing sector. This proportion continues to fall. Britain is not unique; other Western European economies show the same trends and manufacturing employment in the USA is now only one-fifth of the total.

The decline of manufacturing need not be a problem as long as the workforce is re-employed in tertiary employment. Examples of tertiary occupations include many associated with *information*. More and more people in a post-industrial economy are involved with recording, processing or transmitting information. Some examples are:

accounting   meter reading
book publishing   music-making
data processing   newspapers
market research   stock control

However, new types of employment are not immediately available in many declining manufacturing areas. Factory closures can leave whole communities without work (Fig D). Certain groups of people are excluded from obtaining new types of employment. They might not be qualified, or near to it (labour is *immobile* and not all people choose to *migrate* to find work). With fewer jobs available, some people may be discriminated against; young black people find it difficult to find jobs, as do older people, and women may fare less well than men.

The areas of Britain that have suffered most from the decline of manufacturing are the old industrial areas. The coalfield areas and major conurbations have lost the largest number of jobs.

Where large numbers of manufacturing jobs have been lost, the problem needs help from local and national government. Trafford Park, Manchester, has suffered massive job losses in a small area. At the beginning of the twentieth century, it was Britain's first industrial estate and the busiest square mile of industrial activity in the world. In 1961, 60 000 people were still employed at Trafford Park, but by 1982 only 23 000 people remained. This is only a small percentage of total job losses in the manufacturing industry in the Manchester area.

Where smaller numbers are involved, for instance in small towns, the problem can be more easily tackled. In Hebden Bridge in West Yorkshire, population began to fall after textile mills closed. The town council made efforts to stop the town dying. Its

Fig. D An empty factory in Liverpool

policy for survival included tourism, housing renovation and the attraction of small-scale industry. Today, Hebden Bridge is learning to live in a post-industrial society. Its local economy is no longer dependent on manufacturing. Old mills have been put to new uses, the old canal is used for leisure cruising and workers' cottages have been modernised. The town now has a high-technology microphone equipment company and a horse-stud centre, a complete contrast to its original industry.

QUESTIONS
A1 List the reasons for the decline of manufacturing industry.
 2 List five of your own household products that have been imported.
 3 Write brief notes about each of the stages of development given in Fig C.
 4 Give examples of tertiary or service occupations (excluding information services).
 5 What do you understand by information employment? Add other employment areas to the list given.
B1 What do you understand by a post-industrial economy?
 2 Discuss the problems of moving from a manufacturing or industrial economy to a post-industrial economy.
C Describe and account for the recent decline in manufacturing employment in Britain. Outline ways of combating manufacturing decline.

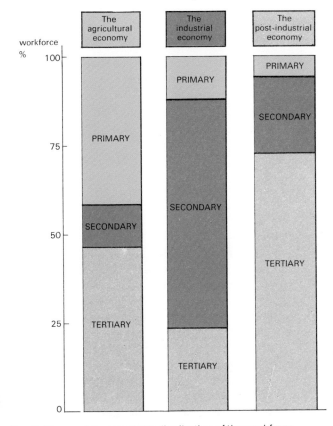
Fig. C Stages of development: distribution of the workforce

5.2 UNEMPLOYMENT

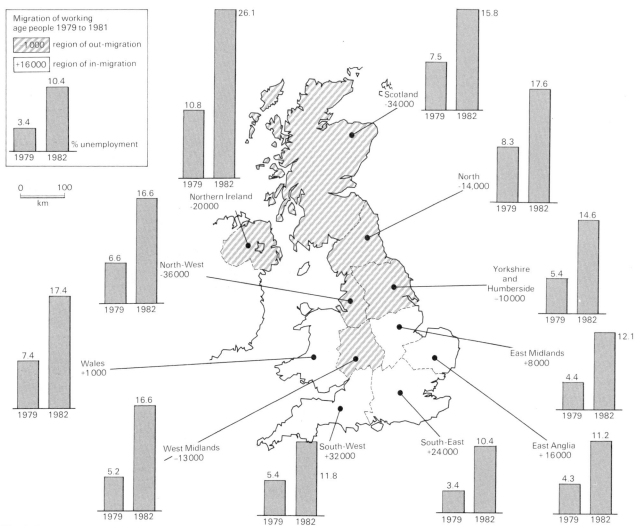

Fig. A Employment and migration

After World War II, British workers were promised 'a new and better world'. All political parties aimed for 'the maintenance of high and stable employment'. For twenty years the promise was fulfilled, but in the 1960s unemployment began to rise. By 1973 there were half a million unemployed out of a workforce of 26 million. But after the oil crisis unemployment reached 2 million by 1980 and over 3 million in 1982.

The reasons for increased unemployment include:
1 The decline of manufacturing industry, especially the heavy industries.
2 The world recession, which meant that throughout the world there was less business and industrial output.
3 The larger numbers of people of working age in the mid-1970s to 1980. This was the result of the large population growth rate of the 1950s and 1960s. Babies born in the mid-sixties left school and looked for work in 1980.
4 The introduction of new technology, especially computerisation.

New technology means that firms, government departments and other employers can work more efficiently. Machines are more productive than people, and employers have saved on labour costs. One example is the increasing use of computers in offices (Fig C). Filing clerks and secretaries are disappearing, and it has been predicted that several hundreds of thousands of office jobs in the City of London could be lost by 1990. Car assembly lines are being fitted with robots; production costs have dropped, but so has employment.

Fig. B

Fig. C Computerised offices need fewer people

The effects of unemployment

Figure A shows the rise in unemployment between 1979 and 1982. The northern industrial regions of Britain, Northern Ireland and Wales have higher rates than southern England, but average figures cover up unemployment blackspots. The map also shows that the regions with highest unemployment were those where people were leaving to find work elsewhere. Some towns have higher-than-average rates (Fig D). For example, Consett and Ebbw Vale have lost steel jobs. The Northern Ireland towns have suffered partly because of continuing political trouble. Some places suffer from seasonal unemployment: seaside resorts employ people in the summer season but there is no work in the winter. Farming regions will always have higher unemployment rates in the winter.

Within towns and cities, unemployment will vary.

The census reveals very high rates in inner-city wards. Unemployment is high in the areas where ethnic groups are concentrated. The Scarman Report which followed the inner city riots of 1981 said that unemployment was a major factor behind the riots. The police link serious crime with unemployment blackspots.

High unemployment need not be permanent in Britain. The economy could successfully move into a post-industrial stage where more people can be employed in information and leisure industries. Jobs could be shared and people could work less time per week. The old ideas of everyone working a set time in a week may well be replaced. Being occupied could be as acceptable as being employed.

Area	Town	%
North-west	Birkenhead	20.9
	Wigan	19.2
North-east	Consett	27.4
South Wales	Ebbw Vale	23.5
Northern Ireland	Newry	32.9
	Strabane	39.2
	Londonderry	28.8

Fig. D   (1982 figures)

QUESTIONS

A1 (a) List the eleven regions in rank order of unemployment and migration.
Arrange your work like this:

Region	Unemployment rank	Migration rank
Northern Ireland	1	3
North	2	4
Wales	3	etc

Note: The region with highest positive number of migrants will have the lowest rank order.

(b) What conclusions can you draw from your rank orders?
Note: You have used percentages for unemployment and whole numbers for migration, so there may not be perfect links.

2 List the reasons for the increasing unemployment of recent years.

B1 Suggest reasons for the higher-than-average figures shown in Fig D.

2 Give reasons for higher-than-average unemployment in old industrial regions and inner-city areas.

3 In what ways could unemployment be reduced in the British economy in the future?

5.3 TRADE

Until World War II, Britain exported mainly manufactured goods and imported food and raw materials. There have been major changes in our trade since then. In 1950, the United Kingdom's share of the world manufactured exports was 25.5 per cent. By 1970, it had dropped to 10.8 per cent and by 1980 to 7.9 per cent. In 1970, only 8 per cent of motor vehicles were imported, but by the early 1980s this had risen to over half. In 1970, 53 per cent of watches and clocks were imported; by the early 1980s, the figure was over 80 per cent. These figures show the size of *import penetration*.

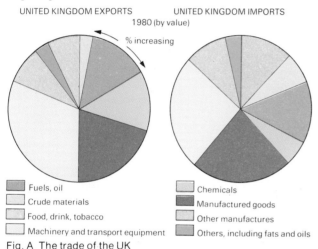

UNITED KINGDOM EXPORTS   UNITED KINGDOM IMPORTS
1980 (by value)

% increasing

Fuels, oil
Crude materials
Food, drink, tobacco
Machinery and transport equipment

Chemicals
Manufactured goods
Other manufactures
Others, including fats and oils

Fig. A The trade of the UK

We now import fewer foodstuffs. British agriculture has improved its efficiency and we have become more *self sufficient* in food production, but Britain will always need to import some foods — oranges, bananas, tea and coffee are never going to grow here. The most recent change in Britain's trade has been concerned with oil. Until the 1970s, oil had to be imported, mainly from the Middle East. By the

1980s, however, oil represented over 8 per cent of total export earnings. Its share has risen since, but it will be an export earner only if production can be maintained.

The sources and destinations of trade have also changed (Fig B). Since Britain joined the EEC in 1973, an increasing amount of trade has been with member countries. The well-established trading links with North America and the British commonwealth countries have declined. For example, in 1965 New Zealand sent half of her exports to Britain, but in 1980 less than one-quarter were sent.

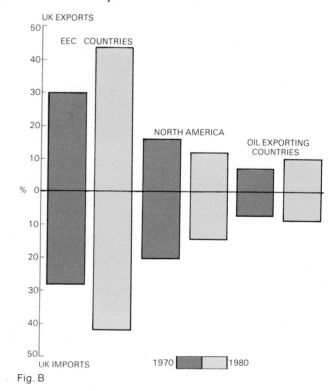

UK EXPORTS
EEC COUNTRIES
NORTH AMERICA
OIL EXPORTING COUNTRIES
UK IMPORTS
1970   1980
Fig. B

Exports to	Percentage of total exports	Imports from	Percentage of total imports
1 USA	12.3	1 USA	11.9
2 West Germany	10.8	2 West Germany	11.6
3 Netherlands	7.9	3 France	7.7
4 France	7.1	4 Netherlands	7.6
5 Ireland	5.5	5 Belgium/Luxembourg	4.8
6 Belgium/Luxembourg	4.1	6 Italy	4.6
7 Italy	3.4	7 Japan	4.3
8 Sweden	3.1	8 Norway	3.8
9 Switzerland	2.9	9 Saudi Arabia	3.7
10 Nigeria	2.8	10 Irish Republic	3.5

Fig. C Britain's trading partners

Fig. G The Seaforth grain terminal

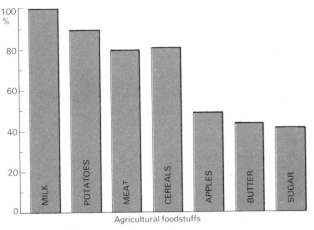
Fig. D Britain's self-sufficiency in food

Fig. E 75% of the country's exports and imports are moved by sea

Commodity	Thousand tonnes
Fish and fish preparations	14.0
Wheat	733.2
Maize	420.7
Other milled cereals	21.5
Dried vegetables	39.1
Molasses	16.1
Animal feeding stuffs	128.3
Soya beans	348.8
Other oil seeds, nuts and kernels	35.0
Softwood	50.5
Pulp and waste paper	22.3
Clays	21.9
Asbestos	34.8
Coal, lignite and peat	496.7
Pitches, waxes and jelly	84.8
Plastics	11.8
Chemical materials and products	10.4
Iron and steel	19.8
Copper	56.4
Lead	20.8
Zinc	17.5
Total	2604.4

Fig. F North American imports entering Liverpool

The balance of payments

The difference in value between exports and imports of goods (*visible* items) is referred to as the *balance of trade* (Fig A). *Invisible trade* includes buying and selling services such as insurance, banking, sea transport, civil aviation and tourism. When the visible and invisible items are combined, the result is the *balance of payments*. The United Kingdom usually has a positive balance on invisible trade, and in the early 1980s had a positive balance on visible trade. The positive visible balance was mainly due to increased export earnings from North Sea oil.

Three-quarters of Britain's foreign trade is handled by the seaports. The changing nature of trade has been responsible for the decline of western seaports and the rise of east and south-east coast ports (Fig E shows Dover). Airports, especially Heathrow, are handling an increasing proportion of our trade.

QUESTIONS

A1 Look at Fig A. Name two categories of goods of which the United Kingdom imports more than she exports.

2 State the main changes shown in Fig B.

3 (a) What is meant by self-sufficiency in food?
  (b) For which products is Britain most self-sufficient?
  (c) What imported foods have you eaten during the last 24 hours?

4 Define briefly: import penetration; visible trade; invisible trade; balance of payments.

5 Construct a bar graph to show the seven main imports into Liverpool from North America (Fig F). Use the same colour to indicate foodstuffs for human consumption.
List next to your graph other foods imported from North America.

6 Describe the port facilities in Fig G. Which North American imports (Fig F) are likely to be handled at the grain terminal?

B Outline the main changes in the trade of the United Kingdom during recent years.

87

5.4 THE LEISURE REVOLUTION

In a post-industrial society, people have more time and money to spend on leisure. In the 1960s, most British workers received two weeks' holiday with pay. By the 1980s, about half were getting four weeks. People now take more holidays and day trips and spend more on them. Travelling to leisure areas, the *journey to play*, has become easier. More people have cars, and roads and motorways are improved.

The British are attracted to many types of leisure areas or *tourist environments* which possess one or more of the following:

Tourist amenities	Natural environment	Historical environment
somewhere to stay	seaside	villages
accessibility	forests	castles
special provisions	mountains	churches
(car parks, toilets,	lakes	harbours
picnic sites,	sunshine	crafts
arcades, museums)	snow	customs

Holidaying abroad

In 1960, four million British people went on a foreign holiday. By the early 1980s, over thirteen million were going abroad annually. The USA follows closely behind the countries in Fig A, with Eire, West Germany and the Canaries next. The rank order may change over the years. For example, if the pound is worth a lot of dollars the USA is popular (as in 1980 and 1981). In recent years, long-distance holidays have increased in popularity: for some, a holiday in Peru or Thailand is now a possibility.

Sixty-nine per cent of those going abroad travel by air, 27 per cent by boat and about 3 per cent by hovercraft. The English Channel has become one of the world's busiest sea-crossings. Sealink operate over 140 sailings a day, most of which are across the Channel, but other routes link Britain with Northern Ireland and Eire. The shortest crossing is 1¾ hours (Dover to Calais or Boulogne). Hovercraft services take about half an hour. Train services link up with boats (Fig C), and other trains carry cars (Motorail).

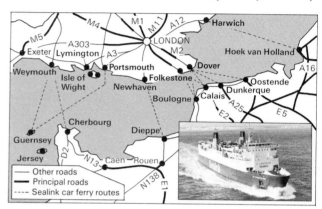

Fig. B Crossing the Channel with Sealink

LONDRES-VIC.	Départ	7.50	8.00	9.58	11.58	13.58	20.10	20.58
	via	DIEPPE	BOULOGNE	CALAIS	BOULOGNE	CALAIS	DIEPPE	DUNKERQUE
PARIS-NORD	Arr.	18.10 ST LAZARE	16.18	18.25	20.20	22.25	6.25 ST LAZARE	8.43

Fig. C The boat-train service: summer timetable

There are over thirty different car ferry services operating from British ports to the continent, Scandinavia and Ireland. Some of the longer routes take over 20 hours (Newcastle to Gothenburg 27 hours, and Scrabster (near Thurso) to Seydisfjordur (Iceland) 37 hours). About fifteen operators are in competition, as a result of which prices have been kept down.

Foreign holidays in the UK

Visits to the UK by foreign residents

1970	6 692 000
1975	9 490 000
1980	12 393 000

When a foreign visitor comes to Britain, the country earns money. This is an *invisible export*. The country is 'exporting' its history, heritage, way of life and scenery. In 1977, a billion pounds more was spent by foreigners visiting Britain than was spent by British holidaymakers going abroad. This surplus has dwindled recently and in 1982 it was claimed that tourism was 'in the red'. Even so, in 1982 an estimated eight million overseas visitors went to London, more than a quarter of them from North America.

% of people going abroad

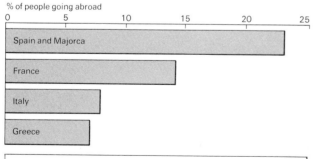

FALL IN £ attracts AMERICANS
Americans are now getting more pounds for their dollars. Put another way £1 used to cost $2 – now they cost less!
In 1982 more than a quarter of all London's overseas visitors came from North America. An estimated eight million overseas visitors came to London in 1982. They contributed some £2000 million to the capital's economy.

Fig. A The most holiday popular destinations

Leisure in Britain

Figure D shows the most popular regions for holidays. The rank order of the regions changes slightly over time. Scotland has lost some of its popularity because of rising petrol prices and its relative inaccessibility from the south. People have chosen to go on holiday nearer home. The English and Welsh motorways have improved accessibility to the south-west, which has slightly increased its popularity.

National parks: Areas which attract visitors all experience *tourist pressure* and many have been protected by conservation laws. National parks cover

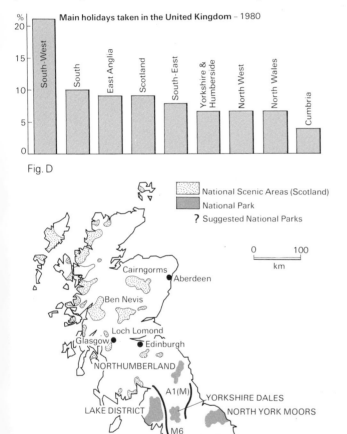

Fig. D

Fig. E The national parks and national scenic areas

about 9 per cent of England and Wales. They were established in 1949, the intention being to:
Preserve the natural landscape
Protect wildlife and places of interest
Maintain the traditional landscapes
Control and manage developments
Provide access to the general public
Provide facilities and information for the visitors.

Most of the land in the national parks is part of the 'wildscape' of Britain. It belongs to landowners and farmers, the Forestry Commission, the Ministry of Defence, water authorities and the National Trust. In the Northumberland National Park, a higher proportion is owned by government bodies: the Forestry Commission (20 per cent) and the Ministry of Defence (20 per cent). In the Lake District, a higher proportion is owned by the National Trust. Motorways have made national parks accessible. About one-third of Britain's population is within day-tripping distance of the Peak District National Park. More than 8 million visits are made to the Peak District every year, which can lead to serious traffic problems. Some parks have developed improved public transport for visitors. The Peak Pathfinder bus in the Peak District and the Snowdon Sherpa in Snowdonia link car parks and walking routes.

Scotland's equivalent of national parks are called national scenic areas (Fig E).

QUESTIONS

A1 What is a tourist environment? What else can you add to the lists given?
2 Why are there so many more visits to these tourist areas than there used to be?
3 Give reasons for the big increase in foreign holidays.
4 Figure A shows only the four most popular countries for foreign holidays. Name other countries you know that are popular.
B1 Look at the following exchange rates:
year X £1 = $2; year Y £1 = $1.50.
(a) In which year will Americans find holidaying in Britain the cheapest?
(b) In which year will the British get most for their money in the USA?
2 How does Britain benefit from foreign tourists?
3 What is meant by 'tourism in the red'?
4 Outline how the national parks have tried to conserve some popular tourist environments in the wildscape areas of Britain.
5 Describe the location of the national parks in England and Wales.
6 Which major cities are within 100 kilometres of the centre of the Peak District National Park? Why is this park particularly accessible?

5.5 CONSERVATION AND LEISURE

Britain's natural environment — countryside and wildlife in particular — is under pressure, and since World War II many state and private bodies have concerned themselves with conservation. All local authorities have planning departments which control development. Most building is controlled; *planning permission* is needed by the householder who wants to build a garage or extension and the company which plans a new factory. Planning controls are often strict: the extension may be allowed only if a certain building stone is used. The factory may be permitted only if landscaping is to be carried out.

Conservation is usually linked to providing leisure amenities. It is only by raising money from the public that some conservation measures can be financed. One of the best-known private bodies conserving land and historic buildings is the *National Trust*. People pay to join this charity, which uses the money to buy land and buildings 'for the benefit of the nation'. The Trust owns coastal stretches and mountain areas. In the north of England, it owns and preserves parts of Hadrian's Wall. There are also many specialist conservation organisations.

The *Forestry Commission* opens its forests to the public. Most have information boards, picnic sites, marked footpaths and car parks. The *Forest Parks* (Fig A) are tourist areas on a larger scale and include camping and caravan sites. The New Forest is the most visited forest park, with millions of visitors a year. A new Commission venture is the building of holiday cabins in some of its forests.

	England	Wales	Scotland
Camping and caravan sites	25	1	9
Picnic places	368	104	122
Forest walks and nature trails	282	141	231
Visitor centres	13	6	11
Arboreta	11	7	5
Forest drives	3	1	2
Forest cabins and holiday houses	108	4	46

(Courtesy of the Forestry Commission)

Fig. B The Forestry Commission leisure facilities

As well as establishing national parks, the government has encouraged a range of conservation measures. Local authorities are increasingly involved in managing conservation areas. *Areas of Outstanding Natural Beauty* (AONBs) have been designated in several parts of the country (Fig A). They are not wildscape, like the national parks, but in coastal and farmland areas. Some small sites are of special environmental interest. Within forty kilometres of the Cairngorm mountains in the Highlands of Scotland are over twenty protected scientific sites

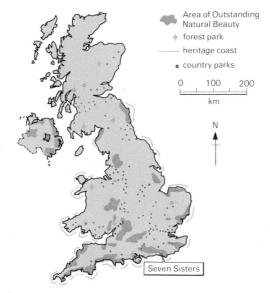

Fig. A

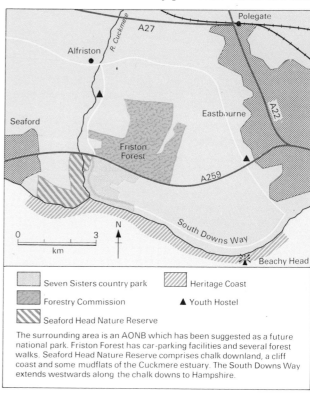

The surrounding area is an AONB which has been suggested as a future national park. Friston Forest has car-parking facilities and several forest walks. Seaford Head Nature Reserve comprises chalk downland, a cliff coast and some mudflats of the Cuckmere estuary. The South Downs Way extends westwards along the chalk downs to Hampshire.

Fig. C The Seven Sisters Country Park

termed SSSIs (Sites of Special Scientific Interest). The most scenic coasts are known as *Heritage Coast*.

The latest conservation/leisure area is the *Country Park*. Many are recognised by the Countryside Commission, the government body which oversees conservation. The parks were set up by local authorities using government grants. They are small, and many are in densely populated areas (Fig A). They are located in a variety of natural and man-made environments.

The Seven Sisters Country Park, East Sussex: This country park was acquired by East Sussex County Council in 1971. It covers 280 hectares of the Cuckmere Valley and part of the Seven Sisters chalk cliffs. Positive action was taken during the 1970s to conserve the scenic beauty, relative remoteness and wildlife of the district and to provide opportunities for people to enjoy and appreciate its qualities.

Vehicles are banned from the park. Sheep-grazing is controlled by licences. A shallow lake has been made for feeding and nesting birds; and there is a park trail. A small campsite has been opened. A park centre occupies an eighteenth-century barn at Exeat Farm and offers literature, maps, displays and exhibitions to visitors.

Other conservation measures have been taken in this area of chalk downland and coast, each with something for visitors. Conservation and leisure provision are linked.

Fig. D The Seven Sisters Country Park

QUESTIONS

A1 Why do you think new buildings must have planning permission?

2 Briefly describe the work of the National Trust.

3 In what ways does the Forestry Commission cater for recreation activities?

4 Suggest reasons why the Beachy Head area of the South Downs has been made a Heritage Coast.

5 In what ways have leisure activities and conservation been linked in the Seven Sisters Country Park?

6 Describe the landscape in the country park (Fig D).

B1 Look at the graph below. Attempt to explain the traffic flow at the times indicated by the letters (a) to (e).

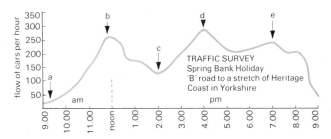

2 What conflicts are likely to arise on this part of Heritage Coast on a spring bank holiday, similar to the one referred to on the graph (question B1)?

3 Suggest what tourist provision the local authority might provide in one settlement in the vicinity of this Heritage Coast.

4 Look at the venn diagram below. Link the following words with the overlap areas (the intersecting sets): wetland habitat, birdwatching hide, footpath.

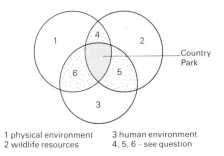

1 physical environment   3 human environment
2 wildlife resources   4, 5, 6 – see question

With special reference to the Seven Sisters Country Park, name some more resources or tourist amenities that are represented by the intersecting sets.

5 With reference to the same country park, explain the phrase 'Conservation and leisure provision are linked.'

91

5.6 SEASIDE RESORTS

Seaside resorts grew at the same time as the industrial areas of industrial Britain, when doctors began to recommend visits to the seaside. Healthy air contrasted with the polluted atmosphere of towns and cities. Today, seaside towns such as Bournemouth, Worthing, Brighton and Eastbourne have grown while industrial towns have declined.

Today's seaside resort is often a retirement town, a conference centre and a focus for regional entertainment. Fewer people see seaside towns as places for holidays, and many visit them only on day trips or for shopping and service facilities. It is increasingly likely that they stay outside the resorts, on caravan and camping sites. Major seaside town development has been in England and Wales (Fig A). The weather in the south of Britain is generally more favourable.

Fig. A Seaside resorts in England and Wales

Brighton

Brighton's population is over 150 000. It was a small fishing village in the eighteenth century when a doctor recommended it as a resort. In 1783, the Prince Regent began to visit the town and soon made it fashionable and famous.

Like most older seaside resorts, Brighton grew quickly with the coming of the railways. It benefited especially from being only seventy-five kilometres to the south of London. The fashionable image attracted the rich, but behind the seafront properties were cramped the homes of the poorly paid servants, shop assistants and craftsmen. The workers' cottages have now been turned into small, expensive residences and second homes. Brighton is still a town of social contrasts. Many large properties have been subdivided into flats and bedsitters but this is an aspect of Brighton not known to the visitors. These are the homes of students, the elderly and the poor.

The town has retained its resort functions but it is also an important conference centre. Political parties and major unions have their annual conferences in the 5000-seat Brighton Centre, opened in 1977. The town has developed light industry and spread westwards, joining up with Hove and the port of Shoreham.

Year	No. of conferences and exhibitions	No. of delegates and associated visitors	Estimated value £ (millions)
1975	286	89 600	6.5
1976	346	94 200	9.0
1977	395	105 200	11.7
1978	469	121 000	13.2
1979	690	162 000	24.8
1980	1034	185 500	32.4

Fig. B Brighton — a centre for conferences

1 The average spending of overseas delegates in 1978 was £240.

2 47% of delegates' spending was on hotel accommodation.

3 5% of the delegates stayed in hotels or guest houses outside Brighton.

4 24% of the delegates would have preferred superior accommodation in 5–3 star hotels.

Fig. C Brighton — a popular seaside resort

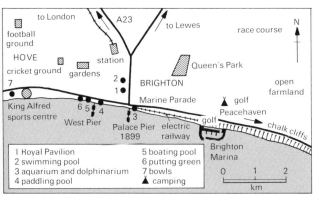

Fig. D The Sussex coast near Brighton

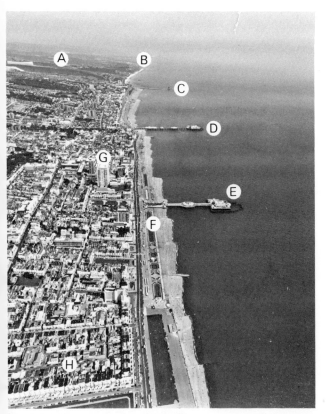

Fig. E Brighton — seen from above Hove

Brighton's present importance is still based on its resort characteristics and leisure and recreational functions. It is estimated that over six million people go there on 'day trips' and up to half a million a year spend more than one night in the town. As in other coast towns, the average age of residents has been increasing. The fast, regular train service to London encourages many people to live in Brighton and work in the capital.

Brighton Marina (Fig F) can take 2000 yachts and is Europe's largest, offering facilities for small-boat sailors and holidaymakers. The marina was built as part of an overall plan to keep Brighton's *resort functions* alive.

Fig. F Brighton Marina

QUESTIONS

A1 Using an atlas, locate and name the seaside resorts lettered on Fig A.

2 Why did Brighton develop as a seaside resort in the eighteenth century?

3 Look at Figs D and E.
   (a) Which way was the camera pointing?
   (b) Describe the landscapes at A and B?
   (c) Name the resort facilities at C, D and E
   (d) Suggest what sports are played along the sea-front at F.
   (e) Why do you think the buildings at G are so high?
   (f) Describe the housing at H. Why do you think it is so closely packed?

4 Apart from being a seaside resort, what other functions does Brighton have?

5 Look at Fig F.
   (a) Describe the site of Brighton Marina.
   (b) Describe its shape and function.
   (c) Which way was the camera pointing?

B1 Look at the beach. Why have groynes been built?

2 Most seaside resorts have developed through the following stages:
   (i) pre-resort stage, (ii) pioneering stage, (iii) period of fast growth, (iv) decline of resort functions and increase of other functions. Attempt to give time-periods and dates to these four stages.

3 Why does Brighton not wholly fit in with stage (iv) in question 2?

4 What evidence is there that Brighton is a town of social contrasts? Why have there always been social contrasts in the town?

5 Explain the attraction of Brighton for (a) retirement, and (b) commuting.

6 Study Fig B. Comment on the growth of Brighton as a conference centre. Suggest possible future accommodation building programmes that would benefit Brighton.

7 Why is the climate of Brighton favourable for seaside holidays? (See pages 8 and 191.)

6.1 RAILWAYS

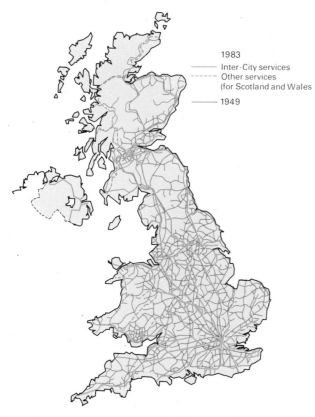

Fig. A The British Railways network 1949 and 1983

1983
— Inter-City services
----- Other services
(for Scotland and Wales
— 1949

The modern rail network is a shadow of what it was (Fig A). The reasons are:

1 Competition from road transport. At first, road transport could compete only over short distances, but with the construction of the motorway network much long-distance rail traffic has been lost to road transport.

2 Air transport is a serious competitor over long-distance journeys such as London to Glasgow.

3 The reduced demand for the transport of bulk cargoes, especially coal, has cut rail freight traffic.

4 Lack of investment meant that much of the railway system was using old, slow and inefficient methods.

In 1963, Dr Beeching proposed the closure of unprofitable lines and the improvement of money-making routes. The 'Beeching axe' closed hundreds of lines and thousands of stations. The closures have not been spread evenly throughout the country. More of the network in the South-East has survived compared with the networks in East Anglia, South-West England and South Wales.

British Rail

Passengers: British Rail's mainline passenger ser-

vices are called 'Inter-City'. A new suspension system gives a smoother ride and computer-controlled signalling improves timekeeping and safety.

High-speed trains (the HST 125s) operate on certain routes at up to 200 kph. Each HST has a streamlined diesel locomotive at either end, and is built of lightweight aluminium to achieve higher speeds. A second new design, the APT (advanced passenger train), has not been successful because of technical problems, but a modified version may enter service.

Inter-City services are efficient and comfortable, but many cross-country routes linking provincial towns remain slow and uncomfortable. DMUs (diesel multiple units) operate these low-income, high-cost services. British Rail has developed the Railbus (Fig B) to provide a cheaper service to run for these routes.

Freight: Only 10 per cent of freight transported within Britain is handled by rail compared to 85 per cent by road. Railways cannot compete in the local delivery of small or varied loads. However, the false economy and environmental threat of the heavy lorry has given rise to pressure to transfer some cargoes from road to rail.

British Rail could handle much long-distance lorry traffic and some shorter-distance traffic as well. At present, the roads are supreme and the railways are undervalued, but traffic congestion and road damage by heavy lorries may force a move back to rail.

A rapid-transit system

Tyneside faces problems which are typical in British cities: congested roads, pollution from exhausts, declining use of buses and trains, increasing demands on land for car parks and road developments. Elsewhere, the solution was to build motorway

Fig. B A railbus

networks. In Tyneside, the emphasis was placed on an entirely new 'light rapid transit' system, the Metro.

The Metro is not a railway although it uses standard railway track. The rolling stock is light, articulated eighty-four-seat trams. Forty-three kilometres of British Rail track has been electrified and twelve of new line laid, half of it under the centre of Newcastle. There are forty-one stations, and eight interchanges where transfer can be made between Metro, bus and car. In this way, the flexibility of road transport can be combined with the speed and efficiency of the Metro. The whole system is computer-controlled. The controllers are linked by radio with the Metro drivers, and the unmanned stations are watched by video cameras.

Seventy per cent of the £280 million cost of the Metro was met by the government. There were doubts about the wisdom of spending so much in an area of severe unemployment, but the Metro has given Tyneside a system that is second to none in Britain. It will be studied by city authorities elsewhere and may be the first of other rapid transit systems.

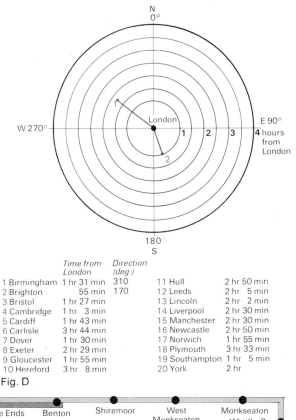

	Time from London	Direction (deg.)
1 Birmingham	1 hr 31 min	310
2 Brighton	55 min	170
3 Bristol	1 hr 27 min	
4 Cambridge	1 hr 3 min	
5 Cardiff	1 hr 43 min	
6 Carlisle	3 hr 44 min	
7 Dover	1 hr 30 min	
8 Exeter	2 hr 29 min	
9 Gloucester	1 hr 55 min	
10 Hereford	3 hr 8 min	

	Time from London
11 Hull	2 hr 50 min
12 Leeds	2 hr 5 min
13 Lincoln	2 hr 2 min
14 Liverpool	2 hr 30 min
15 Manchester	2 hr 30 min
16 Newcastle	2 hr 50 min
17 Norwich	1 hr 55 min
18 Plymouth	3 hr 33 min
19 Southampton	1 hr 5 min
20 York	2 hr

Fig. D

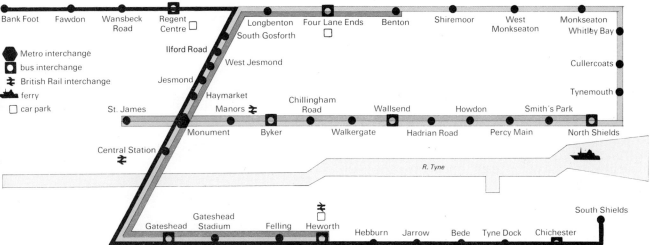

Fig. C The Tyneside Metro network

QUESTIONS

A1 What was the 'Beeching axe'?

2 What is Inter-City?

3 What are (a) HSTs, (b) APTs, (c) DMUs, (d) Railbuses?

4 (a) What transport problems faced Tyneside?
   (b) How have the problems been tackled?

B1 Explain the decline of Britain's rail system as shown by the statistics below:

	1960	1983
Route length open (kilometres)	29 562	17 950
Number of stations open	4 877	2 120

2 Suggest some uses for closed railway lines.

3 (a) Describe the Tyneside Metro system.
   (b) Most British cities have adopted extensive urban motorway networks. Compare and contrast the effects of such motorway networks with a Metro system.

4 Figure D shows the time by fastest train from London to twenty British towns and cities. Copy the radial graph and, using an atlas and a protractor, find the direction of each from London (Birmingham and Brighton have been done for you). Then plot the positions on the graph and draw a line representing the time from London.

6.2 ROADS

Road transport is the main means of travel for passengers and freight, and has several advantages over other modes:

1 Flexibility. Lorries can deliver goods from door to door in a way which railways or canals cannot.

2 Road vehicles do not need expensive loading and unloading facilities.

3 For short journeys, lorries can be fast and cheap.

Eighty-two per cent of Britain's freight is carried by road. In 1983, there were 350 000 km of roads and 18 million vehicles, of which 2 million were goods vehicles.

Motorways

Motorways were designed mainly for the transport of goods over long distances. All have dual carriageways, usually with three lanes each and a limited number of junctions. There are no roundabouts, traffic lights, sharp bends or steep slopes. Serious accidents occur and make headline news, but motorways have proved to be the safest of all roads.

The time saved by motorway journeys represents money saved by road-haulage companies. Accessibility to the motorway network has become an important factor in the location of industry. Factories, warehouses and industrial estates have been built at most motorway junctions.

Passenger journeys by road increased from 79 per cent of the total in 1953 to 93 per cent by 1983. This reflects the decline in rail services. Bus and coach services have declined while travel by car has increased. In the early 1950s, there were 2 million cars in Britain. By 1983, there were 16 million cars and 56 per cent of all households had a car. People like the privacy and comfort which a car provides. Cars are fast and reliable, and often more convenient. Car ownership allows people to live further away from their place of work and to travel for pleasure at weekends. This freedom leads to road congestion, and reduced public transport. Large areas of cities

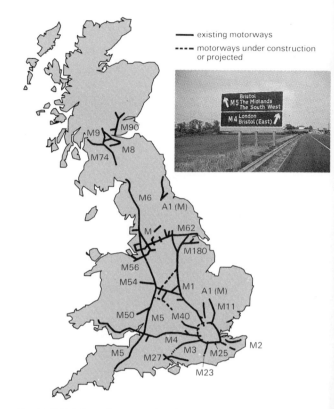

Fig. B Britain's motorway network

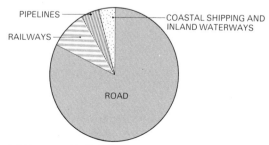

Fig. A Freight transport in Britain

Fig. C Spaghetti Junction: Gravelly Hill, Birmingham

are devoted to the car: roads, flyovers, garages, car parks.

Opposition to motorways: There has been concern about the effect of motorways on the environment. Several campaigns have been fought, notably against the M40 through the Chiltern Hills and the M3 through the Itchen Valley near Winchester. Countryside and farmland has been destroyed, whole areas blighted and many buildings demolished.

It costs over £1 million to build one kilometre of motorway in open country, and much more in difficult terrain or in a city. Heavy traffic has damaged the motorways, and congestion occurs at busy times. Expensive repairs are necessary.

Juggernauts: In 1982 the government raised the weight limit for lorries using British roads from 32 to 38 tonnes. A 38-tonne lorry is nearly 10 per cent

cheaper to operate than a 32-tonner because it saves fuel and reduces the number of journeys needed. Our economy depends heavily upon the heavy lorry, but disadvantages have become obvious:

1 Rising fuel costs have increased running costs. Lorries use more fuel than trains or barges.
2 Weight and vibration damage roads and buildings.
3 Lorries are noisy and pollute the atmosphere.
4 Lorries can be dangerous to other road users.

Many of Britain's roads cannot cope with heavy lorries. New by-passes are being built but many more are needed.

No other European country is as dependent upon road transport as Britain. Our rail and canal systems have been neglected even though they could be used to carry bulk cargoes over long distances. Britain needs a national plan for transport.

Fig. D Expensive motorway repairs

Fig. E Juggernauts driving through the historic town of Louth

QUESTIONS

A1 What are the advantages of road transport?
 2 List the special features of a motorway.
 3 Name four areas of the country poorly served by the motorway network.
 4 List the advantages and disadvantages of cars.
 5 Why have motorways been criticised?
B1 'Motorways have become victims of their own success.' Explain this.
 2 The M40 motorway may be extended from Oxford to Birmingham. It will take traffic away from old towns and villages, but will pass through some of the most attractive countryside in the south of England. The M40 will improve the main routes from Birmingham to the Channel ports and relieve the congested M1. It has been called 'the last link in the motorway chain'.
 Either write a letter to a newspaper supporting the M40's construction or write a letter opposing the new motorway. Whichever letter you write, state clearly the reasons for your opinion.

 3 Describe the problems caused by large lorries and suggest possible solutions.
 4 The table below shows passenger transport within Britain in 1956, 1966 and 1982:

year	Percentage of total passengers			
	rail	bus/coach	car	air
1956	18	36	45	0.2
1966	10	18	72	0.5
1982	7	8	85	0.6

 (a) Construct three proportional bars to illustrate the statistics.
 (b) Describe and explain the changes.
 (c) Explain the dominance of road transport in passenger and cargo transport within Britain.
C Suggest reasons for the pattern of motorway development in Britain. Describe the effects of motorway development on (i) an industrial area, (ii) an urban centre, (iii) a rural area.

6.3 SEAPORTS

There are over two hundred seaports around the British coast. The major cargo ports (Fig A) are Britain's main gateways to world trade.

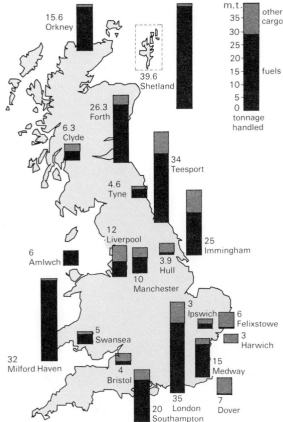

Fig. A The trade of the major British ports

Change in Britain's ports

Two recent developments in shipping have had a profound effect upon British ports: the increasing size of ships and the introduction of specialised cargo ships.

The introduction in the 1960s of supertankers of over 100 000 tonnes has led to the construction of deepwater oil terminals such as Milford Haven in south-west Wales. With tankers of over 300 000 tonnes entering service in the 1970s, offshore oil buoys were needed at places such as Amlwch off Anglesey. Smaller oil ports such as Swansea and Tranmere have lost trade because large ships cannot reach them.

Bulk iron-ore carriers of 100 000 tonnes needed deepwater ports like Hunterston, Port Talbot and Immingham. Established seaports had to build new deepwater berths: Royal Seaforth Dock at Liverpool and the Royal Portbury Dock at Bristol are examples. Seaports which were unable to construct berths for

the larger cargo ships faced decline.

The introduction of specialised bulk and unitised cargo ships (Fig C) has forced seaports to build facilities to handle them. Roll on–roll off facilities allow container lorries to be transported without unloading. The transport of cargo in large ships has meant that fewer are needed. Ports have had to close their older, smaller docks and reduce the size of their workforces. British ports have been involved in fierce competition to attract shipowners:

1 The west coast ports have all declined despite new dock systems at several of the ports. The decline is due mainly to the depressed *hinterlands* (the area which the port serves) and remoteness from trade links with Europe.

2 The smaller ports of East Anglia and south-east England have expanded rapidly to cater for the increased trade between Britain and the EEC. Some of the larger east coast ports have declined because of the closure of old and inadequate dock systems.

3 A select group of seaports handling North Sea oil have expanded rapidly. These include Flotta in the Orkneys, Sullom Voe in the Shetlands, the Forth and Teesport. Sullom Voe became Britain's leading seaport by tonnage of cargo handled in 1981.

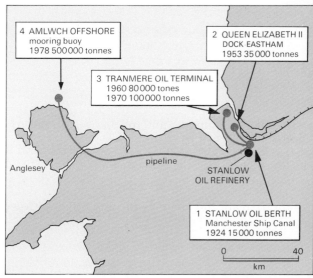

Fig. B The changing location of oil terminals serving Stanlow

QUESTIONS

A1 Name the five largest ports in Britain in terms of tonnage of trade.

2 Why have ships increased in size?

3 List the advantages and disadvantages of (i) container transport, (ii) roll on–roll off transport.

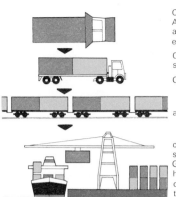

CONTAINERS

A container is a steel box built to a standard size and transported easily by road, rail and sea.

Containers can be loaded and sealed at the factory.

Container lorries........

and freightliner trains.......

carry the containers to specialised container ports. Giant gantry cranes load the huge container ships. The ship can turn round in hours rather than days.

ROLL ON-ROLL OFF

roll on-roll off (RO/RO) means that lorries drive straight on to a specially designed ship. This cuts handling time and costs to a minimum

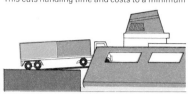

RO/RO has one big drawback: the lorries take up a great deal of valuable cargo space. RO/RO services are most suited to short journeys where handling costs form a high proportion of the total transport costs.

Advantages of containers
1 Quick loading saves time and money
2 Can be carried by several modes of transport
3 Sealed containers reduce theft
4 Carry a variety of goods

Disadvantages of containers
1 Fewer workers are needed to handle the same cargo
2 Because a container ship does the work of several older vessels, ports lie idle for long periods
3 Container handling facilities are very expensive

Fig. C The container revolution

Fig. D The world's largest ship at Amlwch

4 Name (i) the five fastest-growing British ports, (ii) the five fastest-declining British ports.

B1 What effects have (i) the increasing size of cargo ships, and (ii) the introduction of unitised cargo handling had on Britain's ports?

2 Describe and explain the changing importance of Britain's ports?

3 The table below shows the tonnage of cargo handled in container and roll on–roll off traffic in the leading British ports:

(a) Draw a line graph to illustrate the tonnage handled between 1971 and 1981 in container and ro–ro traffic in the six ports.

(b) Explain the changes in rank order between 1971 and 1981. (The 1981 figure for Southampton was unusually low because of a strike.)

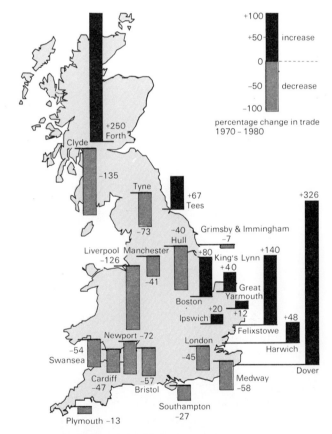

Fig. E The changes in British ports 1970-80

	1971	1972	1973	1974	1975	1976	1977	1978	1979	1980	1981
Dover	1.6	2.0	2.3	2.9	3.1	3.6	4.5	5.0	5.7	6.0	6.4
Felixstowe	1.5	1.9	2.5	2.9	3.2	3.7	3.8	4.4	4.4	5.0	5.8
London	2.4	2.7	2.9	3.0	2.5	2.9	3.1	3.6	3.6	3.5	4.1
Southampton	1.1	1.7	2.8	2.9	2.2	2.8	2.9	3.2	3.9	3.8	1.7
Hull	1.0	1.3	2.1	2.2	1.9	2.2	2.2	2.0	1.9	2.1	2.3
Liverpool	1.6	1.5	1.9	1.5	1.6	1.8	2.0	2.1	1.8	1.9	1.7

(Figures are in million tonnes.)

6.4 PORTS AND WATERWAYS

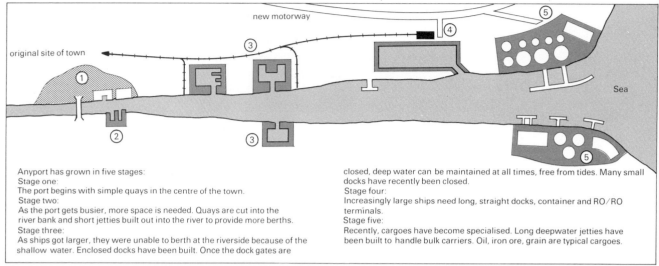

Anyport has grown in five stages:
Stage one:
The port begins with simple quays in the centre of the town.
Stage two:
As the port gets busier, more space is needed. Quays are cut into the river bank and short jetties built out into the river to provide more berths.
Stage three:
As ships got larger, they were unable to berth at the riverside because of the shallow water. Enclosed docks have been built. Once the dock gates are closed, deep water can be maintained at all times, free from tides. Many small docks have recently been closed.
Stage four:
Increasingly large ships need long, straight docks, container and RO/RO terminals.
Stage five:
Recently, cargoes have become specialised. Long deepwater jetties have been built to handle bulk carriers. Oil, iron ore, grain are typical cargoes.

Fig. A Anyport: a model port

'Anyport' (Fig A) is a *model* which summarises seaport development. Real ports vary, but the idea of downriver development usually holds true. The geography of a port such as Bristol can be understood only through studying its historical development:

1 Bristol was founded in the eleventh century at *the lowest bridging point* of the river Avon, 13 kilometres from the open sea (this was the nearest place to the sea where the river was still narrow enough to build a bridge). Ships rested on the rocky bed of the Avon at low tide, but this strained the hulls of large vessels.

2 In 1245, the river Frome, a tributary of the Avon, was diverted into an artificial channel to provide soft mud for the ships to rest on.

3 By the nineteenth century, ships had become too large to rest on the river bed. The Avon was diverted and the old course of the river made into a 33-hectare *dock*. Behind the lock gates, deep water was maintained at all states of the tide.

4 By the later nineteenth century, many ships were too large to sail up the Avon because of the tight meanders. New docks were built where the Avon

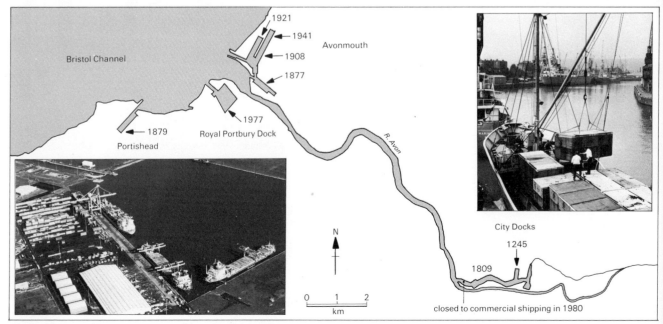

Fig. B The port of Bristol

enters the Bristol Channel. Extensions were built at Avonmouth during this century.

5 The increasing size of ships made Avonmouth inadequate. In 1977, a deepwater dock was opened opposite Avonmouth: the Royal Portbury Dock, suitable for ships of up to 70 000 tonnes. There are container and roll on–roll off facilities.

6 The movement downstream of the port facilities was completed when the City Docks in the heart of Bristol were closed to commercial traffic in 1980. Today, only pleasure craft use the City Docks and some of the warehouses have been converted to other uses such as theatres, arts centres and restaurants.

Inland waterways

Canals were the first transport network designed to carry the materials and products of the Industrial Revolution. They were a great improvement over the poor road system of the late 1700s. Many have fallen into disuse and those which remain are used mainly for pleasure boating. Canal holidays have become popular. Boat-hire centres, boatbuilding and repair yards, canalside shops and pubs have benefited from the increased use of canals for pleasure.

However, inland waterways are still important for commercial freight traffic. Over 60 million tonnes of cargo are carried annually on Britain's canals and rivers. Ten million tonnes are carried on the Manchester Ship Canal alone. Ocean-going vessels of up to 12 700 tonnes can sail 56 kilometres inland to the port of Manchester. Other important inland ports are Goole, Ipswich, Sharpness and Gainsborough.

The most complete network of waterways is that centred on the Humber Estuary; coasters and barges

Fig. D An oil tanker on the Gloucester and Sharpness Canal

of over 500 tonnes navigate far inland. A major improvement scheme to the Sheffield and South Yorkshire Navigation was completed in 1983. This was the first significant investment in Britain's inland waterways since 1905, and may pioneer a return to canal transport. Britain has lagged behind West Germany, France and the Netherlands in inland waterway development. This is to Britain's cost because modern waterways provide cheap and efficient transport. Canal transport does much less damage to the environment than heavy lorries on which transport here is increasingly based.

A new interest is slowly emerging in inland waterways. The British Waterways Board proposes to follow the Sheffield and South Yorkshire Navigation scheme with improvements to the Severn Navigation to allow ships to reach Worcester from the Bristol Channel.

QUESTIONS

A1 How has the location of the Port of Bristol changed since it began in the eleventh century?
2 What does 'lowest bridging point' mean?
3 Why were new docks built at Avonmouth and Portishead rather than in Bristol itself?
4 What has happened to the old docks and warehouses in Bristol?
5 (a) Which canal has been recently improved?
  (b) Why is this scheme important?
B1 (a) What does the Anyport model describe?
  (b) What is the major cause of the stages of development of Anyport?
  (c) How far does Bristol accord with this model?
  (d) Look at the following ports: London (page 182), Liverpool (page 154), Felixstowe (page 126). How far do they accord with Anyport? Explain the differences.
C Comment on the current and future role of inland waterways in Britain.

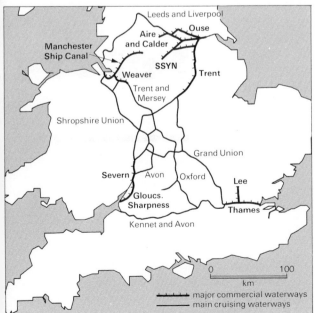

Fig. C The inland waterways of England and Wales

6.5 AIR TRAVEL

Three per cent of passengers travelling on public transport between British cities use airlines. This amounts to over ten million people a year. Air transport competes most strongly with other forms of transport over long distances or where sea crossings are necessary, thus the three major routes are between London and Glasgow, Edinburgh and Belfast.

London (Heathrow): Heathrow is by far the largest airport in the UK and handles half the passengers and cargo using British airports. Three passenger terminals are used by 26 million passengers each year, and a fourth is under construction. Over eighty airlines fly to almost every major city in the world. Heathrow is the world's leading international airport with nearly twice as many passengers on international flights as its nearest rival, New York. In 1981, there were 266 000 aircraft movements (take-offs and landings), equivalent to one movement every two minutes.

Heathrow covers 1200 hectares and the main runway is 4 kilometres long. The airport was sited here because of the existence of a long runway, left over from World War II, which was only 20 kilometres from central London. The airport is like a small city, with shops, offices, factories, car parks, petrol stations and an Underground station. Around 50 000 people work at Heathrow, making it one of the largest single centres of employment in Britain.

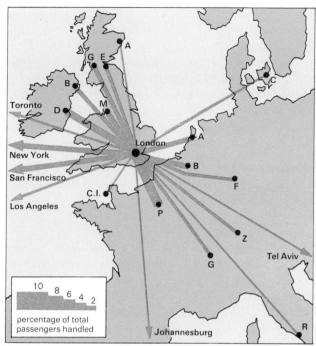

Fig. A The major air routes from Heathrow

There is a limit to the growth of Heathrow. Congestion and delays occur. Services have been encouraged to move to Gatwick, to reduce pressure on Heathrow.

In 1963, Stansted in Essex was chosen as the site of London's third airport. Strong opposition from local people led to a public enquiry and Stansted was

For Stansted	Against Stansted
★ The Government forecasts between 56 and 67 million passengers a year using London's airports by 1990. Heathrow, Gatwick and Luton cannot handle this.	★ Growth in air transport will continue to be slow because of rising fuel costs and the economic recession.
★ Stansted already has an airport which can be expanded quickly and fairly cheaply. It is at present underused.	★ New airport development should occur outside the prosperous south-east of England in order to bring jobs to the depressed regions.
★ Expansion at Stansted will create thousands of new jobs.	★ Stansted has failed to attract airlines or passengers during the 1970s and has lost a great deal of money.
★ Stansted will make high profits, as Heathrow and Gatwick do now.	★ The area around Stansted airport is peaceful, attractive countryside with high-quality farmland and historic towns.
★ If Stansted is not built, many airlines will use European airports such as Amsterdam and Frankfurt.	★ A fifth terminal could easily be built at Heathrow if a neighbouring sewage works was moved.

Fig. B Arguments *for* and *against* Stansted

rejected. In 1978, a new study was launched into the need for a third airport. Another public enquiry followed, and Stansted was chosen as the most suitable site. It has a 3000-metre runway and a small passenger terminal. The government plans to build a terminal to handle 15 million passengers by 1987, with future growth to 25 million. The public enquiry in 1981–3 was the longest and most expensive ever held. The British Airports Authority found itself facing strong opposition from local councils and environmental groups.

Regional airports

Most of Britain's major cities have their own airports. There may be too many. There are advantages in concentrating services at one airport to serve regions wider than an individual city:

1 Money can be concentrated at one place so that better facilities can be provided.

2 More frequent flights can be provided to more destinations.

3 The opportunities for passengers to transfer from one flight to another increase.

The government has divided the airports of England and Wales into four categories (Fig C). The south-east of England is well provided for, but elsewhere only Manchester is a category A airport.

Services will be concentrated at category B airports. The government controls the issue of permits to use airports, and can therefore prevent services being established at unsuitable airports. The government hopes that this policy will encourage a rapid growth of air travel in the regions of England and Wales. Scotland's airports have not yet been classified.

QUESTIONS

A1 (a) Name the largest airport in the British Isles.

(b) How many passengers use this airport each year?

(c) How many people are employed at the airport?

2 (a) What are the four categories of airport in England and Wales?

(b) List the category A and B airports.

B1 (a) Copy the proportional flow lines from Fig A.

(b) Using an atlas, identify the towns indicated by capital letters.

(c) Name the six major routes indicated by Fig A.

2 On an outline map of Britain, locate the ten largest airports listed below and draw circles proportional to the *square root* of their passenger traffic. You will have to calculate the square roots and decide upon a suitable diameter for the circles:

	passengers (million)	square root
Heathrow	26.4	5.14
Gatwick	10.7	?
Manchester	4.7	?
Glasgow	2.3	?
Luton	2.0	?
Aberdeen	1.5	?
Birmingham	1.5	?
Belfast	1.4	?
Jersey	1.3	?
Edinburgh	1.1	?

Why were you asked to draw circles proportional to the square root rather than to the actual figures?

3 The following people are preparing their cases for the enquiry into the development of Stansted airport:

Stansted Residents' Association

British Airways

Local union official

Department of Transport

The local district council

A local businessman

Which people are likely to be in favour of the airport? Briefly state their case.

Which people are likely to be against the airport? Briefly state their case.

C (a) Describe and account for the importance of Heathrow.

(b) Discuss the problems associated with the development of London's airports since 1963.

Fig. C The major airports of the British Isles

6.6 TRANSPORT NETWORKS

A network is the pattern that routes make. We can compare networks in different areas by looking at a map, and can say that the road network of one area appears to be dense while that of a second area is less so. Such observations may be of general use but a more accurate way to compare networks is needed.

The following terms are used:

Node (or vertex): a node is a town, or a junction of two or more routes.

Route (or edge): a route is a line joining two nodes.

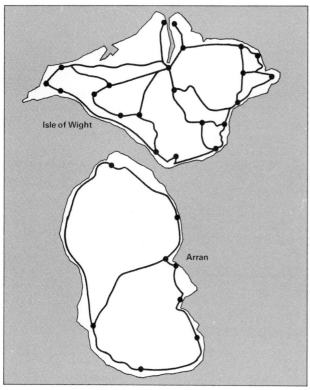

Fig. A

Figure A shows the road networks of the Isles of Wight and Arran. Figure B shows the Arran network on a *topological diagram*, which has the same information but in a simpler form. Networks can be studied by three techniques: the beta index, the alpha index and network density.

The beta index: The beta index measures how many choices of routes there are within the network. It is calculated using this formula:

$$B = \frac{R}{N}$$

where R is the number of routes and N is the number of nodes.

Values of B range from 0.5 to 3.0. The higher the value, the higher the *connectivity* (choice of routes).

The calculations of the beta index for the Isles of Wight and Arran are:

Arran	Wight
$B = \dfrac{9}{8}$	$B = \dfrac{30}{21}$
B = 1.125	B = 1.43

The alpha index: This is a more complicated formula which gives a range of values from 0 to 100 and allows for the fact that there may be two or more separate networks within a region. The alpha index is calculated using this formula:

$$a = \frac{(R - N) + T}{2N - 5} \times 100$$

where R is the number of routes, N is the number of nodes and T is the total number of separate networks.

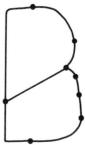

Fig. B A topological road diagram: Arran

The calculations are:

Arran	Wight
$a = \dfrac{(9 - 8) + 1}{16 - 5} \times 100$	$a = \dfrac{(30 - 21) + 1}{42 - 5} \times 100$
$= \dfrac{1 + 1}{11} \times 100$	$= \dfrac{9 + 1}{37} \times 100$
= 18.18	= 27.03

Network density: The density of a network is calculated by this formula:

$$ND = \frac{N}{A}$$

where N is the number of nodes and A is the total area in km².

The calculations are:

Arran	Wight
$ND = \dfrac{8}{427}$	$ND = \dfrac{21}{381}$
= 0.019 per km²	= 0.055 per km².

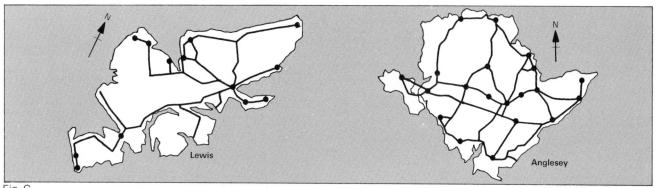

Fig. C

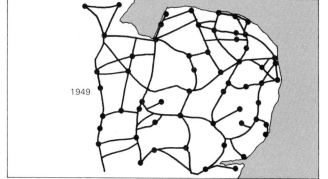

Fig. D

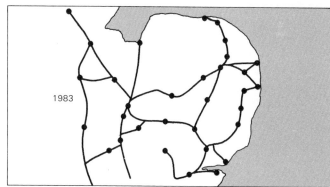

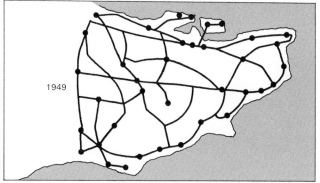

Fig. E

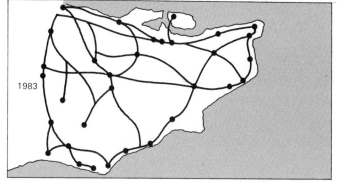

All three techniques show us that the road network of the Isle of Wight is more complex than that of the Isle of Arran. We could have arrived at the same conclusion simply by looking at the maps, but the calculations allow us to make accurate comparisons.

	Wight	Arran	Anglesey	Lewis
alpha index	27.03	18.18		
beta index	1.43	1.125		
network density	0.055	0.019		

QUESTIONS

A1 What is a network?

2 Define (i) a node, (ii) a route, (iii) a vertex, (iv) a topological diagram.

3 What are the formulae for the alpha index, the beta index and network density?

B1 Figure C shows the road networks of the Isles of Anglesey and Lewis. Calculate the alpha and beta indices and the network densities. The area of Anglesey is 715 km² and of Lewis 1994 km². Write your calculations into this table:

2 Network analysis can be used to study the development of an area's network over a period of time. Figures D and E show the railway networks of East Anglia and south-east England in 1949 and 1983. The area of the East Anglian network is 13 000 km²; the south-east network's area is 6350 km².

(a) Calculate the alpha and beta indices and the network density for both areas in each year.

(b) Compare and contrast the results.

(c) Account for the differences.

105

7.1 GROWTH AND CHANGE

More than 80 per cent of Britain's population lives in urban areas. This is the name we use to describe towns and cities, whether they still have a separate identity (Bristol, Edinburgh, Newport), or are part of a *conurbation* (a group of towns and cities like Greater Manchester).

The only towns in Britain before the Romans came were tribal capitals such as Colchester, Canterbury and St Albans. They were few. The Romans built many towns, and Roman origins can be detected today in place-names ending in 'cester', 'chester' and 'eter'. They were well-defended, and linked by a network of roads. They became market centres and trading posts serving the surrounding rural areas.

The Romans left Britain in the fifth century, but few new towns were founded until the tenth century. The Danes made York the major city of the north and developed five borough towns: Lincoln, Nottingham, Derby, Leicester and Stamford. The Anglo-Saxons built a series of burghs or fortresses in southern England which became towns such as Winchester, Southampton, Wareham, Oxford and Warwick.

The Normans built castles throughout England, many in existing towns, after the invasion in 1066. Some, at new sites, later developed into towns such as Ludlow and Leominster. In the Middle Ages, towns slowly grew. Most served as markets for the surrounding farms and villages. They grew up at intervals, acting as *central places* serving the

Fig. A

Fig. B The Barbican: redevelopment in central London

surrounding area or *hinterland*. The most accessible towns developed more rapidly than those with small hinterlands.

Towns can be arranged in order of importance. This *central place hierarchy* is shown below:

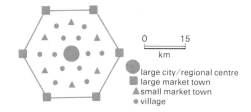

Fig. C

Until about 1750, only 20 per cent of the British population lived in towns. The only large towns, London, Bristol and Norwich, were important seaports. After 1800, the proportion of people living in towns increased very quickly. The Agricultural Revolution was producing more food with fewer workers, and there was large-scale migration from the country to the towns and cities in search of jobs. Because of the Industrial Revolution many new towns were established and existing towns expanded rapidly. This was especially true in the coalfield areas. The hierarchy of settlement changed: there were more towns, and they contained an increasing number of people. The process of urbanisation was closely linked to industrialisation.

Changes in the types of urban centres: Early this century, it was possible to identify types of towns or cities. Towns often had one main industry or type of employment and most people earned their living by it.

It would be impossible to classify towns like this today. Towns and cities now have many functions, although one may still be dominant. A central place in modern Britain has a range of functions. In

Specialised towns of the early twentieth century

cotton spinning town	Oldham
woollen town	Leeds
railway town	Crewe
seaside resort	Blackpool
university city	Oxford
fishing port	Wick
market town	Banbury
steel town	Port Talbot

Fig. D

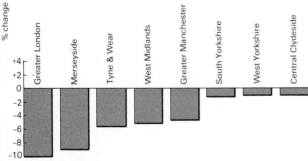

Fig. E Britain's declining conurbations

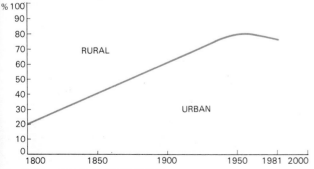

Fig. F The growth of urban Britain

Oxford, for example, cars are made and industry is established in estates around the city. The information, service and retail trades are well represented. The university has not declined, but it no longer dominates the modern city.

Urban population changes

There was a steady increase in the number of people living in urban areas until the 1950s, since when there have been changes:

1 Urban centres have lost population.

2 The older suburbs of metropolitan areas have gained population.

3 The main conurbations have declined.

4 Small towns away from large urban areas have grown quickly.

5 People have moved within the large towns and cities as redevelopment has taken place.

6 Immigrant groups have moved into the central areas of cities.

7 New towns have been built.

8 Existing towns have been designated as expanded towns.

QUESTIONS

A1 Since what date have there been more urban than rural people in Britain?

2 Name some important towns of Roman origin.

3 Briefly define conurbation; hinterland; and hierarchy.

4 Give an example of a settlement hierarchy in your area (name a village, market town, large town and city).

5 Which city would you say was at the top of your local hierarchy?

6 (a) Name four specialised towns other than those listed in Fig D.

  (b) Why are there now fewer specialised towns?

B1 Write a brief explanation of the following:

  (a) 'The conurbations of Britain are declining but smaller towns continue to grow.'

  (b) 'The urban cores are losing population but the outer metropolitan areas are gaining population.'

  (c) 'Immigrants have been attracted to the declining centres of British cities.'

2 Study the population figures for the south-east region:

	1971	1981
Greater London	7 452 346	6 713 165
outer metropolitan area	5 152 338	5 400 152
outer south-east	4 325 946	4 682 439

State briefly how population has changed in the region between 1971 and 1981.

7.2 CITY STRUCTURE

Cities and large towns have their own character, but all have similar types of areas. The areas may be in *concentric rings* or *sectors*. There may be specialist centres in large urban areas which are called *nuclei*, where there are single functions. For example, all industry may be located in one area and recreation facilities in another. The city shown here combines many of the characteristics found in typical large urban areas in Britain.

The city has grown outwards from the centre and has developed specialist sectors. The redeveloped residential area has been planned to keep housing separate from industry. Today, there are nuclei of industry on the edge of the *built-up area*. Near the airport, a conference and hotel complex has been built.

The *central business district* (CBD) is the most accessible place in the city. This accessibility attracts shops and offices:

large shops   department stores
specialist shops   video
finance   banks, building societies
public buildings   council offices
entertainments   theatre
education   university
transport   bus station
offices   firm's headquarters

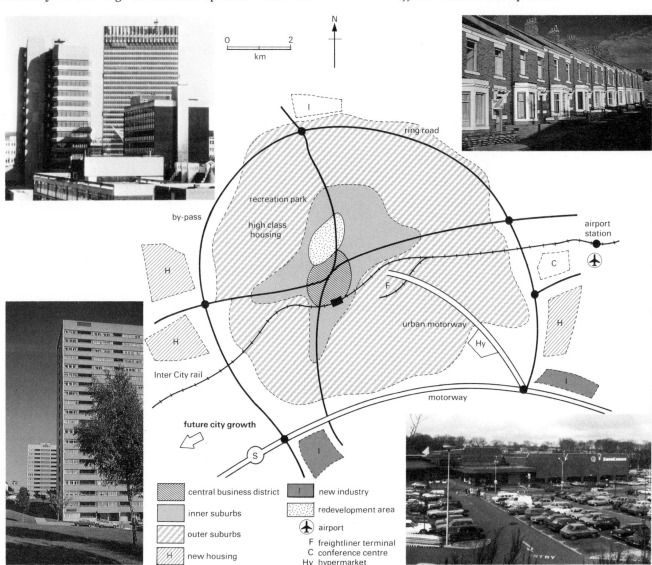

central business district
inner suburbs
outer suburbs
H new housing
I new industry
redevelopment area
airport
F freightliner terminal
C conference centre
Hy hypermarket

Fig. A Sectors within a city

Many of the buildings in the CBD are high-rise. There can be several functions in one tower block. At street level, there may be shops and services; above may be insurance offices, and then company offices on the upper floors. Profits are high in the CBD; because there is a demand for sites there, *land values are high*. Away from the city centre, land values are lower because there is less demand (Fig B).

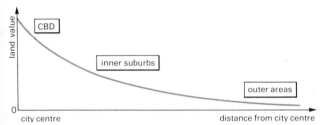

Fig. B Land values within a city

Cities and towns grew outwards from the centre, and spread along railways and roads. Housing strung out along main roads is called *ribbon development*. Industry located near the centre, close to the homes of the workers. Inner suburbs often consist of terraced housing mixed with industry, in buildings which are often old and sometimes run down.

In areas awaiting redevelopment, people may move out and empty property stands next to homes which are still lived in. This is a *twilight zone*, often where the poorest people live. The census statistics show people here may not have an inside toilet or bath, and there is more overcrowding and higher unemployment. The percentage of owner-occupied housing will be among the lowest in the city. The inner suburbs house many *ethnic minority groups*, whose members are not necessarily immigrants — they may have been born in Britain.

Further out the housing is newer. Housing densities are lower and there is more open space. Neighbourhood shopping centres serve the suburbs which have distinct communities. In recent years, planning has played an important role in city growth. The local authorities *zone* land for specific functions, and industrial estates are often financed by them.

Transport improvements explain the changing city. The motorway has taken over from the railway. New growth is increasingly attracted to the land accessible to motorway interchanges. Most cities now have urban motorways which make it easy to reach the inner city.

Britain's cities have expanded outwards and losses of agricultural land have been high. *Urban sprawl* is seen as a continued threat to the countryside. *Green belts* have been used to control sprawl. *Green wedges* help to keep land for leisure and farming around cities.

 inner cities 114, 154, 166, 184   green belt 171, 179
multi-racial Britain 220

QUESTIONS

A1 What attracts shops and offices to city centres?

2 Make a list of functions in the CBD. Give one more example of each function, e.g. *large shops: department stores* and *chain stores*.

3 Give examples of transport improvements in the typical British city.

B1 Explain the location of the following functions on the map: conference centre; hypermarket; new industrial estates.

2 Suggest why 'future city growth' is being planned towards the south-west.

3 Where will future redevelopments be started?

4 Suggest why land values decline away from the city centre.

5 The following statistics are taken from the 1981 Census for selected wards of Birmingham.

Wards	% born outside United Kingdom	% women unemployed	% with no car
Brandwood	7.6	5.1	43.2
Moseley	18.0	7.3	46.2
Deritend	35.2	11.3	72.4

Suggest locations in the city for these three wards.

What types of housing do you think are to be found in each of the three wards?

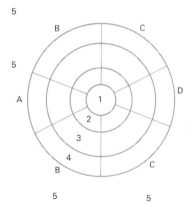

A middle-class sector
B lower middle-class sector
C working-class sector (including council estates)
D industry and lowest working-class sector

1 CBD
2 transition zone
3 zone of small terraced houses in sectors C and D; larger by-law housing in sector B; large old houses in sector A
4 post-1918 residential areas, with post-1945 housing on the periphery
5 dormitory towns within commuting distance

Fig. C Model of a British city

C1 Using the model in Fig C, describe and explain the land use in any town or city you have studied.

2 Outline recent changes in the structure of a typical British city.

7.3 NEW AND EXPANDED TOWNS

The population of Greater London fell from 8.6 million in 1939 to 6.71 million in 1981. Londoners were encouraged to leave the congested city and move to 'overspill' towns specially built to take them.

Britain's first new towns came into being after the New Towns Act of 1946, and today over two million people live in them. Not all were built solely for overspill. Corby was planned to house workers for a new iron and steel works and Peterlee was planned to provide new homes and new jobs for people of the Durham coalfield. Peterborough and Northampton were already large when they became new towns.

London's new towns

New town	Date of establish- ment	Population 1981	Planned population
The original ring:			
Basildon	1949	94 277	130 000
Bracknell	1949	48 752	60 000
Crawley	1947	44 309	75 000
Harlow	1947	79 276	90 000
Hatfield	1948	25 160	29 000
Hemel Hempstead	1947	76 257	85 000
Stevenage	1946	74 365	100 000
Welwyn	1948	40 496	50 000
The new city:			
Milton Keynes	1967	96 130	200 000
Second generation:			
Peterborough	1967	114 108	160 000
Northampton	1968	156 853	180 000

London's expanded towns: London has entered into house-building agreements with the local authorities of various towns. The agreements began with the Town Development Act (1952). There are over thirty expanded towns, some as far from London as Bodmin in Cornwall.

The problems of new towns: The ring of eight new towns around London was built immediately after

Fig. A Britain's new towns

World War II. To keep them separate from London's suburbs, a green belt was established where most new building was prohibited. The land was preserved for farming and recreation. This has not been totally successful in stopping growth.

New towns were planned to be 'self-contained environments for work and living', and were intended to attract people from the older inner areas of London. New industry would be encouraged. However, they were all within 50 kilometres of London and people can commute to work in the capital. The towns have become extensions to the 'dormitory suburbs' of London. New town inhabitants do not settle easily into a fresh environ-

Expanded towns

	Population		% increase	Year of overspill agreement	Number of houses in agreement
	1951	1981			
Swindon	68 932	91 136	32.2	1953	9080
Basingstoke	16 979	67 447	297.2	1959	9250
Aylesbury	21 054	48 159	128.7	1958	3700
Huntingdon	5 282	17 467	230.6	1958	2600

It must be the Peterborough Effect

Peterborough
Cathedral city – new town

Fig. B

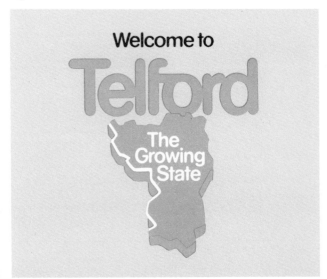

Fig. C

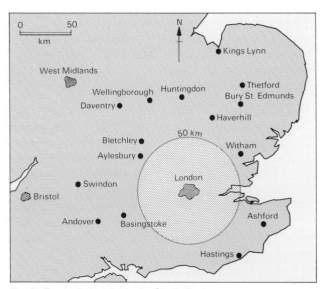

Fig. D Expanded towns in the South East

ment, especially if social and leisure facilities are poorly developed to start with. Another problem is that the cost of living is often higher than in the older centres: rents are high and transport can be expensive. Many of the estates are large and impersonal. Crime, divorce and suicide rates are higher in new towns than elsewhere.

Many towns have been worried about the success of new and expanded towns in attracting new industry. Older towns have often stagnated. Recently, official policy has begun to favour redevelopment of the inner areas of major cities. Overspill has taken people and industry away from the cities, and now there must be attempts to make city life attractive. It is likely that overspill movements will decline in future years for this reason, and also because population growth throughout Britain has slowed.

QUESTIONS

A1 What do you understand by a new town; an expanded town; an overspill town?

2 Why were eight new towns built around London after World War II?

3 Name two new towns that were not built for overspill reasons?

4 (a) Using the scale on Fig A, measure the distance from Crawley and Stevenage to the centre of London.

(b) What happened as a result of the original new towns' nearness to London?

(c) On Fig D, measure the distance from Swindon and Basingstoke to the centre of London. Suggest why the expanded towns are further from the centre of London.

B1 Write what you understand by 'The Peterborough Effect'.

2 You live in London and have decided to take advantage of new GLC housing in an expanded town. Write a letter to a friend telling him/her of your decision but explaining your worries about moving.

3 Why are we likely to hear less of overspill movements in the future?

C Write an account of Britain's new town policy. From examples known to you, discuss the main features of new towns.

111

7.4 MILTON KEYNES

Milton Keynes is a new city in the south-east Midlands of England. When industrial premises and shops were being closed elsewhere, and city populations were falling, Milton Keynes was expanding. Industry, offices and shopping areas were under construction, promising new jobs for the fast-growing population. Between 1967 and 1981, the population increased by 60 000 to 124 000, over half-way to the 1990s target of 200 000.

The new city, designated in 1967, is being built midway between London and Birmingham. It is on the main electrified railway line from London to the Midlands and the north-west. The M1 motorway forms its north-eastern boundary.

Building a new city

The idea was that Milton Keynes should be a major *growth pole*. It was to be a self-sufficient hub of industrial, office and service activity. Being centrally placed, it has good links with Europe. The ports of Felixstowe and Harwich are within 150 kilometres by road, and Luton Airport is only half an hour's drive. The area of the new city was not entirely a 'green field' site, but included the existing towns of Bletchley and Wolverton.

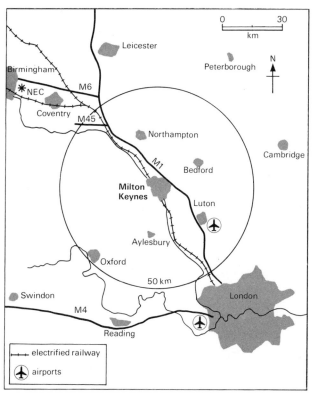

Fig. A The location of Milton Keynes

Financing the new city: Forty-five per cent of the total investment has come from the Milton Keynes Development Corporation (MKDC), which borrows money from the government. It has to be repaid over sixty years. To repay the loans, the corporation must be successful. To ensure success, it must attract industry and offices to the New City (Fig B).

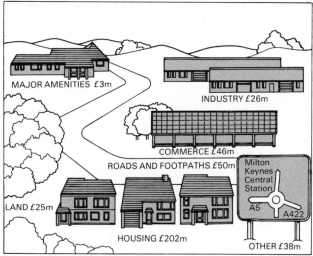

Fig. B MKDC investment

Attracting businesses: The MKDC says 'there is a compelling commercial logic in choosing Milton Keynes as a place to do business. Whether manufacturing, distribution or service industry, large or small, the city offers the ideal location . . .'

Over 450 companies support this view. They include Coca-Cola, Aston Martin Lagonda, VAG (Volkswagen), GEC-Marconi and Minolta Cameras. Hoechst Chemicals have a research centre there and the John Lewis Partnership their distribution warehouse. Office development has been successful and the city is now one of the main office centres in south-east Britain. The Open University has established its headquarters there. The Abbey National Building Society has a computer centre and the Institute of Chartered Accountants has moved some of its administration out of London to Milton Keynes.

Living in a new city: Figure C shows how housing, shopping, employment and recreation areas have been dispersed. They are linked by a grid of main roads. The plan is that the roads will never be blocked with rush hour traffic. Buses serve all the housing areas and there is a bus stop within a few minutes of every house. The separation of different land uses helps to avoid *land use conflict*. Industrial activity does not affect housing areas, for example.

Milton Keynes has no sense of 'home' to most people until they have lived there for some years. Many are lonely on arrival and miss the neighbourhood of their former homes. To create a 'sense of belonging', the city has neighbourhood areas called urban villages. Most new towns use this planning concept—each separate residential area is served by its own shops, schools and community centre. Although the new city was meant to be self-sufficient, over 2000 people travel daily to London. For them, Milton Keynes is a new dormitory town. Many more commute to work in towns like Luton and Dunstable.

People's reactions to living in Milton Keynes are mixed. They may enjoy the amenities but miss their original home. Some object to living in a place where so much building is going on, but this problem will be solved as the city nears completion. It takes many years to establish a settled community.

The city covers a large area and some have said that the sprawl should have been limited. Many more are questioning the sense of building on good-quality farmland when there are large areas of derelict land in our major cities. The size of the place causes problems of movement between areas and with this in mind over 80 kilometres of cycleway have been built. The first generation of residents is living with expansion, a situation unfamiliar to most British cities in the early 1980s.

Fig. D Milton Keynes' Shopping Centre

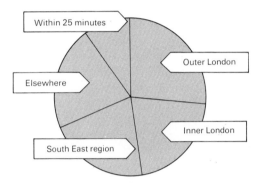

Fig. E Where the people come from

QUESTIONS

A1 Why is the location of Milton Keynes between London and Birmingham an advantage?

2 Name six companies or organisations that have located in Milton Keynes.

3 'A manufacturing or distribution firm locating in Milton Keynes will enjoy good transport facilities.' What are these transport advantages?

4 Draw a bar graph to show the different types of investment by the MKDC (Fig B).

5 Why is the MKDC so interested in attracting successful businesses to the new city?

6 List the advantages and disadvantages of Milton Keynes as a growth pole for Britain.

B1 Look at the plan for Milton Keynes (Fig C). Write about the road network, the location of industry and the distribution of open space.

2 How does a new city like Milton Keynes 'swallow up land'? Suggest alternative ways of providing new growth areas for Britain which are not so 'land hungry'.

C Name three new urban settlements and state their purpose. For one you have studied, outline the original plans and discuss their success.

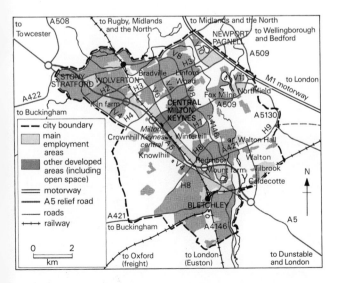

Fig. C The New City plans

7.5 THE INNER CITY

The problems of living in our once-busy city cores were brought to the public's attention in the early 1980s when several cities experienced riots (Liverpool, London and Bristol). It is possible to explain the build-up of tensions in decaying, *deprived* inner city areas which led to these outbursts of violence.

Inner city areas grew fast with early industrialisation. Now, factories have closed and the housing is old. People and industry have been attracted to the outskirts or suburbs of the city, but the poor and unemployed have been unable to move. Ethnic minorities are in the main poor and often suffer *racial disadvantage* in getting work, which gives rise to a sense of frustration and injustice.

The solutions are not easy and the scale of the problem is large. Under the Inner Urban Areas Act (1978), some local authorities were given powers to stop decay and decline in *inner city partnership areas*. They include Liverpool, Manchester/Salford, Birmingham, Newcastle/Gateshead and parts of inner London including the docklands. Government grants and European Regional Fund aid are available. Enterprise zones have also been set up in several city areas such as Liverpool, Manchester, Newcastle and London.

Financial help will not guarantee revival. For decades, there has been movement away from the big cities. Life in outer urban areas, small towns and rural areas is more attractive. In future, inner city areas need new industry which is at present enticed to out-of-town locations. Bradford has successfully established microelectronics (hi-tech) companies, but there is no sign of a movement back to cities generally. If our big cities fail to attract re-building schemes, their future could be in the balance.

QUESTIONS

A1 With the help of Figs A to D, outline some of the problems of the inner city.

2 People in inner cities are often deprived. The graphs (Fig F) compare the inner city areas of Liverpool and Manchester with the whole conurbations. How are the inner city areas deprived?

3 Study the maps (Fig E) of inner Liverpool.
   (a) Which wards are most deprived?
   (b) Which ward is least deprived?

4 What other maps could be drawn to show the inner city of Liverpool as a deprived area?

Fig. A Housing in inner Liverpool: vandalised, dirty courtyards and no private gardens

Fig. B Redevelopment in inner Birmingham: high-rise homes create problems for the young and old and a dual-carriageway cuts through the new community

Fig. C A dangerous play area in inner Liverpool

Fig. D Derelict housing in inner Birmingham: the roofs offer a lethal playground

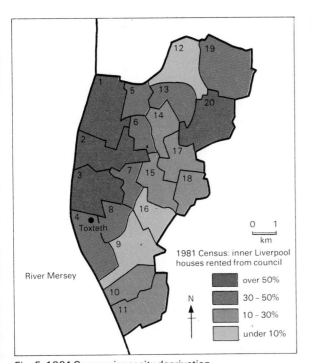

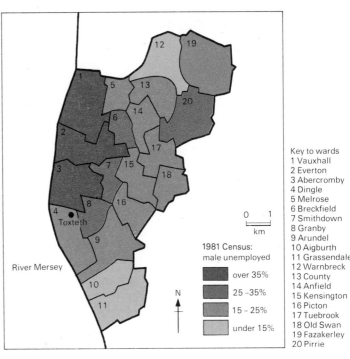

Key to wards
1 Vauxhall
2 Everton
3 Abercromby
4 Dingle
5 Melrose
6 Breckfield
7 Smithdown
8 Granby
9 Arundel
10 Aigburth
11 Grassendale
12 Warnbreck
13 County
14 Anfield
15 Kensington
16 Picton
17 Tuebrook
18 Old Swan
19 Fazakerley
20 Pirrie

Fig. E 1981 Census: inner city deprivation

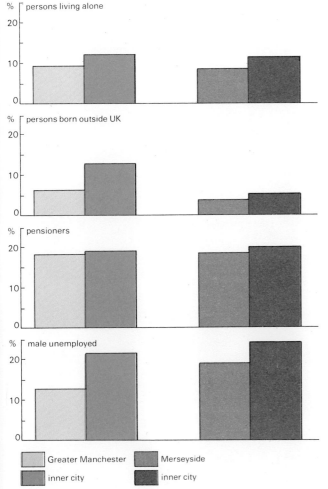

Fig. F 1981 Census: inner Liverpool

B1 Draw similar graphs to Fig F to show the following inner city characteristics:

households	Greater Manchester	inner city	Merseyside	inner city
owner-occupied	57.0	31.5	52.0	39.2
with no car	47.2	68.9	50.1	66.9

2 Attempt to compare the two maps of the Liverpool inner city area (Fig E).

3 Study the figures below and Fig C on p 179. What do the statistics reveal about
   (a) population changes in the Greater London area as a whole?
   (b) changes in population distribution within the Greater London area?

Population density, persons per hectare

Borough	1971	1981
Kensington and Chelsea	158	116
Islington	136	108
Hackney	113	93
Lambeth	107	90
Bexley	36	35
Harrow	40	39
Barnet	34	33

Population changes, 1971–1981

Greater London	– 9.9%
Inner London	– 18.0%
Outer Suburbs	– 5.1%

115

7.6 POPULATION CHANGE: CENSUS 1981

The information in Figs A to D has been taken from the 1981 Census, one of a series of censuses held in Britain every ten years (except 1941) since 1801. The census covers every household in Britain and its results are more accurate than surveys using samples. Its findings are published at a variety of scales: national, regional, town or district, and *ward*. The wards of towns and districts are areas of similar size. They are further divided into *enumeration districts*, each with about 150 to 200 households.

The census provides facts which are used for a range of policies and planning. Government grants to local authorities are based on the figures. Local authorities can plan for schools, housing and old people's homes by using the data. The statistics are used in medical research and the planning of future

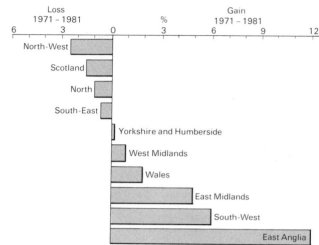

Fig. B Population changes in the regions

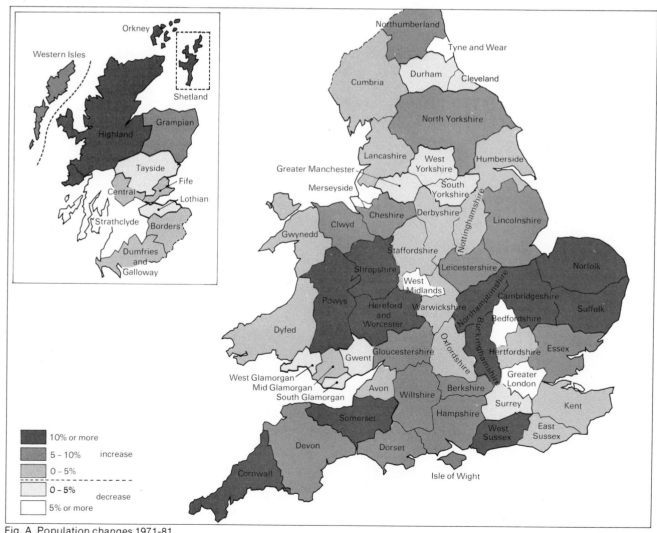

Fig. A Population changes 1971-81

transport services. The census cannot provide all information required and must be supplemented from other sources. Figure E is an example of population change information that comes from the Registrar General.

	% population change
Great Britain	+ 0.6
Greater London	– 10.1
Metropolitan districts	– 4.6
Non-metropolitan districts	+ 5.3
(a) Large cities	– 5.1
(b) Smaller cities	– 3.2
(c) New town areas	+ 15.1
(d) Resort/seaside areas	+ 4.9
(e) Remoter rural areas	+ 10.3

Fig. C

QUESTIONS

A1 Use Figs A and B:

(a) Which four regions in Great Britain increased the most between 1971 and 1981?

(b) Name a county in each of these four regions where population increased by 10 per cent or more.

(c) Which counties in the declining Scotland region increased by 10 per cent or more?

(d) What is common about the five counties that decreased by 5 per cent or more?

(e) Figure B shows north-west England as losing population. What is misleading about this (see Fig A)?

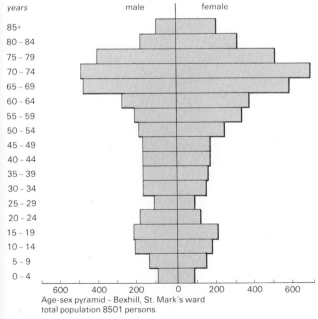

Fig. D Age-sex pyramid: St Mary's Ward, Bexhill

2 Look at Fig D, which shows distribution by age and sex in a ward of Bexhill, East Sussex.

(a) Which age-group has the least persons?

(b) Which age-group has the most persons?

(c) Are there more of one sex than the other? If so, in which age-group is this most pronounced?

3 Suggest a possible type of housing area for this ward in Bexhill.

4 Think about the housing area you live in. What shape of age–sex pyramid would you think it has?

B1 Comment on the population changes shown in Fig C.

2 Describe the characteristics of the age–sex pyramid (Fig D).

3 Suggest how this age–sex pyramid would differ from that of Great Britain as a whole (*Bexhill, St. Mark's*: 51.3 per cent of pensionable age, *Great Britain*: 17.7 per cent; *Bexhill, St. Mark's*: 1.9 per cent 0–4 years, *Great Britain*: 6.0 per cent).

4 Sketch the shape for an age–sex pyramid for an area of new three-bedroomed houses on the outskirts of a city.

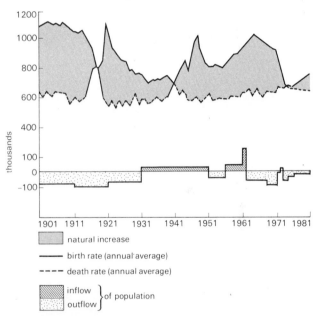

Fig. E The population of Great Britain

C Study Fig E:

(a) Describe the general trends of births and deaths between 1901 and 1981.

(b) The population of a country is sometimes compared to the water in a domestic bath which has two taps, a plughole and an overflow. Explain how this comparison helps us to understand Fig E.

(c) Suggest future trends in the population of Britain.

8.1 EAST ANGLIA AND THE FENS

If you asked people to talk about East Anglia they would probably describe a scene similar to that in Fig A: large wheat fields, a flat landscape and broad skies. East Anglia presents a peaceful rural face, and the regional tourist authority makes the most of it. East Anglia is a popular holiday playground for the industrial Midlands and south-east England, but the traditional pattern of the area is changing fast.

Although it has the smallest population of any British region, East Anglia's population is increasing at the fastest rate. In the last twenty years it has grown by one-quarter, which is significant when considered against a 6 per cent increase for England as a whole.

East Anglia is the fastest-growing industrial region in Britain. High-technology firms have established themselves in the area. Growth is occurring in the

Fig. A

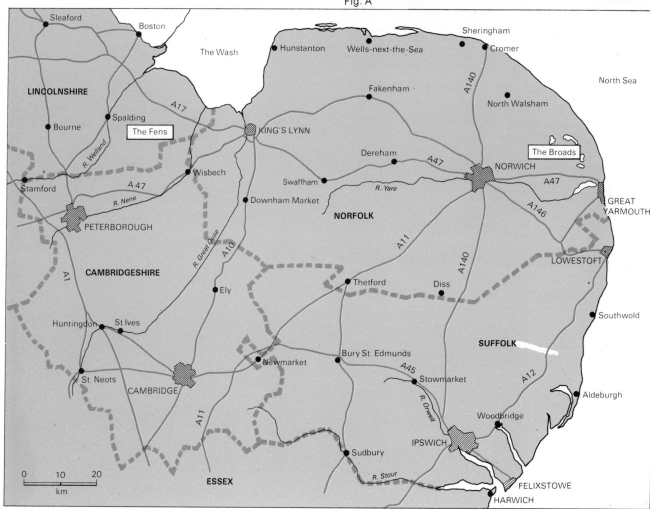

Fig. B East Anglia

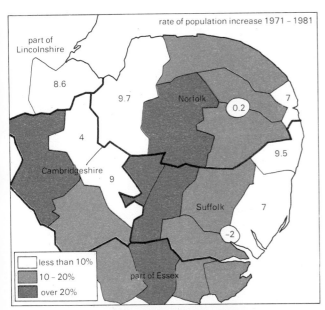

Fig. C Population increase in East Anglia, 1961-81

Fig. D Weavers' cottages in Lavenham

Fig. E 'The Cornfield' by Constable

Fig. F Boats on the Norfolk Broads

seaports, and the trade of Felixstowe, Harwich, Ipswich and King's Lynn is booming whilst ports in other regions are declining. Agricultural production is increasing. East Anglia's farms operate on an intensive, industrial basis.

This rapid growth in population, industry, trade and farm production has changed the character of East Anglia. The traditional dependence upon agriculture has vanished. The farming workforce has declined so greatly that many villages have completely lost their links with farming. Despite the overall growth, many of the remote areas are suffering from the effects of rural decline. Job opportunities in villages have decreased sharply, and young people have been forced to travel or move to find work. The population structure of villages has aged as a result. Services in the rural areas have suffered. Village shops find it difficult to compete with supermarkets on price or range of stock, and many have been forced to close. Village schools have closed as the number of children has declined. Village clinics, post offices and banks have gone. Bus fares have increased and the number of services has been cut. Car ownership in East Anglia is among the highest in Britain; 66 per cent of homes have a car. The elderly suffer most from the decline of the village services. Many do not have cars, and bus fares drain their pensions. Some elderly people in rural regions such as East Anglia face hardship due to the decrease in services.

East Anglia is a region of growth and decline; the outsider's image of a peaceful, unchanging area is an illusion.

QUESTIONS

A1 In what ways is East Anglia growing?

2 In what ways is East Anglia declining?

B1 Use the population map, and an atlas, to explain the pattern of population increase.

2 What are the causes and effects of rural decline?

119

8.2 AGRICULTURE IN EAST ANGLIA

East Anglia and the Fens is the most important farming region in Britain. A higher proportion of the region's workforce is employed in farming than in any other region, but amounts only to 6.5 per cent of the total workforce. The area makes a vital contribution to Britain's food supplies (Fig A).

During the Middle Ages East Anglia was famous for its woollen industry, but there are few sheep left in the region now.

Arable farming is most important today. The region has several **physical advantages**:

1 The summers are warm (daytime average over 21°C in July) and sunny (over 6.5 sunshine hours per day in July), which ripens the crops.

2 Rainfall is low (less than 650 millimetres over most of the region), but much of it is during the growing season from April to August when it is most needed.

3 The cold winters (average 3°C in January) have hard frosts which help to kill disease and break up the soil for ploughing.

4 There is a wide variety of soils and many of them are fertile (Fig C).

5 Much of the land is flat or undulating. It is suitable for large-scale farming and fields are large.

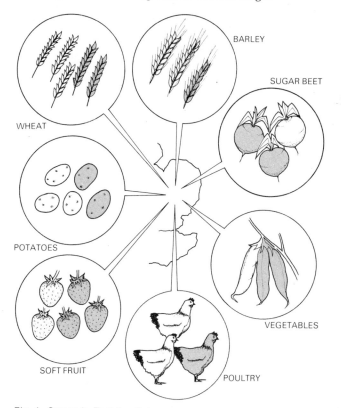

Fig. A Grown in East Anglia!

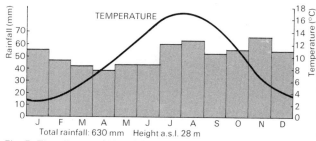

Fig. B The climate of Norwich
Total rainfall: 630 mm   Height a.s.l. 28 m

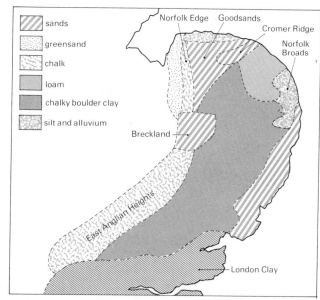

Fig. C The soil types of East Anglia

Fig. D Farming regions

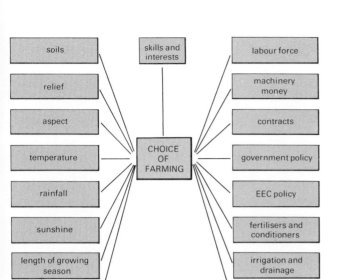

Fig. E Farming decisions

The region's **economic advantages** include:
1 The accessibility of the markets in London, the south-east and the West Midlands.
2 The region's long history of farming innovation. This continues today with the use of modern farming practices including mechanisation, controlled grazing, factory farming, seed selection and the intensive use of fertilisers.
3 The existence of large efficient farms (arable farms are often over 200 hectares).
4 Specialisation: the traditional mixed farm is becoming rare. As a result, the output of certain crops, such as oilseed rape, has increased, while others, such as oats, have declined.
5 The development of *contract farming* in which a food company agrees to purchase a crop, usually fruit or vegetables, for processing.
6 A willingness to invest in farming and to intensify production: building storage silos, purchasing sprinkler irrigation systems and renewing field drainage systems.

Agricultural sub-regions

The chalky boulder clay soils: This is the largest sub-region, a low plateau covered by chalky boulder clay deposited by ice sheets during the Ice Age. Soils are deep and the land is flat or gently undulating. In recent years, hedgerows have been uprooted to form large fields which are suitable for the intensive use of machinery. There are broad expanses of wheat and barley (the 'English Prairies'). Sugar beet and potatoes are important. There are dairy cattle pastures on the heavier clay soils.

Sandy soils: Sandy soils are naturally infertile, but can be improved by fertilisers and irrigation. Barley, wheat and sugar beet are the major crops, but some areas are important for specialised crops: e.g.
Peas, carrots and cabbages in the Goodsands area
Blackcurrants and apples in the greensand area
Part of the Breckland, used only for forestry until recently, has been improved. Carrots, parsnips and asparagus are grown. Two hundred square kilometres remain forested with coniferous plantations.

The light, sandy soils are good for fruit and vegetable crops because they warm up early in the year.

Loam soils: This small area in north-east Norfolk is one of the most productive farming regions in Britain. The crops grown here have changed recently, with peas and beans more important than wheat and sugar beet because of the increased demand for frozen foods and the building of quick-freezing plants. Fifty per cent of British homes have a freezer.

Agriculture in East Anglia has changed during the last twenty years and the region will continue to supply a great deal of food for Britain.

QUESTIONS

A1 What physical advantages does East Anglia have for arable farming?
 2 How have farmers overcome the problems of sandy soils?
 3 How has the land use of Breckland changed?
 4 Why has the farming on the loam soils changed?
B1 Study the major land uses in East Anglia:

land use	% of total area
barley	31
wheat	19
permanent pasture	10
vegetables	8
potatoes	6
soft fruit	4
sugar beet	8
other crops	3
temporary grassland	8
rough grazing	3

(a) Use these statistics to construct a triangular graph similar to Fig D, page 21. which shows the agricultural land use of England and Wales.
(b) Compare and contrast the two graphs and explain the differences you observe.
 2 Study Fig E and write an essay accounting for the importance of arable farming in East Anglia.

8.3 AGRICULTURE IN THE FENS

Fig. A The Fenland landscape near Downham Market

The Fenland is one of the most unusual landscapes in Britain. Flat land stretches as far as the eye can see, and has a geometric appearance. Roads, rivers, ditches, embankments and lines of trees run in straight lines. How has this unique landscape developed?

After the Ice Age, the rising seas flooded this area and formed a large shallow bay. Currents built up silt across the seaward end of the bay to form the silt fen (marshy area) shown on Fig B. The peat fen was formed by the slow decay of vegetation in the marshes and lagoons which surrounded the silt fen. Villages and towns such as Ely developed on the islands of clay rising above the marshes.

Figure A shows a largely man-made landscape. It was not until the seventeenth century that man was able to begin large-scale reclamation of the Fens. A group led by the Fourth Duke of Bedford realised the potential of the marshland for farming, and called in the experts in land reclamation — the Dutch. Dutch engineers drained the Fens along the River Ouse and built a network of drainage ditches which took the water to the Ouse. The river was straightened to increase its speed by the cutting of two artificial channels, the Old and New Bedford Levels (Fig B).

Reclamation has continued ever since, mainly one field at a time by local farmers. They are rewarded by some of the best farmland in Britain, and 80 per cent of the Fens is under arable land, the highest proportion in the country. However, reclamation has caused problems:

1 *Shrinkage and flooding:* When peat dries, it shrinks. In some places, the level of the land has fallen by over four metres and is now below sea-level. Rivers are raised above the surrounding land, protecting embankments have to be built and water from drains pumped up to the river. Windmills were once used, but diesel pumps do the job today.

2 *Wildlife and conservation:* Dutch engineers at work in the seventeenth century were attacked and some of their embankments destroyed by local men who lived by fishing and wildfowling. They were protesting at the loss of their living. Many waterbirds had to find other breeding places. There are now nature reserves at places like Wicken Fen in Cambridgeshire which preserve the few remaining areas of natural fenland.

Some people are worried by the possible effects of a proposed barrage across the Wash, to create a fresh-water reservoir to supply England's demands well into the next century. It would have a disastrous effect upon local wildlife by removing part of the tidal silt flats, the breeding and feeding ground for many species.

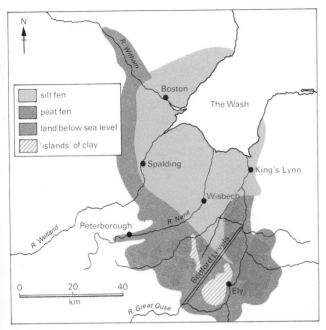

Fig. B The Fens

Fig. C Bulbfields at Spalding

Fig. D

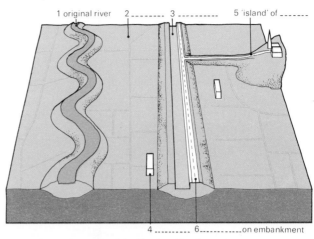

Fig. E Some features of the Fenland landscape

Farming in the Fens: Throughout the Fens, the main crops are wheat, barley, potatoes and sugar beet. Market gardening is important, especially on the silt fens. Peas, carrots, celery and other vegetables are grown and taken by road to London and the Midlands. Around Wisbech, soft fruit and apples are grown. The Spalding area is famous for its tulip and daffodil bulbs.

Intensive cultivation of the fertile fenland soils brings high yields. However, the farmers have created problems:

1 The soil has been exhausted in some areas after decades of overcropping. Much fertiliser is needed.
2 The removal of hedges to allow easier use of machines has encouraged soil erosion. The strong winds blow away the topsoil.

QUESTIONS

A1 Copy Fig E and label the numbered features.
 2 How were the Fens originally formed?
 3 How were the Fens reclaimed?
 4 What problems were caused by the reclamation schemes?
 5 Describe agriculture in the Fens.
B1 What advantages do the Fens have for arable farming?
 2 What problems face Fenland agriculture? How have the problems been caused, and how can they be solved?
 3 The average farm size in the Fens is only twenty hectares. How can such small farms be profitable?
 4 Study Fig A and answer the following questions:
   (a) A and B are both watercourses. Which is a river and which a drainage canal?
   (b) What is the construction at C and what is its function?
   (c) Describe and explain the agricultural landscape shown in Fig A.

8.4 INDUSTRY IN EAST ANGLIA

East Anglia is Britain's fastest-growing industrial region. This growth is based largely upon movement of companies and people from the south-east and especially from London.

Agricultural industries

Most towns in East Anglia have firms involved in agricultural processing and farm engineering. There may be a flour mill, brewery, sugar refinery, canning or freezing factory as well as firms making and servicing farm machinery. Most are small concerns, but there are larger factories in the main towns.

Figure B shows the sites of two important industries, sugar beet refining and freezing factories. Sugar beet is a bulky crop of which only about 15 per cent is the valuable sugar, so refineries are spread throughout the areas suitable for sugar beet to reduce transport costs. The refineries are owned by the British Sugar Corporation. The corporation controls the growing of the crop and transports it to the refineries. The sugar is extracted from the beet and the remaining pulp is sold as animal feed.

Transport costs are not so heavy for most vegetables, so the freezer factories need not be spread throughout the region but can be concentrated in the largest towns. Freezer factories are usually large units employing over 1000 workers. Vegetables cannot be grown too far from the factories since they must be frozen soon after harvesting to prevent loss of quality. This is especially true of peas. Farmers grow their crop under contract to the big freezing companies such as Bird's Eye and Ross.

New industries

Engineering is the most important industry in East Anglia. Agricultural engineering has long been important, but a much wider range has recently developed: radios, computers, light bulbs, dynamos, televisions and telephones are made in East Anglia. Many of the light engineering firms have moved from London and south-east England. The expanded towns and new town shown in Fig A have grown rapidly; Peterborough provides an example of the industrial growth typical of East Anglian towns. It was designated a new town in 1967 when it had a population of 81 000, but had been growing rapidly in any case. In 1961, the population was 61 000. Peterborough was well placed for industrial expansion, midway between the Midlands industrial area and the East Anglian seaports. High-speed trains have brought London within an hour's travelling. The A1

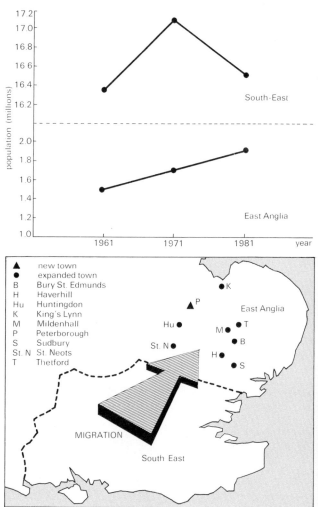

Fig. A Expansion in East Anglia

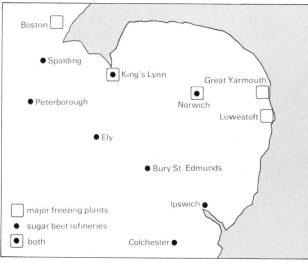

Fig. B Freezing plants and sugar factories

links Peterborough with the north.

By 1982, Peterborough's population had reached 124 000. Two hundred companies had moved to the city within twelve years. Peterborough had a long tradition of agricultural engineering and food processing, but the new companies broadened the city's range of employment. Here are some of the major industries:

Old-established industry
diesel engines, compressors, agricultural machinery, sugar refining
New industry
electronics, engineering, office equipment, pet foods, double glazing, furniture, microcomputers, toys, scientific instruments
New offices
Thomas Cook Travel, Pearl Assurance, Trustee Savings Bank,

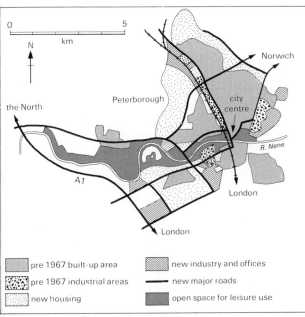

pre 1967 built-up area

pre 1967 industrial areas

new housing

new industry and offices

new major roads

open space for leisure use

Fig. C Peterborough grows

Other towns also have grown quickly. Industry has been attracted for several reasons:
1 Large industrial sites are available cheaply.
2 Local authorities provide incentives and services.
3 The region is attractive and uncongested.
4 The market of London is within easy reach.
5 The efficient East Anglian seaports offer rapid trade with Europe.

An East Anglian town: Norwich
Like most towns in East Anglia, Norwich was founded in Saxon times. It was sited at the lowest bridging point of the River Wensum and became a route centre. An atlas will show that Norwich remains an important route centre today. Until recently, it was a river port. This accessibility made Norwich an important market town and it became a centre of the woollen industry during the Middle Ages.

Norwich is an attractive city of 120 000 people. Its castle, cathedral and narrow streets of old buildings bring tourists, it has a growing number of modern industries and is the shopping and service centre for much of East Anglia.

QUESTIONS
A1 What types of industry would you expect to find in an East Anglian town?
2 Why has industry been attracted to East Anglia?
3 List four reasons for the importance of Norwich to East Anglia today.
B1 Here is a list of the main industries in Norwich. Place each under the correct heading:
    Industries based upon agriculture
    Other manufacturing industries
    Service industries

brewing	dynamos	shoes
metal fencing	insurance	printing
confectionery	clothing	fertilisers
sugar refining	vinegar	soft drinks
banking	council offices	mustard
electrical switches	fruit/vegetable	farm machinery
shops	wholesaling	animal feed

2 Calculate the percentage increase in the population of East Anglia between 1961 and 1981, from Fig A. How does this compare with the percentage increase in the population of other regions during the same period? (See Fig B, page 116.)
3 This table shows the employment structure of East Anglia:

	Percentage of total employment	
	East Anglia	**UK**
agriculture, forestry and fishing	6.5	1.8
food, drink and tobacco	21	10
engineering and vehicles	40	37
metal manufacture	1.7	7.2
textiles	1.7	7.6
clothing and footwear	5.6	5.4
others	23.5	31

(a) Draw pie graphs to show the figures for East Anglia and the UK as a whole.
(b) Calculate location quotients for East Anglia. Comment on your results.

8.5 SEAPORTS IN EAST ANGLIA

Fig. A The port of Felixstowe

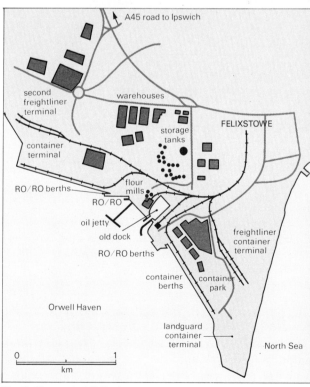

Fig. B The port of Felixstowe

Felixstowe

Felixstowe is Britain's fastest-growing port. Over seven million tonnes of cargo pass through its modern docks annually. Its growth has taken place since 1953, when flooding almost destroyed the small dock. The port had been in decline before that, and Felixstowe was known mainly as a small seaside resort.

The port owners built warehouses, dredged a deepwater channel and constructed new berths, some on reclaimed land. They were among the first to introduce roll on–roll off and container-handling services. In 1953, there were only twelve dockers; now there are over a thousand. There are three separate container terminals and two rail Freight-liner terminals. In 1982, 428 000 containers were

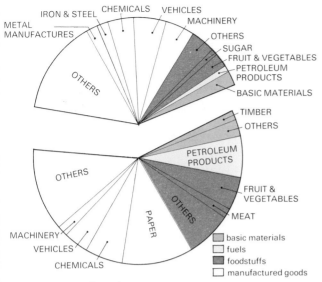

Fig. C Felixstowe's trade

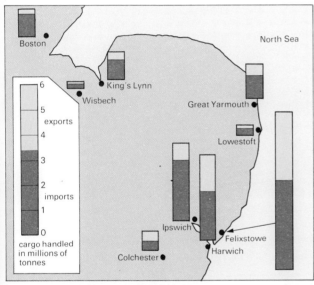

Fig. D The trade of seaports 1981

handled — more than any other British port.

Felixstowe's modern facilities and its reputation for efficiency have attracted several big shipping lines from other ports. The port's managing director puts the success of Felixstowe down to 'good geography — well-set for industrial England and Europe'.

Increasing trade between Britain and the EEC is an important factor in Felixstowe's growth. Over half the port's foreign trade is with EEC nations, especially Denmark, West Germany and the Netherlands. Container ships of up to 25 000 tonnes operate regular services to North America and the Far East. Most of the trade involves manufactured goods. Felixstowe is the fifth most important British seaport by value of trade.

Other ports in East Anglia

All the East Anglian ports have grown since the 1960s, though not as dramatically as Felixstowe:

1 Harwich, opposite Felixstowe, is an important container terminal with roll on–roll off and passenger services to northern Europe.

2 King's Lynn and Boston are increasingly important for the import of steel, wood and paper and the export of manufactured goods from factories in the Midlands.

3 Great Yarmouth is the main supply base for the North Sea natural gas rigs, and a growing general cargo port.

4 Ipswich has an important trade in chemicals and foodstuffs, and a new container terminal.

5 Colchester, Wisbech and Lowestoft are small ports of local significance; Lowestoft is an important fishing port.

QUESTIONS

A1 Why has Felixstowe become an important port within the last thirty years?

2 List the three most important imports and the three most important exports of the Port of Felixstowe.

3 Using the text and Fig D to help you, complete the table:

Rank order	Port	Imports (million tonnes)	Exports (million tonnes)	Total trade
1	Felixstowe	3.2	2.2	5.4
2				
3				
4				
5				
6				
7				
8				
9	Wisbech	0.2	0.1	0.3

For each port briefly state its main functions.

B1 Using the completed table from question A3, answer the following questions:

(a) What percentage of the trade from East Anglian ports is export?

(b) Why is this percentage so low?

(c) If we studied the value of trade rather than the tonnage, would there be any difference in the percentage of exports and imports? If so, why?

2 Design an advertisement for the Port of Felixstowe to attract shipping companies to use the port. You should include details of the port's facilities and its advantages over other seaports in Britain.

8.6 SOUTH-WEST ENGLAND

This section deals with the South-West peninsula of England. Its distinctive characteristics are its southerly and westerly position, its proximity to the sea, its maritime climate and its variety of geology and relief. Much of the economy of the south-west has been influenced by its physical geography. Many of its problems are the result of location and environment.

Agriculture

The variety of agriculture is a result of the different local climates, relief and soils, as well as a range of economic factors. Throughout the region, *subsidies* are available to farmers. The government and the EEC give financial help for hill-sheep farming, draining and fencing, and building projects. The region is peripheral to the British economy, and has had to compete with France and other European countries for markets. With improved transport, farm produce from Europe can be in Britain within hours.

Early vegetables: Around the mild coasts (6–7°C mean, January), especially in southern Cornwall, there are small intensive vegetable farms. Mount's Bay near Penzance is especially important. Here *raised beaches* about half a kilometre wide have light,

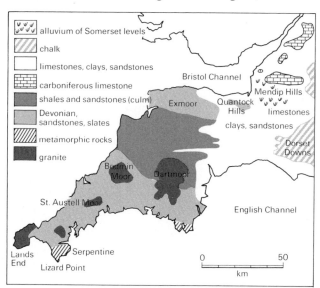

Fig. A The geology of south-west England

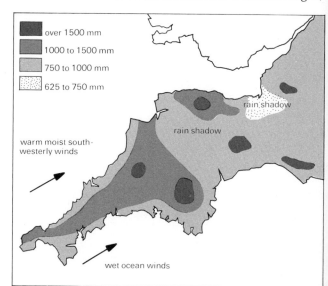

Fig. C The annual rainfall of the region

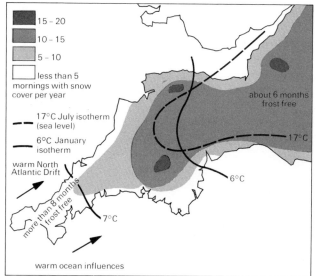

Fig. B The climate of south-west England

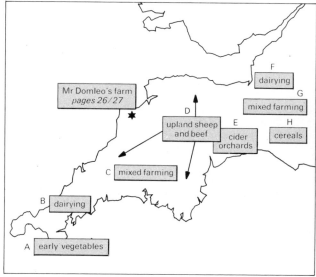

Fig. D Farming in the south-west

sandy soil which drains well. Broccoli, spring cabbage, cauliflower and potatoes are ready for the market before those grown elsewhere in the country. The railway was once used to transport the crops, but road transport is used increasingly.

Horticulture or the growing of flowers is important in sheltered coastal areas such as the Tamar valley near Plymouth. The Isles of Scilly, which lie off Land's End and have an even milder climate than mainland Cornwall, grow early daffodils.

Dairying: About 42 per cent of the south-west's farmland is under permanent pasture which is grazed by about 20 per cent of the country's cattle. Grass grows well in the damp, mild conditions in the lower areas of the region. Milk production is the main source of revenue for the majority of farms.

Mixed farming: This is important where conditions for arable farming are favourable. The wetter parts of the farms are used for livestock-grazing and the drier parts for crop-growing. Fodder crops such as kale, barley or oats are fed to the cattle or sold to local farmers. Pigs are kept throughout the region and fed on a variety of feeds including *skimmed milk* left over from cream-making. Further east, more cereal crops are grown on the mixed farms.

Hill farming or upland sheep and beef is found in the higher and more exposed areas. In the granite areas, the land is often rugged and hilltops have *tors*, the weathered remains of granite blocks (Fig E). Farming is restricted where soils are thin and acidic and climate is harsh. On the highest moors, farming has often been replaced by forestry. Hill farming continues because government subsidies enable it to do so.

Fig. E A Dartmoor tor

Fruit farms are a declining speciality in parts of east Devon and Somerset. Cider-apple orchards benefit from the lack of frost and the warm summer temperatures (17°C mean, July).

In the extreme east, especially on the chalk downs

of Dorset, there is more *arable farming*. Lower rainfall and higher summer temperatures favour wheat and barley. Fields increase in size, farms are bigger and more mechanised. Maize (corn on the cob) grows well, and it is generally used as a fodder crop.

QUESTIONS

A1 What is the approximate length of the peninsula from the Mendip Hills to Land's End?

2 What is the most southerly point, and what is its latitude?

3 Fill in the blanks:

(a) The extreme south-west of Cornwall has more than _____ months free from frost. The prevailing winds blow from the _____ _____. Average January temperatures are above _____°C. The inland higher areas have more than _____ millimetres annual rainfall.

(b) The three wettest areas in the peninsula are _____, _____ and _____. The Exe valley is in a _____ shadow, and is drier. The driest area is the _____ _____ and has only _____ to _____ millimetres rainfall.

4 Explain the following: early vegetables are grown in the Penzance area; dairy farming is found throughout the south-west; upland sheep farming is found on Dartmoor.

5 Explain the differences between the following land use statistics:

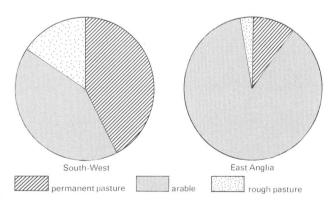

South-West   East Anglia

permanent pasture   arable   rough pasture

B1 Write a reasoned account of farming in the south-west.

2 Using a physical geography book, draw a diagram to show how a raised beach is formed.

3 Draw a sketch of the tor in Fig E and label its main characteristics.

C The proportion of small farms in the south-west region is higher than the national average. Suggest reasons for this and describe the problems that it may cause.

129

8.7 SOUTH-WEST ENGLAND

Industry

Primary industries are more important in the south-west than in Great Britain as a whole.

	south-west %	Great Britain %
agriculture, forestry and fishing	3.1	1.7
food, drink and tobacco	3.5	2.9

In Cornwall, over 6 per cent of the workforce is engaged in agriculture, forestry and fishing. Many small towns throughout the region have important agricultural processing industries. Figure A shows some of the industries that have developed using farm products. Not all are based on food and drink, and the old-established industries do not necessarily use local farm products. Skins and leathers used in Yeovil are now imported and many of the new materials for clothes and shoes are not animal products. In the past, there was greater dependence on farm products. Devon had a widespread woollen industry based on local sheep and water power.

Fishing

With the indented coastline and many natural sheltered harbours, Devon and Cornwall developed an important fishing industry. Brixham once dominated, and sent long-distance trawlers to the fishing grounds off Newfoundland. The fortunes of the fishing ports changed, and in the late 1970s and early 1980s mackerel-fishing provided large revenues. The shoals were exploited, mainly by foreign boats and large Scottish vessels. Fish stocks were reduced to such an extent that since 1983 they have been reserved for local fishermen.

Today, shellfish are providing the greatest proportion of the fishing revenues. *Spider crabs*, once thrown back into the sea, are exported to Spain and France. In 1980, three towns shared £250 000 from the European Agricultural Fund to build premises to process shellfish. At Newlyn, W Harvey & Sons can store twenty-four tonnes of live crab, lobster and crayfish. They shrink-wrap *brown crabs* for the Swedish market. In winter, the firm's forty employees fillet mackerel which go to be smoked.

Fish is still landed in the outer harbour of Polperro

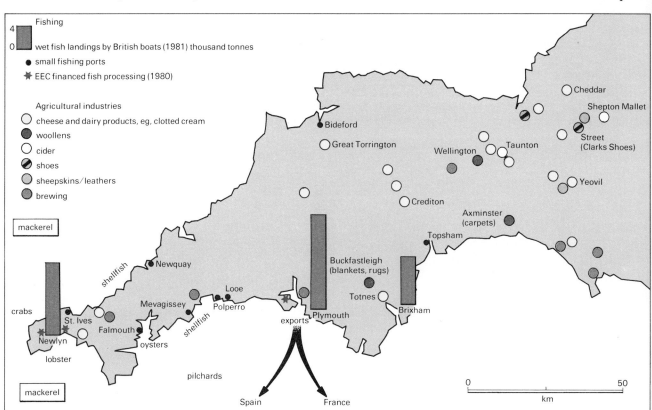

Fig. A Agricultural industries and fishing

Fig. B Polperro

(Fig B) and the quayside is busy each morning, but it is no longer just a fishing community. Holidaymakers provide Polperro with a more secure income. The old village is crowded with tourist shops, restaurants and holiday accommodation.

Mining and quarrying

The population of Cornwall in the nineteenth century indicates the importance of mining in the county. Between 1801 and 1861, the population rose from 192 000 to 369 000. In the next thirty years, it fell to 323 000. *Tin* has been found in Cornwall since Roman times and underground mining began in medieval times. By the mid-nineteenth century, Cornwall was the world centre of tin and copper mining. These minerals were found in rock veins or *lodes*. The ores had been formed when igneous rocks (*magma*) cooled. Towards the end of the nineteenth century, Cornish mines were forced to close because of low-cost ores coming from abroad, for example tin from present-day Malaysia. In many parts of the tin and copper zone (Fig C) there are remnants of old mining activities. Mines would employ up to 500 people. The ore was sent by rail to southern ports.

In recent years, only a few mines have been working. The mines of Geevor-Levant near St Just and of South Crofty-Wheal Pendarves in the Camborne/Redruth area were operating in the early 1980s. The Wheal Jane mine near Truro re-opened in 1979 and in 1983 employed about 400 men. At this mine, new underground areas are being explored and old waste is being re-processed. There is renewed interest in non-ferrous metal mining. Mines are being modernised, extended and new ones contemplated. Zinc, copper, tin and tungsten are more valuable than ever before. At Hemerdon, valuable tungsten deposits are being exploited in a tiered open pit. Three hundred and fifty jobs will be provided and the 4500 tonnes of tungsten per year will save Britain £22 million in imports. Tungsten is used to make hardened steels for drill bits and cutting machines. At the beginning of the 1980s, Cornwall was producing about 20 per cent of Britain's tin, a figure which could double, but tin prices must remain high to encourage investment.

QUESTIONS

A1 What industries are based on agriculture in the south-west?

2 Suggest why Cornwall has always been important for fishing. What types of fish are important in the region?

3 Describe the scene in Fig B.

4 Why might tourism bring in a more steady income than fishing?

5 Why did mining decline in Cornwall at the end of the nineteenth century?

6 Why is there now more interest in developing the mining industry?

B1 Calculate the location quotient for agriculture, forestry and fishing in the south-west.

2 'The fortunes of fishing ports change.' Why do you think this happens?

3 Why did the population of Cornwall decline after 1861?

4 The population of Cornwall has risen since 1961:

1961	343 278
1971	381 621
1981	430 506

Suggest possible reasons for this recent population growth.

5 What is the significance of the rising price of tin for the future of tin-mining in Devon and Cornwall?

6 What are the advantages of the new tungsten extractions at Hemerdon? What could some of the disadvantages be?

C Account for the changing fortunes of mining and fishing in the south-west.

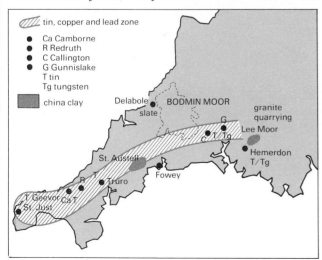

Fig. C Mining and quarrying

131

8.8 SOUTH-WEST ENGLAND

Towns and cities

Most of the towns in the South-West are small by national standards and there are only two large cities, Bristol and Plymouth. Exeter is an old-established city with a population of less than 100 000.

Most towns are growing, but Bristol reflects the trend in large British cities and it is losing population. Plymouth is still expanding.

Bristol in medieval times was England's second port after London. In the eighteenth century, the city became the second largest in England and some of its merchants made a fortune. Bristol was part of the *slave triangle*. Ships carried trinkets and alcohol to West Africa to trade for slaves. The slaves were transported to the West Indies and North America where they were exchanged for rum, cotton and tobacco. These materials were brought across the Atlantic to Bristol and sold in Britain.

Today, Bristol is a wealthy industrial area. It has not suffered industrial decline as much as other large British cities. Its industries include *port industries* which process raw materials imported from abroad. There is sugar-refining, chocolate, flour-milling, cigarette-making and trade in wines and sherry. The inner Bristol docks have closed to commercial traffic but trade continues downstream where the Avon meets the Severn estuary. Avonmouth has a new range of port industries such as petrochemicals, fertilisers, a zinc smelter and frozen food stores. Another important industry in north Bristol is aero-

space. At Filton, where Concorde was made, 22 000 people are currently employed manufacturing civil and military aircraft, components and aero-engines.

Bristol and its immediate surroundings, *Severnside*, has 25 per cent of the population of the south-west. It has been the main focus for economic growth in the region. It is accessible by Inter-city rail and motorways (Fig B). Since 1966, it has been linked to South Wales by the M5, M4 and Severn Bridge. Bristol is a major educational, entertainment and shopping centre attracting people from a wide area, including South Wales. Increasingly, it has become attractive for offices and has drawn firms from the more expensive London region. In a predominantly rural and agricultural region, Bristol is the only place with inner-city problems similar to those of the large urban areas. Some inner wards are deprived, with housing problems and above-average unemployment. In 1980, there were riots in the St Paul's area, which has a population of ethnic minorities.

Plymouth has been a focus for the navy since the thirteenth century. The Tamar river enters the sea here in the form of a large, sheltered ria (drowned river valley). It is a perfect natural harbour from which to guard Britain's western approaches. Devonport's naval dockyards were the main source of employment. Its naval importance made the city a target for German bombs, and by 1945 a vast area had been destroyed. Since World War II, the naval dockyard

Fig. A Changes in town population 1971-81

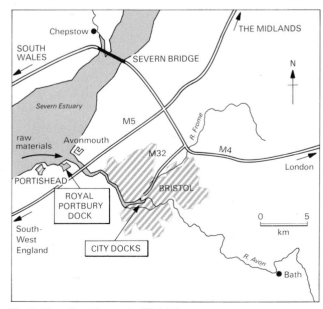

Fig. B The site of the port of Bristol

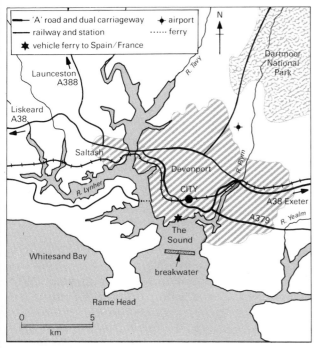

Fig. C Plymouth

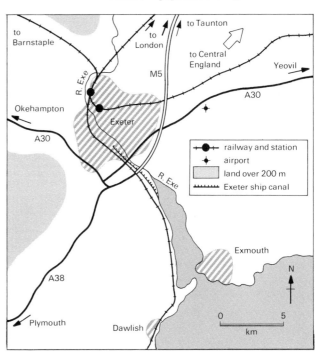

Fig. D Exeter

has declined. The loss of jobs at Devonport led to Plymouth being included in the south-west development area.

The economy of the city has slowly *diversified* and a range of light industry has been attracted. More recently, as road and rail transport have improved, the city has drawn a wide range of industry, making television sets, chewing gum, baby foods, small boats, scientific instruments and hydraulic equipment. There is fish processing at Saltash. The port has developed roll on-roll off ferry services to France and Spain. It attracts shoppers from a wide area and has become a tourist attraction in its own right. There is a naval college, a polytechnic and other educational establishments.

Exeter is much older than Plymouth. It was founded by the Romans in AD 50 on the site of a Celtic tribal capital. By the Middle Ages, it was a thriving market town based on the woollen trade. It has always been an important *nodal centre*. Most routes to the south-west peninsula pass through Exeter, including the M5 motorway. It is not an important port. The old ship canal basin has been converted into a maritime museum.

The city serves a large agricultural hinterland. It has an important livestock market, a regional shopping centre and is the administrative centre for Devon, rather than an industrial settlement. With the reduction in *time-distance* (the travel time) from southern England, light industries have been attracted. As with Plymouth, footloose industry can

benefit from the lower costs of the south-west region and its pleasant working environment. Tourists are attracted to Exeter as a holiday centre.

QUESTIONS

A1 Name the urban settlements in the south-west which are declining.

2 Name three towns that grew by more than 9 per cent between 1971 and 1981.

3 In which areas of the region are most of these towns?

4 Suggest why so many coastal towns are growing.

5 What part did Bristol play in the slave triangle?

6 What are port industries?

7 What are some of the social problems of inner Bristol?

8 Why was Plymouth an obvious choice for a naval centre?

9 'Plymouth's economy has diversified.' What does this mean?

B1 Explain why Exeter and Plymouth serve large agricultural hinterlands.

2 Study the geology map of south-west England on page 128 and Fig D on this page, then explain why Exeter is an important route and nodal centre.

3 Explain how the reduction of time-distance has favoured industrial growth in Plymouth and Exeter.

4 Compare two of the large urban areas in the south-west under the headings the port; industries; communications.

133

8.9 SOUTH-WEST ENGLAND: TOURISM

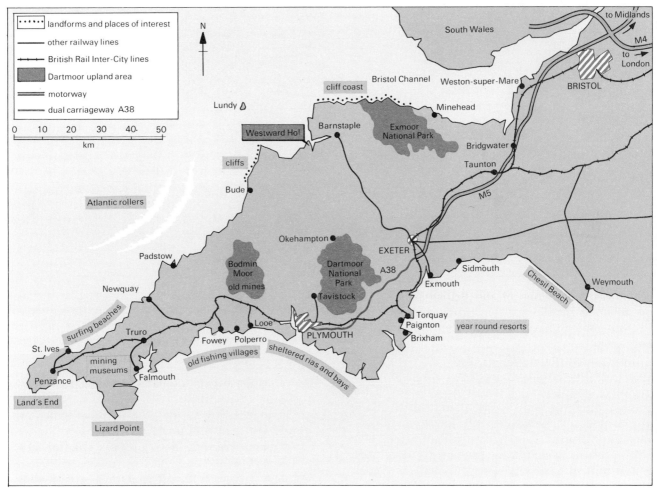

Fig. A Holidaying in the south-west

About 20 per cent of all people holidaying in Britain go to the south-west. Before the railways were built, this region was remote from the main population centres. Today, travel to the region by road and rail is straightforward. It is well-equipped with a variety of holiday accomodation.

QUESTIONS

A1 Look at Fig A and answer the following:
  (a) Which motorway serves the south-west?
  (b) How far is the region served by dual-carriage-way road?
  (c) Name the region's two national parks.
  (d) List the coastal attractions.
  (e) What inland attractions are shown on the map? Suggest other places of interest you are likely to find in a major holiday region such as the south-west.

  (f) Which area is most suited to year-round holidays? Suggest reasons for this.
  (g) Why do you think July and August are the busiest months for holidays in the region?
  (h) Briefly state some of the problems for the south-west region of a large influx of people in the holiday season.

2 (a) What are the attractions of the Newquay area for holidaymakers?
  (b) How far is Newquay from Land's End?
  (c) How far is it from the granite moors of Bodmin?

B1 Suggest why Newquay is (i) a surfing centre and, (ii) mainly a summer-only holiday centre.

2 Why is seasonal unemployment a problem in the town?

3 Use an atlas to help you discover the climate of Newquay. Note rainfall totals and temperatures.

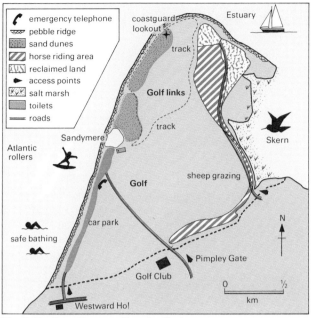

Fig. B Northam Burrows Country Park

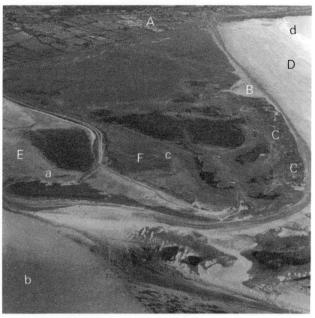

Fig. C Northam Burrows

C Account for the development of tourism in two contrasting regions of the British Isles. What particular problems are likely to occur when a region is developed as a recreation environment?

Northam Burrows Country Park

At the mouth of the Taw and Torridge rivers, a 263-hectare area of sand dunes, salt marsh and pasture has been run by Devon County Council since 1973 as a country park. Figures B and C show some of the attractions. The area is suited to walking and picnics. The estuary is often busy with small fishing boats and coasters. The Skern area is well-known for its cockle beds and flocks of wintering birds. Edible seaweed (laver) is collected from the pebbles of the estuary. The most important economic activity is sheep, which mingle with the tourists.

Northam Burrows illustrates some of the holiday activities available to a wide range of people. The case study reminds us of the pressures of tourism on south-west England. In the country park, there is careful separation of tourist activities. Car access is controlled and there is only one main car-parking area. Horse-riding is restricted to one area and one access route.

There is tourist pressure elsewhere. Some of the old fishing ports such as Polperro ban cars at peak holiday times. A large car park has been provided outside the village. The two national parks have clearly defined parking spots, picnic areas and walks. Around the coast are well sign-posted paths, including the long-distance South-west Peninsula Coast Path. Much of the coast is being conserved.

The National Trust owns several stretches, and paths are generally well maintained.

QUESTIONS

A1 Which way was the camera pointing in Fig C?
  2 (a) Name the settlement at A.
    (c) Name the landforms at B, C, D and E.
  3 The photograph shows the area before the country park was established. What has now happened at F? Suggest how this could have been carried out.
  4 What leisure activities are indicated by letters (a) to (d)? Use the photograph and map.
  5 Approximately how long is the pebble ridge from north to south?
  6 (a) What information is shown on the photograph which is not shown on the map?
    (b) What does the map show that the photograph cannot show?
B1 The area covered by the country park is a recurved spit with infilling behind. From your knowledge of physical geography, draw a map of the area to show how the spit has been formed. What provides the material for the spit and the infilling?
  2 Suggest how Sandymere was formed.
  3 What is meant by 'separating recreational activities' at Northam Burrows?
  4 What types of tourist pressures are there on the country park?
  5 Suggest why there is limited car and pedestrian access to the country park.
  6 In what ways are the tourist attractions in the south-west region being conserved?

135

9.1 NORTH-EAST ENGLAND: COAL

Coal was the basis of industry in the north-east of England, but the Northumberland and Durham coalfield has declined dramatically since World War II. In 1913, at the peak of its development, over 20 per cent of the region's workforce were miners. Today, less than 4 per cent are employed in coalmining.

Figure F shows that mining has declined most in the exposed coalfield in west Durham and Northumberland. Here, the seams are exhausted or too expensive to work. Present-day mining is concentrated in a few mines near the coast or on the concealed field. The modern mines are much larger and shafts are often over 500 metres deep. At the Ellington/Lynemouth Colliery in Northumberland, 1.7 million tonnes a year are produced. The mine employs 2,300 people. The miners work under the sea-bed, producing coal for the 390 mw power station which provides Lynemouth aluminium smelter with electricity. A wide range of by-products come from coal. An example is electrode pitch, produced locally and used at the aluminium smelter.

Coal exports reached a peak before World War I, when it was shipped from ports such as Hartlepool, Seaham Harbour, Sunderland, South Shields, North Shields, Blyth and Amble. Coal is still shipped south to London and the south-east, and power stations along the Thames Estuary still use north-east coal, but exports have almost ceased. Most coal remains in the region and is used to make electricity.

The good-quality coking coal from Durham is used in the blast furnaces of Teesside.

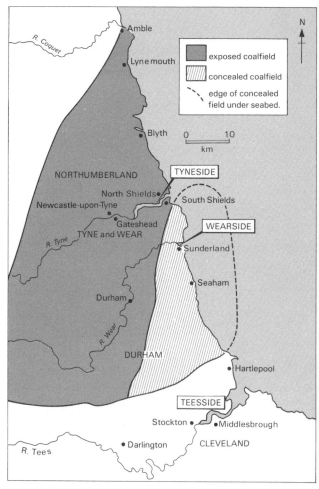

Fig. B The north-east

Fig. A Down the pit

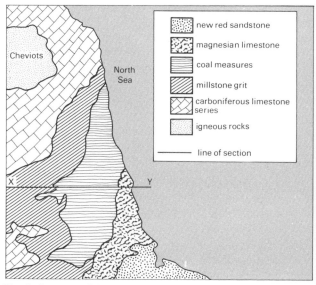

Fig. C Geology of the north-east

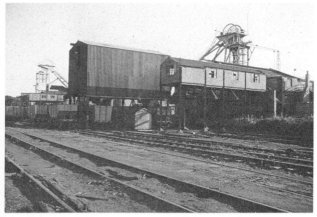

Fig. D Eccles colliery

Fig. E Westoe colliery

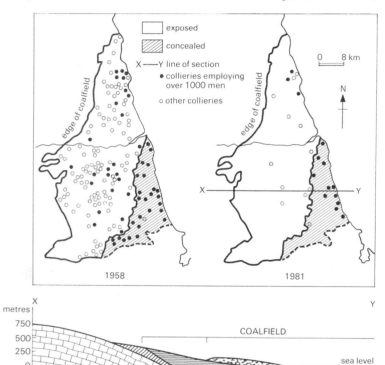

exposed

concealed

X ——— Y line of section

● collieries employing over 1000 men

○ other collieries

0   8 km

N

1958

1981

X

metres
750
500
250
0

Y

COALFIELD

sea level

magnesian limestone   millstone grit

coal measures   carboniferous limestone series

Fig. F

Coal exports
(million tons)
1800   2
1850   8
1910   35
1931   25
1971   0.1
1982   1.9

Coal miners
1913   220 000
1958   145 000
1971   48 000
1983   26 650

Number of collieries
1913   433
1958   186
1978   32
1983   20

QUESTIONS

A1 Draw the cross-section of the Durham coalfield. Label the Pennines, the North Sea, west and east, exposed and concealed coalfield.

Above the appropriate areas of the coalfield, write:

Many small mines now closed;

A few large mines;

Mines extending under the sea-bed.

2 Why did mining start on the exposed field? (See Fig F.) Why has modern mining moved east to the concealed field?

3 Look at the two mining scenes in Figs D and E. Suggest some differences between the two pits.

4 Suggest how working conditions have improved in the mines since the sketch in Fig A was made.

B1 Calculate the percentage decrease in the number of coal miners between (i) 1913 and 1971, (ii) 1971 and 1983. Use Fig F.

2 Coal made the north-east great, but has now declined in importance. Write a paragraph explaining how the decline can be measured.

137

9.2 NORTH-EAST ENGLAND

Shipbuilding

The north-east developed as one of Britain's most important regions for heavy industry. Today, shipbuilding and heavy engineering still have some importance but many jobs have been lost.

The coal trade led to the development of shipbuilding as early as the Middle Ages. The first ships were built from local wood but iron and steel from Tyneside, Derwentside and Teesside were used later. The wide, sheltered river mouths of the Tyne and Wear were ideal locations for larger-scale shipbuilding. Slipways were often built at an angle to the rivers to make launching easier. Over the past few decades, north-east shipbuilding has faced increasing problems and the industry has had to adapt to the changing demand for ships.

One of the north-east's shipbuilding success stories was the development on Wearside of the 15 000-tonne SD14 general cargo vessel. Wearside now builds more tonnage of shipping than Tyneside.

The Tyneside shipyards are crowded and there is a lack of covered building facilities. The shipyards are narrow and there is little room for expansion. The 1970s was a crisis decade for shipbuilding in the north-east, yet large sites suitable for shipyard development on Teesside were not exploited. The failure to move shipbuilding from the Tyne to the Tees is seen as a wasted opportunity.

Heavy engineering

Heavy engineering produces things such as cranes, generating plant, transformers, boilers, engines, pumps, guns and tanks. It is associated particularly with shipbuilding and repairing (pumps and engines are made on Tyneside). On Teesside, girders, bridges, oil-refining and chemical plant are built. Head Wrightson on Teesside have made some of the world's largest engineering products, including blast furnaces and the Sydney Harbour Bridge.

Demand for heavy engineering products has declined and many jobs lost as firms have closed.

Merchant shipbuilding in the north east (1980 figures)

	Gross registered tonnage	% British output
Wearwise	146 029	34
Tyneside	57 174	13
Teesside	34 416	8

The figure for Tyneside of only 57 147 tonnes illustrates the recent sharp decline of shipbuilding there. In the early 1970s, 250 000 tonne tankers were being built at the Wallsend shipyard on Tyneside (formerly Swan Hunter). The numbers employed by British Shipbuilders on Tyneside are now falling.

Fig. A

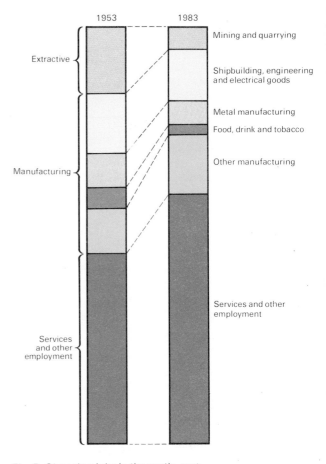

Fig. B Changing jobs in the north-east

Fig. C Deptford Yard, Sunderland Shipbuilders

QUESTIONS

A1 Look at Fig B. Measure the sections of the bar graphs. Which jobs have declined between 1953 and 1983?

2 Why did shipbuilding develop in north-east England in the Middle Ages?

3 Why were the Tyne and Wear ideal locations for shipbuilding?

4 Study Fig C.

(a) Draw a simple sketch map from the photograph. Label the river Wear, construction docks, fabrication sheds, cranes, road, new factory, gasometer.

(b) What are the site advantages of this shipyard?

Can you see any problems in the site?

(c) Suggest why the construction docks have been built at an angle to the river.

5 What do you understand by 'heavy engineering'?

6 Why has this type of engineering declined recently?

B1 What problems are caused by the decline of heavy industry in the north-east?

2 You are a director of a north-east firm producing generators for electricity stations. UK and world demand has declined for generators. Write a letter to the government asking for aid for your firm. Outline in your letter various ways forward for your factory and workers.

9.3 NORTH-EAST ENGLAND: TEESSIDE

Fig. A The Teesport oil refinery

Few places in Britain have so much large-scale industry as Teesside. To the north of Middlesbrough, there is a mass of oil storage tanks and two oil refineries. An oil refinery such as that shown in Fig A covers a vast amount of land and costs hundreds of millions of pounds to build. The Tees estuary is wide, and a steady stream of tankers brings in oil from the North Sea oilfields.

There is industrial activity all around, but also industrial dereliction and wasteland. Teesside has many problems and severe unemployment. Neither Middlesbrough nor Stockton have developed as regional capitals, their shopping centres lack the life and variety of Newcastle upon Tyne.

Industrial development on Teesside did not begin until the nineteenth century. Railways came early, and the world's first railway, the Stockton and Darlington, opened in 1825. From the 1850s, when 'railway mania' started, the iron and steel industry grew up. Over 800 iron furnaces were opened between 1860 and 1880. Population grew rapidly. Middlesbrough rose from 7000 in 1850 to 30 000 in 1881. The Cleveland Hills supplied iron and the Durham coalfield provided coking coal. Railways carried the products to and from Teesside.

Iron and steel are still important although there have been major changes. A proposed integrated iron and steel works at Redcar has not gone ahead; only the first phase has been completed. Meanwhile, smaller works have closed at Skinningrove, Cargo Fleet and Hartlepool. There have been redundancies and closures in the shipbuilding and heavy engineering industries.

During the 1960s and early 1970s, Teesside was a growth area. There were prospects for full employment. This has changed and Teesside is now a problem industrial area.

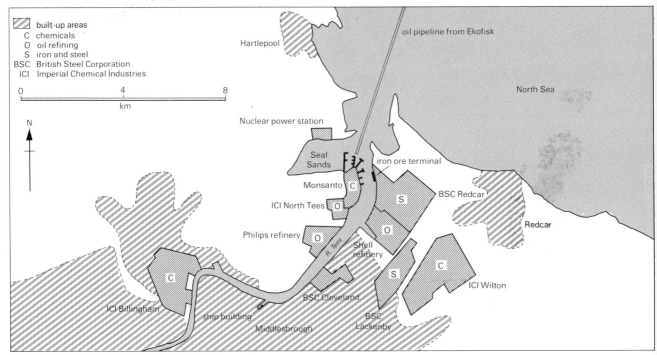

Fig. B

Chemicals

Teesside is one of the world's largest chemical centres. The history of chemical production goes back to World War I when *Billingham* was chosen to make nitric acid for wartime explosives (TNT). It was selected for its road and rail communications, the navigable river Tees, local coal deposits and supplies of water. Salt was present and could be brought to the surface in the form of brine (salt water).

After World War I, *fertilisers* were made. Sulphur was obtained from anhydrite which was mined under the Billingham site. The original reasons for the siting of Billingham are no longer relevant (coal and anhydrite are no longer used). Billingham now uses imported raw materials. The works are an example of *inertia*. As well as fertilisers, Billingham manufactures chlorine and sodium.

In the 1970s Billingham employed 14 000 workers, but there were job losses in the early 1980s.

Petrochemicals

On the south bank of the river Tees, between Middlesbrough and Redcar, is the ICI Wilton site. The development covers more than 550 hectares and about 10 000 people are employed. The raw material is oil from the refineries at Teesport. The plant is linked by an oil pipeline to Billingham and Merseyside.

Ethylene has been produced in 'crackers' since 1951. There are three 'crackers', one with a capacity of 500 000 tonnes. Products are numerous: nylon, polyester, Terylene, Perspex, polyethylene, propylene, PVC, polyurethanes, Butadiene. About 40 per cent is exported, mainly to EEC countries.

Between 1975 and 1981, 5000 jobs were lost at Wilton, which is an example of capital intensive industry. This means it does not employ large amounts of labour in proportion to the amount of money invested in it.

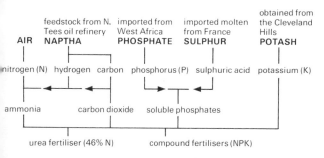

AIR   NAPTHA   PHOSPHATE   SULPHUR   POTASH

feedstock from N. Tees oil refinery | imported from West Africa | imported molten from France | obtained from the Cleveland Hills

nitrogen (N) hydrogen carbon   phosphorus (P) sulphuric acid   potassium (K)

ammonia   carbon dioxide   soluble phosphates

urea fertiliser (46% N)   compound fertilisers (NPK)

Fig. C ICI products: fertiliser

QUESTIONS

A1 Use the following words to write a paragraph on the early development of Teesside:
iron ore, coking coal, railways, Middlesbrough

2 Complete the table, which refers to the Teesside oil and chemical industry. Refer to the text and Fig B.

Product	Raw material	Place of manufacture
fertiliser	?	?
refined oil	?	?
ethylene	?	?
?	?	Wilton

3 Why has Teesside grown up as an oil-refining and petrochemical centre?

B1 Why are tidal mudflats attractive to the oil companies?

2 Study Fig C and write about the manufacture of fertilisers at Billingham. Why are the works an example of inertia?

3 You visit the Tees estuary. Write a letter to a friend describing some of the scenes that have impressed you.

4 'In 1978, Monsanto (a chemicals firm) were spending £180 million on new plant for Seal Sands that would provide no more than 4200 permanent jobs.' Explain the reason for this limited employment. What other jobs would be provided?

C For Northumberland and Durham, including Teesside:

(a) Describe and account for the location and development within the region of two of the following industries: shipbuilding; iron and steel; chemicals.

(b) State some of the present industrial problems associated with the region, and attempts being made to overcome these problems.

9.4 NORTH-EAST ENGLAND: CHANGE

```
NORTH ENGLAND
BASE YEAR ? 1977
POPULATION IN  1977 ? 2541700
NORTH EAST ENGLAND:  1977
SAME PERCENTAGE INCREASE
EVERY YEAR ? YES
PERCENTAGE INCREASE ? -0.6
YEAR        POPN.
            (MILLIONS)
1977        2.542        1989        2.458
1978        2.526        1990        2.443
1979        2.51         1991        2.428
1980        2.594        1992        2.414
1981        2.579        1993        2.399
1982        2.563        1994        2.385
1983        2.549        1995        2.37
1984        2.533        1996        2.356
1985        2.518        1997        2.342
1986        2.502        1998        2.328
1987        2.487        1999        2.314
1988        2.472        2000        2.3


TYNE AND WEAR
BASE YEAR ? 1977
POPULATION IN  1977 ? 1174000
TYNE AND WEAR:  1977 - 1986
SAME PERCENTAGE INCREASE
EVERY YEAR ? YES
PERCENTAGE INCREASE ? -0.8
YEAR        POPN.
            (MILLIONS)
1977        1.174        1989        1.066
1978        1.165        1990        1.059
1979        1.155        1991        1.049
1980        1.146        1992        1.041
1981        1.137        1993        1.032
1982        1.128        1994        1.024
1983        1.119        1995        1.016
1984        1.11         1996        1.008
1985        1.101        1997        1
1986        1.092        1998        .992
1987        1.083        1999        .984
1988        1.075        2000        .976
```

Fig. A

Computer prediction indicates that Tyne and Wear which now has a population of over one million, may be reduced to 976 000 by the year 2000. In places like Consett, County Durham, where the steelworks closed in 1980, the rate of population fall is much greater. Small mining communities (scheduled as 'D villages') have declined to zero because of the closure of the coalmines.

The decline in population is not the only problem in the region. In 1983, the national average unemployment rate was just over 15 per cent. In the north-east, many areas had up to 25 per cent unemployment because of the decline of traditional heavy manufacturing industry such as shipbuilding, engineering and metal working. The region has a lack of light manufacturing industry such as electronics, computers and consumer goods. These growth industries are increasingly located in the south of England and the north-east has been by-passed. The location is a disadvantage. It is away from the main population centres and is not linked to the main motorway network. Modern ports serving Europe, such as Felixstowe and Dover, are nearer to the south-east growth areas.

Housing, roads and other communications have been improved with the help of government grants. The road network has been made more efficient, and the present communications system provides greater incentives for future investment by outside firms. Movement around much of the region is now quick and easy.

In some areas, housing and social conditions remain among the poorest in Britain, but redevelopment schemes are transforming housing environments. In Newcastle upon Tyne, the Byker redevelopment scheme replaced old terraced housing which was densely packed on the slopes of the river Tyne. Figure B shows part of the Scotswood Road redevelopment in Newcastle upon Tyne. This was another area of close-packed nineteenth-century housing. Redevelopment does not necessarily mean a total change in living conditions. The people of the Scotswood area are still relatively poor and for them

Fig. B High-rise flats at Scotswood

Fig. C

Fig. D

Fig. E Small industry

job prospects are few. The high-rise blocks present new problems and many people miss the community feeling of the terraced street.

New development

The government has been helping the north-east to cope with its problems. The region has been a development area since 1934 and has received aid for roads, services and new industry. Industrial diversification has been taking place since the 1930s, when the Team Valley Trading Estate was opened on Tyneside. Today, 20,000 people are employed, and employment for women has been established. In the past, employment opportunities for women were few compared with the south of England. Here, as elsewhere on industrial estates, food, clothing, consumer goods and light engineering products are made.

Figure E shows a small industrial estate on the western outskirts of Newcastle upon Tyne. Several companies enjoy a clean, modern environment with good road links. Products from this estate include blinds and shutters, optical equipment and radar instruments. The region desperately needs much more industry to make the transition from an old industrial region to one with a broader spread of economic activity. Another attempt to revitalise the economy is the enterprise zone established on the north and south banks of the Tyne west of Newcastle and Gateshead. Vickers have a new tank factory in the zone employing 700 people. A range of small businesses is also being attracted.

Another recent source of help is the EEC. Between 1975 and 1980 the whole of northern England (the north-east and Cumbria) received £114 million from the regional fund. Two examples show the type of aid received:

Establishment of cigarette factory, Spennymoor, County Durham, 1980 (grant £4 645 000).

Establishment of British Industrial Plastics factory at Darlington, County Durham, 1980 (grant £1 805 000).

QUESTIONS

A1 Why has the population of the north-east region declined?

2 How will the population of the north-east change over the next ten years?

3 Give reasons for the future changes in the population.

B1 People who move away from a region are usually young. What are the consequences for the region of this type of out-migration?

2 How can the government help to provide more jobs?

3 What does the advertisement for Sunderland emphasise about the location of the city? If you were a manufacturer, would you be attracted to Sunderland? Is it really as near to Europe as the advertisement suggests, or is south-east England or South Wales better located? Calculate the distance to the European countries from (i) Felixstowe, (ii) Cardiff.

9.5 NORTH-EAST ENGLAND: WASHINGTON

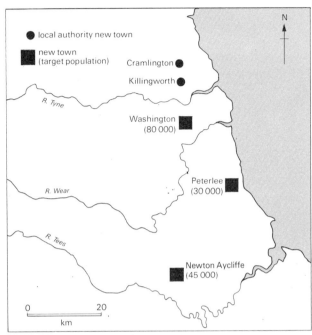

Fig. A New urban centres in the north-east

Fig. B The old 'F' pit at Washington

Washington, Peterlee and Newton Aycliffe are north-east England's new towns. All received grant aid under the government's regional aid programme. Washington was designated in 1964 to:

1 provide homes for an eventual population of 80 000.

2 revitalise the region's economy by attracting industry and providing new retail and service centres.

3 raise the standard of urban environment by setting examples in quality of design, building and layout.

The Armstrong Industrial Estate: Industrial land use has been kept separate from residential and other uses. This is the policy favoured in all new towns. It prevents *land use conflict*, which could arise if factory noise, activity and pollution interfered with people in their homes. Washington Development Corporation established the Armstrong estate to attract business, and therefore jobs, to the area. Maximum grants are available, since the new town is in a special development area, and a choice of buildings is offered, from rented standard factory units to purpose-built units to individual designs on a company's own site. The working and living environment is modern and pleasant, the 'highway' system enables easy, quick movement around the new town and links with other parts of the region. The new town has acted as a growth pole for the region, and retail and service functions have developed. However, an industrial estate does not guarantee success. Units at Washington remain empty and several firms have closed their factories.

QUESTIONS

A1 Link Fig C with Fig D to answer these questions:
   (a) Which way was the camera pointing?
   (b) Describe the layout of the estate.
   (c) Name the empty building in the background of the photograph.

 2 Look at Fig E and the titles at the top of the last three columns. Complete the table, using one or more ticks.

 3 Write a few sentences describing the types of firms in Elswick Road.

 4 How many industrial estates are there in Washington New Town? (Fig C insert.)

 5 Many units on the estates are still empty. What advantages would there be for firms wanting to move into the estate?

B How can a town like Washington provide a 'pocket of growth'? What are the advantages to the surrounding area of such a growth pole?

C Outline the reasons for the designation of new towns in Britain. Briefly describe the planning aims of one new town you have studied. What type of industrial development has taken place?

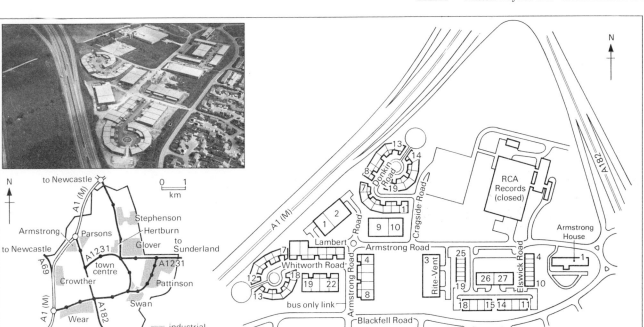

Fig. C

Fig. D The Armstrong industrial estate

No.	Tenants		Storage and distribution	Manufacture	Servicing and repairs
4	Roy Burn	TV and radio repairs			√
5	Peter Cox	Damp proofing			√
6	Fridgrite Limited	} Manufacturing and repair of		√	√
7	Fridgrite Limited	refrigeration equipment			
8	Coral Sea Foods Limited	Frozen food storage			
9	Thorn EMI Television Rentals Ltd	TV rentals			
10	T.T. Print	Printing			
11	Resolute Electronics Limited	Electronic components			
12					
13					
14	Machinery Services (Newcastle) Ltd	Engineering servicing			
15	T.T. Print	As No. 10			
16	Visionhire Limited	TV and radio repairs			
17	Ransomes Hamech Limited	Fork lift trucks sales and service			
18					
19	Lanofilm Limited	Fire protection distribution			
20	Chaldur Frozen Fish Co. Ltd.	Frozen food storage and distribution			
21	Legs Fashion Trousers Limited	} Trouser manufacture			
22	Legs Fashion Trousers Limited				
23	Wacker (Great Britain) Limited	Construction industry service			
24	Kingston Wholesale Supplies	Wholesale distribution			
25	Murray Insulations	Storage and distribution			
26					
27	Chester Metal Company Limited	Metal working			

Fig. E Elswick Road, Armstrong Estate

9.6 NORTH-EAST ENGLAND: NEWCASTLE

Fig. A Newcastle's bridges

Newcastle upon Tyne

Newcastle upon Tyne, the regional capital, is over 900 years old. It has grown from its bridging-point site to become the major urban centre in the north-east region, and dominates the Tyne and Wear metropolitan area. In 1981, the old city area had a population of 192 000 but there were over 277 000 in the Newcastle district of the Tyne and Wear County. Although Newcastle is in a region of industrial decline, it has been able to attract new office developments and commercial enterprises. The city centre has all the facilities of a modern European regional capital. The visitor can fly to the regional airport, travel by Metro rapid-transit, shop in the new Eldon Square Centre and relax in the modern leisure complex. Newcastle attracts shoppers and visitors from all over the northern region and the Scottish Borders.

Fig. B Communications in the north-east

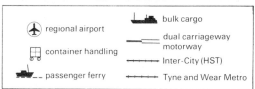

✈ regional airport	⛴ bulk cargo
⊞ container handling	▬ dual carriageway motorway
⛴ passenger ferry	Inter-City (HST)
	Tyne and Wear Metro

Newcastle — the regional capital
shopping centre: Eldon Square
leisure facilities: Eldon Square
Theatre Royal
City Hall: major pop concerts
Tyneside Summer Exhibition
'Hoppings': large June fair
conference hotels
university and polytechnic
museums
local government centre

Summary: the north-east

The north-east region of England has a character of its own. Its people have a distinctive accent and a sense of loyalty to their home area. Heavy industry here reached its peak at the beginning of the twentieth century, but during the great depression of the 1930s the region suffered severe unemployment. After the trough of the 1930s, a search for new employment began. The north-east is still one of Europe's problem areas, but recent changes in fields such as transport and light industrial development have improved its status.

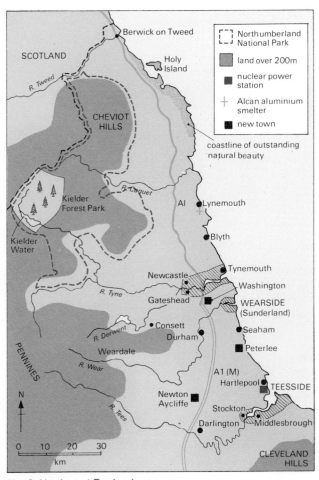

Fig. C North-east England

QUESTIONS

A1 Figure B locates the major transport facilities in the north-east. With the help of this map, answer the following questions:
  (a) Suggest how the rail network has changed since the end of the nineteenth century.
  (b) What changes have there been in the trade of the ports since the north-east was mainly a coal-exporting region?
  (c) How have port handling methods changed?
 2 Use an atlas to calculate how far it is from Newcastle to (i) Esbjerg and (ii) Oslo. In which direction from Newcastle would the ferry travel to each of these Scandinavian ports?
 3 Suggest the advantages of the new Metro rapid-transit network for shoppers and commuters in the Newcastle area (see page 95).

Fig. D

B1 In what ways is Newcastle a regional focus?
 2 Look at the topological diagram (Fig D). Construct a similar diagram to show air routes from Newcastle airport. Let 4 centimetres represent 1 hour. Use the figures below.

Glasgow	45 min
Aberdeen	50 min
Copenhagen	1 hr 30 min
Amsterdam	1 hr 5 min
Paris	1 hr 30 min
London	55 min
Manchester	45 min
Belfast	55 min
Dublin	1 hr

For which routes do you think rail is particularly competitive?
 3 In 1982, the northern region had an unemployment rate of 17.6 per cent. The national average rate was 13.6 per cent. What links can you make with this high unemployment rate and the region's industrial structure?
C For a declining industrial region you have studied, account for the factors which favoured its growth and the reasons for its decline. Refer to specific examples of important industries.

9.7 SOUTH WALES: THE VALLEYS

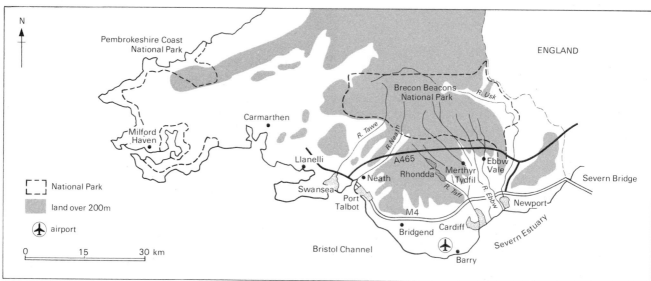

Fig. A South Wales

South Wales, like north-east England, has a distinctive culture and declining traditional industries. Coal and steel were the twin foundations of the region's growth during the nineteenth century.

Before 1800, South Wales was a sparsely populated farming region. The only industries were small-scale ironmaking and coalmining. Drift mines (*adits*) and water-powered ironworks using charcoal and local iron-ore were sited in the valleys of the coalfield.

With the replacement of charcoal by coke, and of the waterwheel by the steam engine, coal became a vital industrial fuel. South Wales, with its coal resources, rapidly became one of Britain's greatest industrial areas. The population increased rapidly and new towns grew as the valleys of the coalfield area began to fill up with mines, ironworks, canals, roads, railways, chapels and rows of terraced houses. People flocked to the Valleys, especially from mid-Wales, Shropshire and south-west England, in search of work. The population of the Rhondda Valley rose from under a thousand in 1801 to 140 000 by 1921. Living conditions were often poor, with up to fifteen people crammed into a tiny terraced cottage.

Employment in the coalmines rose to a peak of 230 000 by 1913 (in 630 mines). Extensive reserves of coking coal allowed the development of an iron and steel industry, especially in the north-eastern area of the coalfield. A string of iron-producing towns grew up, including Merthyr Tydfil and Ebbw Vale. Associated industries such as tinplating, coking plants and chemical works were attracted.

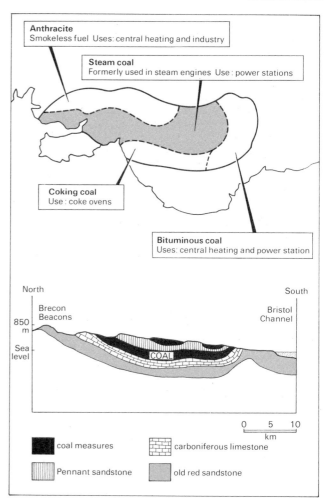

Fig. B (i) Types of coal mined in South Wales (ii) Cross-section through the South Wales coalfield

The years of depression

Over-dependence upon coal and steel led to disaster in the 1920s. Demand for the basic products of South Wales fell rapidly. Coal export declined from 30 million tonnes a year in 1913 to 15 million tonnes by 1936. Coal output dropped and the number of miners fell. In some valleys, over 60 per cent of the men were out of work. This economic collapse forced people to leave. Between 1921 and 1936, over 300 000 people migrated from the Valleys, mainly to south-east England and the Midlands.

Government aid for the Valleys

The consequences of the decline of coal and steel in the Valleys led to the establishment of a regional development policy. From 1934 onwards, the policy encouraged new industry to move into the northern valleys. There have been several successes, such as the establishment of Hoover's factory at Merthyr Tydfil, electronics at Treorchy and vehicle components at Bargoed. However, as a whole the Valleys hold few attractions for large-scale industry:

1 There are few flat sites for large factories.
2 Much of the housing is substandard.
3 There is still much derelict land.
4 The Valleys are relatively inaccessible. The M4 motorway passes well to the south.

Much of the new industrial development in the Valleys has been concentrated in the most favoured parts of the region. Along the north of the coalfield, the modern A465 Heads of the Valleys road has greatly improved the accessibility of towns such as Merthyr Tydfil and Tredegar. A number of industrial estates have been built along the road, notably at Hirwaun where 3800 people are employed. The population of the Valleys continues to decline; the Rhondda, for instance, had a population of 100 300 in 1961, by 1981 it had only 81 725.

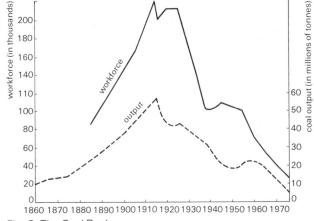

Fig. C The Coal Rush

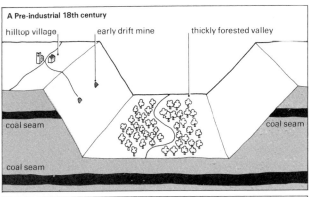

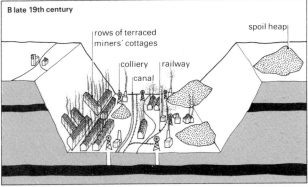

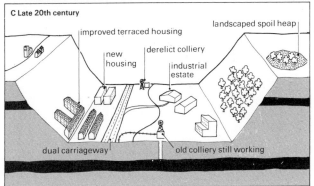

Fig. D Change in a model South Wales valley

QUESTIONS

A1 Why did South Wales become an important industrial region?

2 Using Fig D to help you, describe how a typical valley in the coalfield was altered by the development of large-scale coalmining.

3 List three reasons for the decline of the South Wales coal industry.

4 What disadvantages do the Valleys have for large-scale modern industry?

B1 Using Fig C, calculate the average annual percentage increase in coal output (i) between 1860 and 1880, (ii) between 1880 and 1910.

2 How has the government helped the Valleys?

3 How would you describe the type of industry which has moved into the Valleys in recent times?

9.8 SOUTH WALES: INDUSTRY TODAY

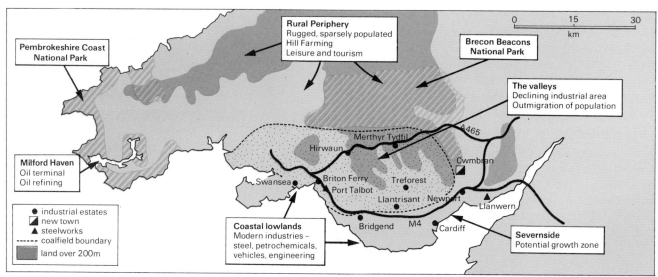

Fig. A South Wales today

The industrial centres of South Wales have moved from the Valleys to the coastal lowlands. The largest and most successful industrial estates have been built at such places as Treforest and Bridgend. A wide range of modern consumer industries from clothing to electronics occupies these estates. Here are the large flat sites needed for modern industry. The completion of the M4 motorway in 1980 has improved accessibility.

Several extensive developments have occurred here, and the cities of Cardiff, Newport and Swansea have become the major administrative and service centres for the whole of South Wales.

Major industries

Coalmining: The long decline of coalmining in the area may have ended. Only 37 mines remain, employing 27 000 miners. Older mines are still closing. However, a number of new mines are opening in response to the improved position of coal in the energy market following the oil crisis of 1973. The Betws drift mine, opened in 1978, is now the most productive mine in the coalfield; 515 000 tonnes are produced annually by 550 men.

Iron and steel: Two major steelworks remain in South Wales. As recently as 1950, there were sixteen separate plants. The workforce has declined from 58 000 in 1968 to less than 20 000 today. The last inland steelworks, at Ebbw Vale, closed in 1978. Only the coastal works at Port Talbot and Llanwern are left open, and these have had their workforces halved since 1980.

Fig. B The Kenfig industrial estate

The new deepwater port at Port Talbot serves as the iron-ore terminal for both works. Bulk carriers bring the ore from Sweden, Canada and Mauritania. Some of the steel produced is used in South Wales but much is sent by rail to the Midlands and south-east England, mainly for use in the vehicle industry.

Tinplate: One of the major Welsh customers for steel is the tinplate industry. Each year, 750 000 tonnes of steel is turned into tinplate by the addition of a thin coating of tin. The tin coating prevents rusting. A tin can is really 98 per cent steel and 2 per cent tin.

Tinplating began in South Wales as a result of the coal trade. Coal was shipped to Cornwall to fuel the steam engines at the tin mines in Cornwall and tin ore was taken on the return journey to South Wales. Today, tin is imported from Malaysia, Bolivia and Nigeria. Tinplate works were widespread until recently. In 1950, there were thirty-eight plants; today there are only three at Trostre, Velindre and Ebbw Vale. The industry has declined because of the introduction of new materials for cans.

Non-ferrous metals: There are *aluminium* rolling mills at Resolven near Neath, at Waunarlwydd near Swansea and at Rogerstone near Newport. About 4000 people are employed producing aluminium foil, trim for cars, wire and sheet. *Nickel* imported from Canada is refined at Clydach north of Swansea. At Waunarlwydd, *titanium* sheets are produced for the aerospace and engineering industries.

Oil refining and petrochemicals: There are three refineries at Milford Haven, and a fourth at Llandarcy near Swansea supplied by pipeline from Milford Haven. Opposite Llandarcy is the BP petrochemical works at Baglan Bay, which uses feedstock from Llandarcy to produce a wide range of chemicals including ethylene and PVC.

Motor vehicle components: South Wales has become an important centre for the manufacture of vehicle components. The major locations are Llanelli (BL radiators and body components), Swansea (Ford axles and transmissions), Bridgend (Ford engines) and Kenfig (automatic transmissions).

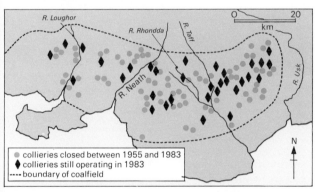

Fig. C Collieries in South Wales

- ● collieries closed between 1955 and 1983
- ◆ collieries still operating in 1983
- ---- boundary of coalfield

Fig. D Ford's Bridgend engine plant

South Wales offers suitable factory sites, a labour force, and good road and rail connections.

Office employment: South Wales has benefited from office decentralisation in the same way as the north-east. Several important government offices have been moved or set up in the region. The major units are the Driver Vehicle Licensing Centre and Land Registry at Swansea, the Royal Mint at Llantrisant and the Welsh Office, Inland Revenue and Ministry of Defence at Cardiff.

QUESTIONS

A1 Describe the coal industry in South Wales today.
  2 How many steelworks remain open in South Wales today? Name them.
  3 (a) What is tinplate?
    (b) How did the tinplate industry begin in South Wales?
    (c) Where are the tinplate works?
  4 Name three non-ferrous metal industries in South Wales.
  5 Why has South Wales attracted vehicle component industries? Name three vehicle component factories.
  6 Name six industrial estates in South Wales.
B1 Why has the coastal lowlands area attracted more new industry than the valleys of the coalfield?
  2 This table shows employment in thousands at the four largest industrial estates in South Wales:

	1966	1976	1983
Treforest	12.5	9.7	5.6
Bridgend	6	6.6	6.4
Hirwaun	4.5	3.7	3.3
Swansea	6.3	6.2	4.1

  (a) Calculate the percentage change of employment between 1966 and 1983.
  (b) Which industrial estate employed more workers in 1983 than in 1966?
  3 The table below shows the changing populations of four towns in South Wales in thousands:

	1911	1921	1931	1951	1961	1971	1981
Maesteg	25	28	26	22	21	20	20.9
Neath	29	32	33	32	31	28	26.6
Port Talbot	32	40	41	44	50	51	47.3
Bridgend	8	9	10	13	15	15	15.7

  (a) Construct a line graph to illustrate these statistics.
  (b) Suggest reasons for the trends revealed by the graph.

9.9 SOUTH WALES: THE FUTURE

South Wales has fine natural scenery which bears the scars of industrial activities. Much of the dereliction is due to coalmining, but the iron industry, smelting and chemicals, docks and railways are also responsible. Coal and iron slag waste tips and derelict industrial buildings dominate the living and working environments of whole communities.

The first big project to reclaim old industrial areas was in the *Lower Swansea Valley* where old metalworkings were reclaimed. In October 1966, 144 people were killed when a waste-tip slipped and engulfed the mining village of Aberfan. This tragedy led to action, and within a month the government had set up a special unit to lead and encourage a programme of reclamation throughout Wales.

Since then a drive has been under way to clear dangerous dereliction and unsightly waste and to restore the land to productive use. The cost has been high (over £90 million), but ugly skylines have been improved, and once-sterile land is providing grazing for farm animals. Factories and industrial estates, houses and schools, country parks and recreation areas are being built on land once written off as worthless.

The removal of dereliction raises property values and makes an area more attractive to outsiders. It encourages local people, who might neglect their houses, to repair and paint them. Whole communities recover their pride. By 1982, 5550 hectares of derelict land had been reclaimed throughout Wales, 85 per cent of it in the south:

1 Figure C shows the Nine Mile Point colliery in

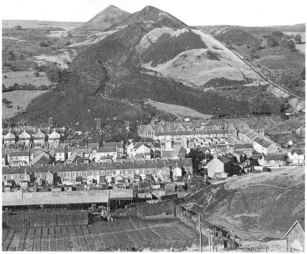

Fig. A The Aberfan Disaster 1966

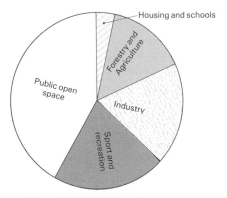

Fig. B How the reclaimed land is used

Fig. C Nine Mile Point colliery

Gwent which closed in 1964. It left behind old pithead buildings, rusting railway tracks and a massive waste tip on the valley floor dominating the village of Cwmfelinfach. In a reclamation project, the derelict buildings were demolished and the tip cleared to leave a plateau on which four factories have been built.

2 The ruins of the 200-year-old Sirhowy ironworks at Tredegar have been renovated and are now preserved as an industrial monument.

3 Gwaun Helyg in Ebbw Vale lay under coal waste tips which have now been flattened and landscaped. Over 100 houses and old people's bungalows were built on the reclaimed site.

4 The Monmouthshire and Brecon Canal, once disused, has been repaired and restored for the use of pleasure craft.

Figure B shows the uses to which reclaimed land

has been put. The most important use is in providing public open space.

Success or failure?

Since 1934, government and local authorities have spent a great deal of time and money on rebuilding the economy of South Wales. It was not until 1976, with the creation of the Welsh Development Agency (WDA), that a single organisation was established to oversee developments. The WDA is concerned with:

Developing industrial estates and sites

Building factories

Investing money in Welsh businesses

Providing advice for businesses

Advertising and promoting Wales as a centre for industry

Clearing and reclaiming derelict land.

Fig. D Nine Mile Point industrial estate

The WDA has attracted businesses providing over 10 000 jobs, but this has not been enough to offset the job losses suffered in the region, especially in the coal and steel industries. The unemployment rate in South Wales has risen from an average of 6 per cent in 1976 to over 15 per cent by 1982.

The policy has concentrated on supporting the faltering coalfield Valleys, but with limited success. The traditional industries have continued their decline and the population of the Valleys has fallen despite all the incentives available.

There is support within Wales for preserving the Valley communities, but there are many opponents of the policy. They point out that the Valleys are mostly unsuitable for large-scale modern industry. Yet the Valleys have received massive government support while the coastal lowlands, where more suitable sites are available, have received less. The most favoured area of all is the Severnside coast between the English border and Cardiff, but this area received no assistance at all until the 1970s.

The failure of the government to provide incentives for industry to move into Severnside may have prevented industry developing there. A more successful policy for South Wales could have involved large-scale developments in the coastal lowlands with government aid and development encouraged only in the most favoured areas of the coalfields.

QUESTIONS

A1 What are the main causes of industrial dereliction in South Wales?

2 What was the Aberfan disaster?

3 To what uses is the reclaimed land put? Give examples.

4 What do the initials WDA stand for?

5 How does the WDA attempt to help the Welsh economy?

B1 Discuss the benefits resulting from the reclamation of derelict land.

2 Study Fig E.

(a) How does the advertisement attempt to attract new industry to Gwent?

(b) Design an advertisement intended to attract industry to South Wales.

3 How can the government's policy of supporting the coalfield valleys be (i) defended, (ii) criticised?

C (a) Explain the factors favouring the growth of South Wales as a major industrial region, referring to specific examples of important industries.

(b) What are its advantages and disadvantages for its continued industrial development and the establishment of new industries?

Today fiction is becoming reality, and the communications revolution is reshaping the way we live. In the forefront of that change is Gwent, the new centre of Britain's high technology industry. Why have so many world leaders like Inmos, Mitel and Ferranti chosen to cross the Severn Bridge to set up their new factories in Gwent? Gwent has first class communications by rail and road. London is only ninety-three minutes by high speed train, and Birmingham is just ninety minutes away by motorway. Heavy investment in high-tech education in Gwent Colleges gives firms a head start when it comes to recruitment. As the most successful companies have proved, a good environment is essential to efficiency. And people like living in this attractive corner of Britain. With factories ready now, and sites available for specialist developments, Gwent is proving a powerful magnet for firms with the future in mind.

the future starts today in Gwent

Take a look at Gwent, the new high-tech centre of the United Kingdom.

Fig. E

9.10 MERSEYSIDE

The Merseyside conurbation has been declining in terms of population and manufacturing industries since the 1960s:

	Population
1961	1 718 186
1971	1 656 545
1981	1 513 070

Liverpool, at the centre of the built-up area, has been declining at a much faster rate than the area as a whole. The port, once one of the world's busiest, has lost a large proportion of its former trade. The government and local authorities are trying hard to regenerate the Merseyside economy, but the task is difficult because of the scale of the problem. Liverpool was a small fishing port until in the eighteenth century trade developed with the North American colonies. During the nineteenth century the port grew fast, importing raw cotton and exporting cotton cloth.

The Port of Liverpool

The majority of goods are now handled at the Royal Seaforth Dock. This 200-hectare site includes specialised facilities for grain, timber and containers, without which Liverpool's port would now be insignificant. Most of its old docks are shallow and

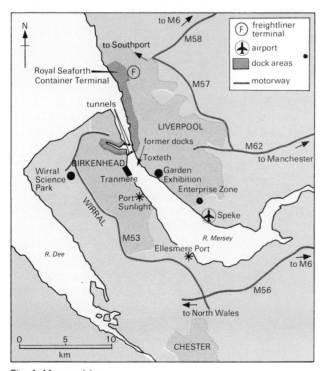

Fig. A Merseyside

	Thousand tonnes
Foreign imports	
Food, drink and tobacco	2345
Raw materials	2150
Manufactured articles	777
Petroleum in bulk	461
	5733
Foreign exports	
Food, drink and tobacco	249
Raw materials	198
Manufactured articles	1481
	1928
Coastwise imports	
Petroleum in bulk	3811
Livestock	30
Other	192
	4033
Coastwise exports	
Petroleum in bulk	36
Other	747
	783
Total imports and exports	12 477
of which containers	1222

Fig. B The trade of the port of Liverpool

have narrow quays. Dockside handling equipment is old and inefficient. In 1972, the South Docks closed. Many of the other docks are being used less and less. Ferries operate to Ireland and Northern Ireland but there are no longer trans-Atlantic passenger services.

There are other reasons for the decline. The heavy industries and textiles in and around Merseyside do not generate as much trade as they once did. There has been a shift in port activity to the east and south coasts of England. In 1965, Liverpool's share of national trade was 10 per cent; by 1980, it was only 3 per cent. Over the same time, its labour force had shrunk from 14 000 to about 2000. Another major cause of total cargo decline is the transfer of crude oil shipments to the Amlwch terminal off Anglesey.

Industry

Port industries in the Liverpool area include flour-milling, oil-seed crushing and cattle feeds, paper-making and paints. Oil is refined at Eastham and Stanlow, with larger tankers off-loading at the Tranmere Oil Terminal. Soaps and margarine are

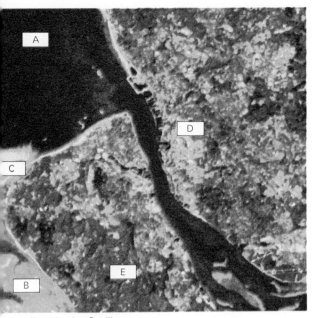

Key to Landsat Satellite
False-colour image

A	sea
B	water with varying amounts of suspended sediment
C	sand and mud
D	urban/residential areas
E	farmland and woodland

The satellite image was taken by the Landsat I satellite. The satellite uses a multispectral scanner (MSS) which 'photographs' from a height of 915 kilometres. The images contain a series of areas of 79 metres square (the 'pixel size'). This map uses false-colour to illustrate different types of land and water. The shades of blues and greys show the built-up nature of Merseyside. The areas of vegetation or farmland are limited to patches of derelict land, the airport and the surrounding countryside.

Fig. C Merseyside from space

made at Unilever's Port Sunlight works. This has its own port, opened in 1883. William Lever built one of the world's first industrial villages for the factory's workers. In the early 1980s, 10 000 were employed at Port Sunlight and the original houses were being conserved.

There is shipbuilding at Birkenhead, opposite Liverpool. There was no town there before the Cammell Laird Shipbuilders' yard was built in 1824. Since the 1960s, this shipyard and other smaller ones have declined. Other industries in Birkenhead which have also lost jobs include the manufacture of vehicle brakes, printing machinery, cardboard cartons, clothes and flour. Some industries that moved to Merseyside because of government development policies have suffered employment cutbacks. The British Leyland factory at Speke closed in 1978 with 5000 job losses. Fords at Halewood have been overmanned on their Escort production lines. Vauxhall at Ellesmere Port have cut back, although in 1983 the company expanded their labour force because of the success of the Astra model.

Fig. D Toxteth

The future

Several developments are promising. There has been aid for the run-down inner-city areas which surround the old docklands. Toxteth (Fig D), the scene of riots in 1981, will be improved. The new initiatives to regenerate Liverpool have been co-ordinated by a civil service task force. It has brought people together to convert derelict land and old industry to new economic life. There will be a high proportion of service industry. Three hundred and fifty hectares of once-derelict land have been reclaimed for the 1984 Garden Festival. A new entertainment/sports hall has been built. In the Speke enterprise zone, new factories are available for light industry. On the Wirral, a new science park is attracting high-technology industry. This is similar to Birchwood Science Park in nearby Warrington. The media have emphasised decline and dereliction, but Merseyside needs to be seen as an area with a future.

QUESTIONS

A1 Why has the port of Liverpool declined?
  2 Study Fig B.
    (a) What goods dominate Liverpool's trade?
    (b) What is meant by coastwise trade?
    (c) What proportion of total trade is carried in containers?
  3 Which of the port's imports are processed in the industries of Merseyside?
B1 Study Fig C and link it with Fig A to answer these questions:
    (a) Identify Speke Airport, Birkenhead Docks, Seaforth Dock, farmland on the Wirral.
    (b) Compare the amount of mud and silt in the Mersey with that in the river Dee estuary.
    (c) Why are there red patches, especially in south Liverpool?
    (d) Which part of Liverpool appears least built-up?
    (e) What does this image show about Merseyside that a normal satellite photograph could not?

155

9.11 NORTH-WEST ENGLAND

The decline of north-west England as one of the world's most important industrial regions began after World War I, and has quickened since the 1960s. As employment in manufacturing industry has fallen there has been a shift to the service industries. Growth in this sector has not provided enough jobs, and unemployment rates are above the national average. Out-migration has been high.

Figure A shows the relative importance of different types of industry in the north-west. In the 1950s and 1960s, one-third of all workers were employed in textiles and engineering. As textiles declined, engineering absorbed former textile workers and

Industrial production	United Kingdom £ million	North-west England £ million
Food, drink and tobacco	8359	1229
Chemicals, coal and petroleum products	9084	1932
Metal manufacture	3330	192
Mechanical engineering	8382	951
Instrument engineering	1171	125
Electrical engineering	5850	826
Shipbuilding, marine engineering and vehicles	7697	1056
Other metal goods	4029	374
Textiles	2919	661
Leather and furs	252	39
Clothing and footwear	1959	285
Bricks, pottery, glass, cement	2744	399
Timber, furniture	2099	264
Paper, printing, publishing	5615	704
Other manufacturing	2858	371
Total manufacturing	66 351	9415

Fig. A   (1979 figures, *Regional Trends* 1982)

mills were converted into engineering factories. Since the end of the 1970s, engineering has declined in importance and many old mills and even new factories now stand empty. The details of change in Bolton (Fig B) are typical of many north-west towns.

Other major industries in the region have suffered also. The coal industry has steadily declined since its peak year of 1907. Pits became exhausted or uneconomic but there are still a few modern deep mines between Wigan and St Helens which have reserves for over 300 years. Much of the output of two million tonnes per year is exported from a new coal export port at Garston. The chemical industry

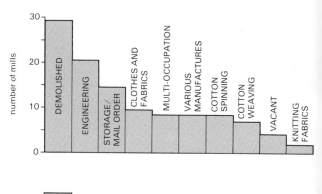

mills in some form of textile manufacture, only 24 in 1982 (15 direct and 9 allied)

	Mills	Employees
1934	122	30 000
1948	111	28 000
1960	61	17 000
1973	25	7000
1977	18	5000
1980	15	4500

TO

Journeymen Spinners

Wanted Immediately,

From Eighty to One Hundred

MULE SPINNERS,

For a New Mill and other Mills, in Great Bolton, which New Mill is complete with new Machinery now ready gaited, and will commence running on Monday Morning next, adjoining to which Mills are a Number of Cottages, for the convenience and accommodation of Spinners: liberal Wages will be given and constant employ.

For further particulars apply to Messrs. ORMROD and HARDCASTLE, of Bolton aforesaid, Cotton Spinners.

BOLTON 7th NOVEMBER, 1816   [EDWARD SMITH, PRINTER.]

Fig. B Growth and decline of cotton in Bolton

declined alongside the textile industry as demands for soaps, dyes and bleaches fell. Petrochemicals have been a growth point in the region. A pipeline from the Shell oil refinery at Stanlow on the Mersey supplies Carrington with liquid by-products from the refining process (feedstock), but this wealth-creating industry is capital intensive. It has never employed many people, and was even shedding jobs in the early 1980s.

The Manchester area has suffered inner-city unemployment and population decline similar to Liverpool's. Jobs in the centre declined from 160 000 in 1966 to about 90 000 in 1981. The designation of a

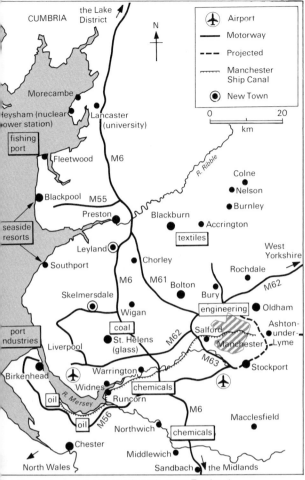

Fig. C The industrial base of north-west England

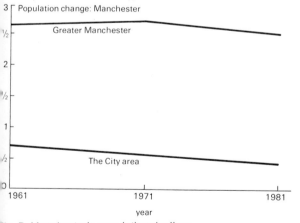

Fig. D Manchester's population declines

artnership area in inner Manchester is intended to :ope with decline. Transport improvements in the Manchester area have received high priority. Figure : shows the plan to complete an orbital motorway n Greater Manchester, which will have Britain's lensest regional motorway network. These infra-tructure improvements should improve the econ- mic prospects of Manchester and the north-west.

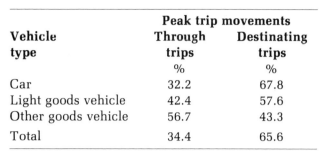

Vehicle type	Peak trip movements	
	Through trips %	Destinating trips %
Car	32.2	67.8
Light goods vehicle	42.4	57.6
Other goods vehicle	56.7	43.3
Total	34.4	65.6

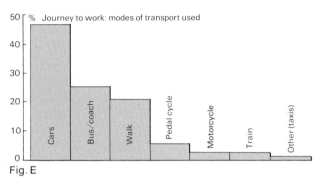

Fig. E

QUESTIONS

A1 List the industrial groups in rank order for the United Kingdom (Fig A). In another column, state the rank order for the north-west. In another column, state the difference in rank. Example:

Industry	UK rank	NW rank	Difference in rank
chemicals	1	1	nil
mechanical eng.	2	4	2

2 Which industries are more important in the north-west than in the United Kingdom as a whole?

3 Make a list of major manufacturing industries in the north-west that have declined. Include industries on Merseyside (page 154).

4 In a recent survey, 24 mills in Bolton were in some way connected with textiles. What pro-portion of all mills was this? (Fig B.)

B1 Using the details in Fig B and the information on pages 68 and 69, write about the growth and decline of Lancashire's cotton industry.

2 Suggest reasons for the changes in population in the city of Manchester area between 1961 and 1981 (Fig D).

3 Study the details about transport in Fig E. Summarise the main facts in a few sentences. Suggest possible solutions to the problems of through traffic and the journey to work.

4 In what ways should an efficient motorway network (Fig C) improve the attractiveness of the north-west region for future economic develop-ments?

9.12 YORKSHIRE AND HUMBERSIDE

This is an area of great variety, with important industrial regions: the woollen textile area of West Yorkshire, the steel and metalworking of South Yorkshire, the Yorkshire coalfield and the modern break-bulk industries of the Humber estuary. In contrast there are the high fells of the Yorkshire Dales National Park, the undulating limestone moors of the North York Moors National Park and the chalk cliffs of Flamborough Head.

Nearly five million people live in Yorkshire and Humberside, three-quarters of them in the metropolitan counties of South and West Yorkshire.

West Yorkshire

The growth of West Yorkshire was based on the woollen textile industry. Hundreds of woollen mills and clothing mills were built and a string of towns grew up around them. At the peak, over a quarter of a million were employed in woollen mills, but by 198 less than 40 000 jobs remained. The job losses hav been serious for major centres like Leeds, Bradfor Huddersfield and Halifax, but the decline has bee disastrous for some of the smaller towns such a Elland and Dewsbury for well over half the wor force was employed in the woollen mills. There ha been large-scale out-migration from these towns an there seems little chance of major industrial growt in many of the smaller settlements, especially thos in the narrow, steep valleys of the Pennines. Som mill towns such as Hebden Bridge and Holmfirth ar finding a new role as tourist centres.

The cities of West Yorkshire have a more divers fied employment base. The most important industr after textiles is engineering. This industry develope from a tradition of manufacturing textile machinery Today, there are a wide range of electrical an

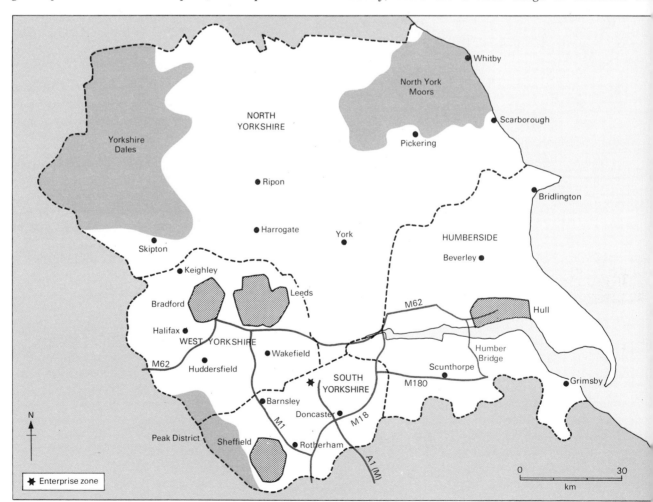

Fig. A Yorkshire and Humberside

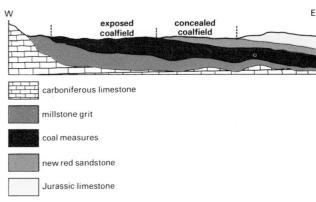

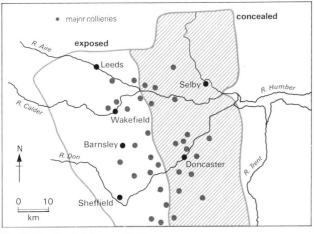

Fig. B The Yorkshire coalfield

Fig. C The Yorkshire Dales

Fig. D Hebden Bridge

general engineering companies.

The largest city in West Yorkshire is Leeds, with a population of 450 000. The city grew up beside the river Aire, which provides an easy route through the Pennines. Leeds was never important for textiles, but was a major centre for clothing. In recent years, Leeds has attracted office employment.

The Yorkshire coalfield

Britain's most important coalfield stretches southwards from Leeds to Nottingham. There are some thick seams of good quality coal, such as the Barnsley

seam which is two metres thick. Thirty million tonnes of coal per year are produced.

The earliest workings were in the exposed coalfield in the west of the area. As mining technology improved, deeper shafts were dug following the dip of the seams eastwards into the concealed field. The smaller, older collieries in the exposed coalfield have closed. The number of miners in the Yorkshire coalfield fell from 117 000 in 1960 to 55 000 by 1983. The opening of a mining complex at Selby is the most obvious sign of the long-term future of the Yorkshire coalfield; there are vast reserves of coal. However, it is likely that employment in mining will continue to decline slowly as production becomes concentrated in a few large, mechanised mines. In an effort to attract new employment to the coalfield area, an enterprise zone has been designated between Wakefield and Doncaster, where an industrial estate opened in 1949. Among the firms moving in are a frozen food distributor, an industrial filter manufacturer and a computer company.

QUESTIONS

A1 List the main industrial areas of Yorkshire and Humberside.

2 Why has the decline of textile employment affected the smaller towns of West Yorkshire more than the larger cities?

3 Why have the coalmines closed in the western sector of the Yorkshire coalfield?

4 What do the figures in the table reveal about the Yorkshire coalfield?

	1960	1983
miners	117 000	55 000
production (million tonnes)	43	33

B1 Why have the industrial areas of Yorkshire and Humberside suffered recent large increases in unemployment?

2 Find Hebden Bridge in your atlas. Suggest reasons why it is well placed for tourism.

159

9.13 SHEFFIELD

Sheffield is England's fourth largest city, and has a population of 560 000. The city's growth was due to a concentration of industrial resources:

1 Iron-ore from the coal measures.
2 Forests providing the wood for charcoal.
3 Fast-flowing streams to operate waterwheels.
4 Millstone grit from which grinding stones were made.
5 Limestone from the Pennines.
6 Local coal.
7 Gannister, a clay for fire-bricks to line the furnaces.

By the fourteenth century, Sheffield was already famous for iron cutlery. The early ironworks used water power to work bellows, drive hammers and turn grindstones. Sheffield built up a reputation for high quality and its knives and tools were in great demand. As the local iron-ore became exhausted, it was replaced by imports from Sweden during the sevententh century.

Steel

When coke replaced charcoal for smelting, and steam replaced water power, Sheffield was able to use local coking coal. The modern steel industry began in the middle of the eighteenth century when Benjamin Huntsman invented the crucible process, an improved way of producing steel which allowed steel to replace iron for tools. In 1742, 'Sheffield plate' was invented, a steel alloy with copper and a silver coating. By 1835, Sheffield had become the national centre of steel tool manufacture. Later developments included electroplating, introduced in 1850, large-scale steel production following the introduction of the Bessemer Converter in 1858, and the invention of stainless steel (a chromium/steel alloy) in 1913.

Sheffield's steel industry spread down the Don valley towards Rotherham and Doncaster where iron and steel works and heavy engineering factories developed. Steel castings, railway carriages and heavy steel goods were produced here. By contrast, Sheffield itself specialised in light steel goods, especially cutlery, tools and high-grade special steels.

The Sheffield area remains important for specialised steel products; over half of Britain's special steels are made here. However, none of the local raw materials on which the industry developed is still used. Iron is no longer produced in the area, but is brought in from Scunthorpe. Scrap steel is used in electric arc furnaces. The coalmines have gone.

Employment in Sheffield's steel industry has declined rapidly in recent years. Low-cost foreign imports have reduced demand for Sheffield's tools and cutlery. The rationalisation of iron and steel production has led to the closure of many blast furnaces, and the introduction of mechanisation and automation has reduced labour demands. Several famous Sheffield steel firms have closed.

Diversification of Sheffield's manufacturing has been slow to happen. Food canning, confectionery

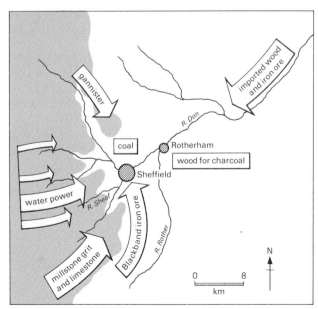

Fig. A Factors of industrial growth

Fig. B An electric arc furnace at the Tinsley Park Works, Sheffield

Fig. C Sheffield's central business district (CBD)

and brewing have traditionally provided some alternative employment from steel and engineering. Despite its problems, Sheffield has one vital geographical advantage — accessibility. Motorway links are excellent. Rail communications are good, and the Sheffield and South Yorkshire Navigation waterway has been the subject of a major improvement scheme.

In an effort to attract new industries, the local authority has established 'a new town within the city' at Mosborough, ten kilometres south-east of the city centre. The area became part of the city of Sheffield in 1967 and rapid housing and industrial development has taken place. Eighteen separate housing estates (or townships) will be completed by 1986, providing housing for 47 000 new residents. At Holbrook, a large industrial estate has been prepared for light engineering, electrical engineering and packaging companies.

Sheffield has attracted office employment. Several new office blocks have been built in the city centre, including the headquarters of the Manpower Services Commission and the Midland Bank.

A tradition of metalworking, engineering and fine craftsmanship established over many centuries is now declining. The face of Sheffield is changing rapidly. The old factories and chimneys have gone and Sheffield boasts that it is the cleanest industrial city in Europe. It is assuming a new role as one of the leading commercial and shopping centres in the north of England. Conferences, leisure and tourism all have a part to play in Sheffield's future.

QUESTIONS

A1 What advantages did Sheffield have for the growth of the iron industry?

2 List the inventions and developments which helped to keep Sheffield a leading iron and steel city.

3 Where was the production of (i) light steel goods and (ii) heavy steel goods concentrated?

4 Why has employment in Sheffield's steel and steelworking industries declined in recent years?

5 How has the employment structure of Sheffield changed recently?

B1 Explain how Sheffield provides an example of industrial inertia.

2 What problems face a city like Sheffield, which has an old industrial employment structure? How can such problems be overcome?

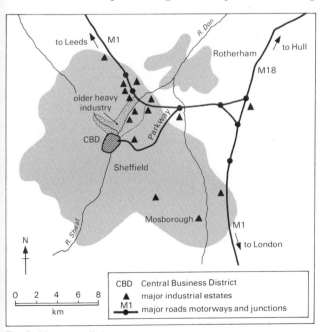

Fig. D Motorway links

9.14 HUMBERSIDE

The county of Humberside was formed in 1974, combining parts of Yorkshire and Lincolnshire. The change gave rise to fierce opposition from people angry at losing their old counties, but the creation of Humberside made geographical sense, especially following the opening of the Humber Bridge linking the north and south banks.

The Humber ports

The region's importance is based upon the ports, which handle over 10 per cent of Britain's trade, over 33 million tonnes per year.

Goole is 90 km from the sea on the river Ouse. Ships of up to 3000 tonnes berth there, and there is much barge traffic. Goole has excellent communications by motorway and waterway with the industrial areas of Yorkshire and the Midlands. It handles 1½ million tonnes of cargo a year. The main imports are cereals, timber and vehicles; the main exports are coal, steel and chemicals.

Hull docks stretch for 7 km along the Humber estuary. The small western dock has closed and development is concentrated at the downriver docks where there are container and roll on–roll off facilities for ships of up to 26 000 tonnes. The main imports are petroleum products, food and timber; the main exports are chemicals, machinery and steel. Hull used to be famous as a fishing port. With the collapse of the deep-sea sector of British fishing, hundreds of fishermen have lost their jobs.

Grimsby's fishing fleet has also suffered badly, and the fish market is now dependent upon fish brought in by road from other ports. Grimsby has an increasing general cargo trade with roll on–roll off services to Esbjerg in Denmark. Danish bacon and butter are important imports, as are foreign cars. The main exports are steel and chemicals and the annual trade is 1½ million tonnes.

Immingham dock handles vessels of up to 30 000 tonnes. There is a modern roll on-roll off terminal with regular services to the Netherlands and Scandinavia. Deepwater jetties handle imports of crude oil, bulk liquids and iron-ore, and coal exports.

Industries

Humberside has many advantages for modern industry, including readily-available level coastal sites, deepwater port facilities and development area incentives. However, the relative remoteness and

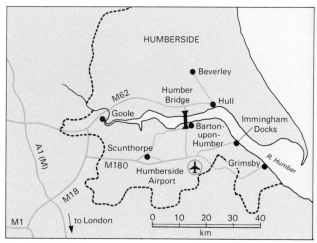

Fig. A Bridging the gap

inaccessibility of the area has discouraged industry. Despite its advantages, Humberside remains the least developed of the major British estuaries.

There is a limited range of industry in the region, much of it concerned with the processing of imported raw materials:

1 *Port industries:* Oilseed crushing, soap and margarine manufacture, saw-milling and flour-milling have been long established at Hull, as have the associated ship repair and marine engineering industries. More recent developments include chemicals and oil storage. There are two oil refineries on the south bank at Killingholme and a range of chemical and petrochemical plants between Grimsby and Immingham. Products include fertilisers, synthetic textiles and pharmaceuticals.

2 *Food processing:* Agriculture is important in Humberside. Potatoes and vegetables are grown along the coastal lowlands and market gardening is important locally. Holderness and the Wolds have large farms growing wheat and barley. There are canning and freezing factories, brewing, flour and biscuit manufacture and agricultural engineering. There are also factories freezing and processing fish and producing fish-meal and fish-oil.

3 *Steel:* Scunthorpe is located on the Jurassic limestone ridge which contains iron-ore. Coking coal was transported from pits in Yorkshire, Nottinghamshire and Durham. Three separate steelworks were built at Scunthorpe. After nationalisation in 1967, a fourth steelworks (the Anchor project) was built using high-quality iron-ore imported through Immingham. By 1983, only one of the older steelworks remained open.

4 *Engineering:* One of Humberside's major employers is British Aerospace. Five thousand people work at Brough designing and building military aircraft. Other engineering products of Humberside include vehicle components, conveyor belts and power transmissions.

Transport

Major motorway and road improvement schemes have been completed to improve the accessibility of Humberside. The M62 links Hull with the A1 and the industrial districts of West and South Yorkshire. The M180 and M18 link South Humberside with South Yorkshire and, via the M1, with the Midlands and south of England. The Humber Bridge, Britain's largest suspension bridge, was opened in 1981. It is over two kilometres long and was built to link North and South Humberside in an effort to bring the two areas together. The people of Hull hoped that the bridge would extend the catchment area of the city's shops, services and industries. The bridge is an engineering success but may be an economic failure. The cost of building it will never be directly recovered, even though the tolls are high. Only 10 000 vehicles a day crossed the bridge during 1982, compared with over 30 000 a day each using the Severn and Forth Bridges. The approach roads to North and South Humberside are now so efficient that many drivers prefer to drive round the estuary.

Fig. B The Humber Bridge

QUESTIONS

A1 Complete the table below:

	Annual trade (million tonnes)	Main imports	Main exports
Hull	3.7		
Goole			coal, steel, chemicals
Grimsby		bacon, butter, cars	
Immingham	23		

2 Why does Immingham handle so much more tonnage of trade than the other three Humber ports?
3 Describe the main industries of Humberside.
4 Why was the Humber Bridge built?
5 Why has the Humber Bridge been called 'an economic failure'?

B1 The *detour index* is a useful mathematical technique for geographers. It gives an accurate measurement of the deviation of a route from the ideal straight line between two points. It is calculated as follows:

$$\text{detour index} = \frac{\text{actual road distance}}{\text{straight line distance}} \times 100$$

Figure A shows the detour around the Humber estuary, now reduced by the Humber Bridge. Here is the calculation of the detour index for the route from Hull to Grimsby before and after the construction of the bridge:

before $DI = \dfrac{138 \text{ km}}{27 \text{ km}} \times 100 = 511$

after $DI = \dfrac{56}{27} \times 100 = 207$

(a) Complete the table at the foot of the page by calculating the detour indices before and after the bridge was built.
(b) Which route has the greatest change in the detour index?
(c) Who would find such calculations useful?
(d) Why do some drivers prefer to drive around the Humber estuary rather than use the new bridge?

2 Why is Humberside the least-developed of the major British estuaries?

Route	Straight line distance	Actual road distance before	after	Detour index before	after	Change
Hull–Grimsby	27	138	56	511	207	304
Hull–Humberside Airport						
Hull–Scunthorpe						
Hull–Immingham						
Goole–Immingham						

10.1 THE WEST MIDLANDS

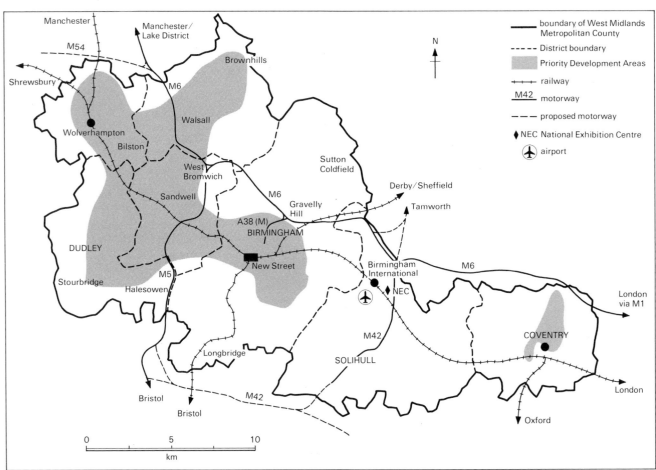

Fig. A The West Midlands metropolitan county

Birmingham, centre of the West Midlands, came to be known as the 'workshop of the world' and 'the city of a thousand trades'. Iron-working provided the basis for industrialisation. Iron-ore was found in Staffordshire and water-power drove bellows and worked hammers. Swords, muskets and pistols were produced for Britain's armies. Coal mined in south Staffordshire supported a rapid increase in industry during the eighteenth century. The building of a canal network linked the West Midlands with the rest of England. By 1790, Birmingham was linked to the Thames, Mersey, Severn and Humber estuaries. World markets were opened up for the manufactured products of the region.

People moved from surrounding agricultural areas to work in the factories. At the beginning of the nineteenth century, Birmingham's population was 70 000. By 1831, it had increased to 170 000 and by the end of the century to 522 000. In 1930, Birmingham had become the country's second

million city. The fast growth was a result of growing industry. The industrial revolution was made in the city by men such as James Watt who invented the rotary steam engine, Matthew Boulton who built one of the early factories, and William Murdoch who developed gas lighting. When railways reached the Birmingham area there was improved accessibility with the outside world. The main line to London was opened in 1833. Railway wagons and coaches were made for the home market as well as for the developing countries of Canada and Australia.

Industrial variety has always been a strength of the area. Birmingham developed a jewellery quarter, a gunmaking quarter and a cocoa and confectionery factory (Cadbury's). Nearby, Coventry produced bicycles in former silk workshops and household goods were made in small workshops throughout the area. In 1905, Herbert Austin built his car factory at Longbridge, south of Birmingham. British Leyland evolved from this start. The success of the car

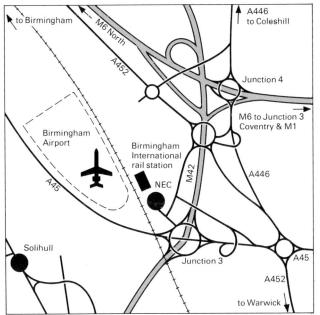

Fig. B

industry gave the region its twentieth-century wealth. Unlike other coalfield industrial areas, the West Midlands was slow to decline. The car industry and its numerous component manufacturers were *growth industries*, but this success led to the region becoming too dependent upon the car industry. The West Midlands became a problem region when the car industry declined in the 1970s.

In the 1960s, population was still increasing. Between 1961 and 1971 there was a 2.25 per cent population increase in the conurbation, through in-migration from northern industrial areas and overseas. The attraction was the prospect of jobs. By 1971, 14 per cent of all New Commonwealth immigrants in the United Kingdom were in the West Midlands. In 1981, 10.9 per cent of the conurbation's population were living in households where the head of household was born in the New Commonwealth or Pakistan.

Communications

The conurbation was well served by canals and, later, by railways. In the second half of the twentieth century, the West Midlands became the 'motorway conurbation'. The M6 winds its way through industrial and residential areas and is joined by the M5 from the south. The M42 almost completes a southern loop. The Aston Expressway links the M6 with the centre of Birmingham. 'Spaghetti Junction', a maze of motorways and slip roads, was opened in 1972. Birmingham has developed inner, middle and outer ring roads to help traffic move around the city.

Figure B shows a late-twentieth-century West Midlands roadscape. The airport, modern industry

and the National Exhibition Centre (NEC) benefit from accessibility. The London to Birmingham electrified railway line has a new station near the NEC. Inter-city has cut travel time to the capital to only ninety minutes.

Within the city of Birmingham, public transport has been encouraged. Fares have been kept as low as possible on buses and trains. The West Midlands Passenger Transport Executive has integrated rail and bus transport. Existing railway lines are being considered for re-opening and electrification. In the city, priority is given to buses, with fast bus lanes and bus-only roads.

The National Exhibition Centre

The NEC is a major exhibition, sporting and concert location for the West Midlands and Britain. It was opened in 1976 and succeeded in enticing the Motor Show away from London on alternate years. The NEC takes about 55 per cent of exhibition business in Britain. It has set high standards and has attracted exhibitions from Europe. The centre cost the Birmingham ratepayers £38 million and began to make a profit after four years.

QUESTIONS

A1 Outline the reasons for early industrial development in Birmingham and the West Midlands.
 2 Draw a line graph to show the growth of Birmingham:

1901	522 000	**1951**	1 113 000
1911	840 000	**1961**	1 183 223
1921	919 000	**1971**	1 097 961
1931	1 003 000	**1981**	1 006 527

 3 Make a list of the men who made the industrial revolution in the Birmingham area, including Cadbury.
 4 Why was there in-migration and immigration into the area, especially in the 1960s?
 5 What has made the West Midlands accessible?
 6 List the transport improvements made within the Birmingham area under the following headings: motorways, ring roads, public transport.
 7 Suggest some possible advantages and disadvantages of urban motorways such as the Aston Expressway (the A38 (M)).
 8 Describe the advantages of the site of the National Exhibition Centre.
 9 Why do you think the NEC was able to entice the Motor Show away from London?
B1 Why was the West Midlands slow to decline? (Consider industrial structure and accessibility.)
 2 What are the advantages and disadvantages to the West Midland's economy of the NEC?

10.2 BIRMINGHAM: A TRANSECT

In any city in the British Isles, there are different land uses as we move from the centre to the outskirts. This transect covers a part of south Birmingham. The pictures were taken along the line of the Stratford Road, the A34. The transect starts in the central business district and passes through the inner city to the newer areas of south Birmingham and Solihull. Much of the area surrounding the CBD has been re-developed, and local authority (council) homes have been built. There are many high-rise blocks but several schemes contain a mix of building.

Redevelopment is planned for areas further away from the city centre and several areas are a mix of old terrace houses and new houses. Where rebuilding is taking place, the residents have to put up with noise, dust and inconvenience (Fig C). In Sparkbrook and Sparkhill, there are still streets of terraced property.

The areas have a high percentage of ethnic minority people, living in owner-occupied and rented homes. The main road is lined with small shops, many selling Asian food and Indian clothing.

Further out of the centre, in Hall Green, there are more semi-detached and detached houses, built in the first half of the twentieth century. The area is well-served by a range of shops including small super-markets and some specialist services such as building societies, dry cleaners and hair salons. The transect ends in Shirley on the edge of the built-up area. The shops are newer and more expensive, the houses are a mix of privately-owned and council property. Some of the houses are large and expensive and several have big gardens. Near the M42 is a large garden centre, new industrial estates and land awaiting development.

Fig. A

Fig. B

Fig. C

Fig. F

Fig. E

Fig. D

Central Birmingham

shops/offices

shops/offices

industry

old industry

new industry

A34

N

A 34

M42

to Stratford

to M6 and National Exhibition Centre

0   5
km

Fig. G

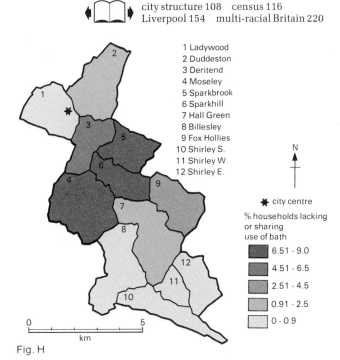

1 Ladywood
2 Duddeston
3 Deritend
4 Moseley
5 Sparkbrook
6 Sparkhill
7 Hall Green
8 Billesley
9 Fox Hollies
10 Shirley S.
11 Shirley W.
12 Shirley E.

★ city centre

% households lacking
or sharing
use of bath

■ 6.51 - 9.0
■ 4.51 - 6.5
■ 2.51 - 4.5
□ 0.91 - 2.5
□ 0 - 0.9

Fig. H

Using the census

Figures G and H were compiled using a computer. The computer program contains information used in the 1981 census. It stores the following statistical information:

1 Percentage of households with no car.

2 Percentage of households lacking or sharing the use of a bath.

3 Percentage of households owner-occupied.

4 Percentage of population born outside the United Kingdom.

When instructed, the computer draws a map of Birmingham divided into wards. It then shades it to show the distribution of one of the sets of information. Figure G shows the distribution of people who have no car. The area of the transect is indicated. The map gives a general picture of the distribution of wealth or *affluence* in the city.

Figure H is a small section of the complete Birmingham map which covers the transect area. This shows a second measure of affluence, but you would need to study several measures (*variables*) to obtain a true picture of wealth distribution.

QUESTIONS

A1 Complete the following details:

Photograph	Details of area shown
A	CBD. Multi-storey car park, no housing.
B	Inner suburbs, old industry, ...
C	
D	
E	
F	

2 In the areas of Sparkbrook and Sparkhill there is a high percentage of ethnic minority people, especially Asians. Describe (i) the types of housing in these areas and (ii) the types of shops.

3 Look at Fig G. Which areas of the city have a high percentage of households with no car? Where in the city are there most cars per household?

B1 Look at Fig H. Describe and comment on the distribution of households that lack or share the use of a bath.

2 Can you see any links between Figs G and H?

3 The following statistics are for the twelve wards shown as the transect area on the two maps:

	% born outside UK	% men unemployed
1 Ladywood	16.6	23.9
2 Duddeston	17.0	29.4
3 Deritend	35.2	30.4
4 Moseley	18.0	15.1
5 Sparkbrook	42.1	28.7
6 Sparkhill	43.7	22.7
7 Hall Green	10.0	9.6
8 Billesley	6.1	14.1
9 Fox Hollies	9.6	17.9
10 Shirley South	3.4	7.5
11 Shirley West	3.0	6.8
12 Shirley East	3.4	6.2

Plot these statistics on an outline map. You will have to decide on different categories and colour shadings. Compare your result with Figs G and H.

5 What other variables could be used to build up a picture of affluence in a city?

10.3 WEST MIDLANDS: INDUSTRY

Industrial diversity has always been a strength of the West Midlands, but since the recession of the 1970s and early 1980s industrial problems have arisen. The car industry with its many component supplies has declined. Figure A shows a few major products used in the vehicle industry. The industrial linkages are

Car assembly	BL, Longbridge
	BL Rover, Solihull
	Talbot, Jaguar, Coventry
Tyres	Goodyear, Wolverhampton
Brakes	Girling, Birmingham
Electrical components	Lucas, Birmingham
Engines	Talbot, Coventry
Wheels	Wolverhampton
Radiators	Coventry
Paint	Birmingham
Transmissions	GKN, Birmingham

Fig. A

many and fewer cars produced has meant that car component firms have less work. The rise in unemployment has been influenced by the problems of vehicle production. In 1982 there was a male unemployment rate of 16.6 per cent, the same as in North-West England. The government's regional policy has not helped industrial growth in the West Midlands. It has not been a development area and several firms have not been allowed to expand there.

	Total employees (thousands)	% of total employment
Food, drink, tobacco	43	2.3
Chemicals, coal, oil products	19	1.0
Metal manufacture	81	4.2
Engineering, vehicles	417	22.1
Textiles, clothing	36	1.9
Bricks, timber, others	129	6.8
Totals	725	38.3

Fig. B

Figure B illustrates the dependence of the West Midlands on manufacturing employment; 38.3 per cent of total employment is in manufacturing compared with 27.8 per cent in the United Kingdom as a whole (1982). With the overall decline in manufacturing it is likely that the loss of job opportunities will increase. The inner city areas are cramped and not attractive to industry. A recent survey (Fig E) shows why businessmen dislike such areas.

Fig. C The former Bilston steelworks

Solutions

Several policies are being followed to attract new industry to the West Midlands. In 1979, the Birmingham partnership area was established, involving the government, Birmingham City Council, West Midlands Metropolitan County and the Birmingham Area Health Authority. The partnership's activities include building factories and improving the environment. It is not difficult to obtain an *industrial development certificate* (necessary before building new factories), and firms are no longer directed away from the region. At the new Gravelly Industrial Park east of Spaghetti Junction, there are seventy-two units on the estate. Some are warehouses and stores, others

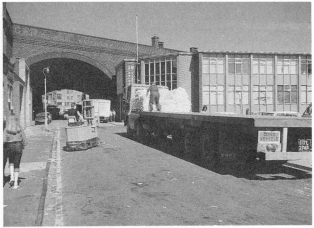

Fig. D Old inner city industry, Birmingham

Why industry avoids inner Birmingham

	points
Vandalism	**101**
Crime	65
Ugliness & urban blight	59
Private transport	58
Poor planning	51
Public transport	49
Poor image	47
Poor housing	38
Poor recreational facilities	21
Poor race relations	7
Shops	2

Fig. E Industry avoids inner Birmingham

are factories and workshops involved in a wide range of activities such as welding supplies, electronics, plastics, lighting, joinery and pumps. The industrial estate is well-served by motorway and main road access. Another new industrial area is the Monkspath Industrial Park (Fig F), on a site in Solihull eleven kilometres from Birmingham. It was built by private enterprise, and units for industrial manufacture or warehousing are leased for twenty-five years. The site is near to the main A34 road and its junction with the M42. Everything has been done to make the site attractive. Because of its locational advantages this industrial area will be successful. What the planners hope is that similar schemes in the derelict parts of the inner city will be equally successful.

Sixteen kilometres from Birmingham in the Dudley area of the Black Country is the West Midlands enterprise zone. It covers 225 hectares of old mining and metalworking industry. One part has been ruined by open-cast coalmining. An access road will be built to link the zone with the M5 motorway. The generous

Fig. F New industry at Monkspath

grants for locating in enterprise zones are attracting firms, but this could be a loss for the surrounding areas, where grants are not available.

QUESTIONS

A1 Why has the fall in car production had such a widespread effect in the West Midlands?

2 The West Midlands has not been a development area. How has this affected industrial growth?

3 State some of the disadvantages for future industrial development in the areas shown in Figs C and D.

4 Why do businessmen sometimes dislike setting up industry in the inner city?

5 What are the advantages for the new industry shown in Fig F?

B1 Account for the recent decline in manufacturing industry in the West Midlands. How is new industry being attracted to the region?

2 Outline the main purpose of the enterprise zone at Dudley.

C (a) Account for the location and development of the motor car manufacturing industry in one important area of production within the British Isles.

(b) Explain briefly why some of the newer manufacturing plants are located away from the older centres of the industry.

(c) Describe briefly the factors which are at present responsible for the industry's growth or decline.

169

10.4 CHANGE IN THE WEST MIDLANDS

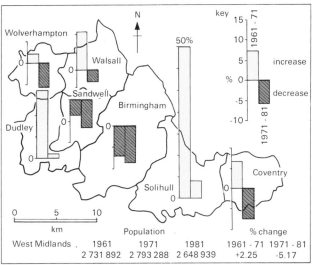

Fig. A

The pattern of population change shown on Fig A is similar to that of the other major conurbations in Britain. The central areas of the metropolitan region were declining between 1961 and 1971. Between 1971 and 1981, the population declined in the outer districts and growth in Dudley and Solihull almost ceased. During this twenty-year period, there was considerable *overspill* of population into surrounding towns. There were extensions to Tamworth, Lichfield, Stafford and Daventry. The new towns of Redditch and Telford developed. By 1981, Telford's population was 104 000 (target population 150 000). The demand for new homes outside the conurbation was a result of:

1 Old housing which needed clearing or improving.
2 A lack of building land within the conurbation.
3 High natural population growth rates in the conurbation.

4 In-migration and immigration which increased the population.

Circumstances have changed and overspill movements have now been reduced. Even so, Birmingham City Council is short of land for housebuilding. New housing will still be required outside Birmingham, or green-belt land will be threatened.

The ethnic structure of the population has changed since World War II. Immigrants were attracted by the prospect of work. In 1981, 9.8 per cent of the West Midlands population was born outside the United Kingdom. Asians have settled especially in the Sparkhill and Sparkbrook areas. West Indians and Irish live in several inner city areas. Birmingham is a multi-cultural city.

Comprehensive redevelopment areas have covered five parts of inner Birmingham. Since 1952, more than 100 000 people have been affected by these redevelopments. The new housing environments have been built at a lower density and now house only half of the original numbers. As in the new towns, housing and industry are separated and public open space has been provided. There is provision for shops, schools and community centres. Through traffic has been kept clear of the residential areas.

As manufacturing employment has declined, jobs have been created in the service sector. Office employment has increased, especially in the city centres of Birmingham and Coventry. Wolverhampton town centre is a third focal point for such employment. In the early 1970s there was surplus office accommodation. This was at the time when firms and government departments were moving out of London. They were not choosing the West Midlands because of its lack of development area status.

Fig. B Multi-cultural Birmingham

Fig. C Development in the CBD

canals 101   green belt 108
population change 116   multi-racial Britain 220

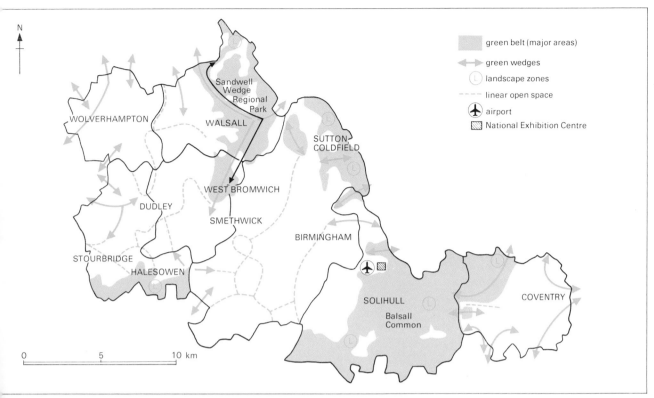

Fig. D Preserving open space

legend:
- green belt (major areas)
- green wedges
- landscape zones
- linear open space
- airport
- National Exhibition Centre

Protecting the environment

Figure D shows various ways of preserving open space. The green belt policy has been adopted to check the growth of the built-up area, to prevent towns from merging, to improve the urban environment and to provide new recreation facilities.

In many parts of the West Midlands, there is derelict land resulting from old mining and industry. Revitalising this land will be essential if the region is to be attractive for future residential development and employment. Over 200 kilometres of canal, no longer used for commerce, provide many possibilities for environmental amenities such as boating,

fishing and walking. The county's 'canal strategy' proposes to give priority to a canal loop which links the centres of Birmingham, Walsall and Wolverhampton.

QUESTIONS

A1 What is overspill population?

2 Use an atlas to find the overspill towns named in the text. Draw a map to show these towns and Birmingham, Wolverhampton and Coventry.

3 Why have there been overspill movements from the West Midlands?

4 (a) Where did Birmingham's immigrants come from?

(b) What attracted them to the area?

(c) Suggest why immigrants have tended to concentrate in certain areas of the inner city.

(d) What do you understand by 'multi-cultural'?

B1 Describe the pattern of population change in the West Midlands (Fig A). What are the reasons for this change?

2 What are the main changes taking place in the West Midlands to protect the environment?

3 What is the future for the West Midlands canal network?

C For a major conurbation in the British Isles, outline the main problems facing the area. Describe some of the strategies being employed to solve these problems.

Fig. E Gas Street Basin, Birmingham

171

10.5 CLYDESIDE

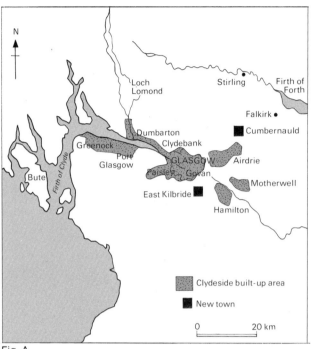

Fig. A

Fig. B The Govan Shipyard, Clydeside

Glasgow, Scotland's largest city and conurbation, grew up at the lowest bridging point on the river Clyde and became the centre of Clydeside, a port and industrial area. Before the eighteenth century, Glasgow was a small market town. As the American colonies were opened up, trade grew. The Clyde was deepened by dredging, and ocean-going vessels were able to reach the city centre. Colonial goods were imported: tobacco, sugar, rum, cotton. Exports to the colonies included furniture, books, clothes and glass, made in small factories in the expanding city.

Large-scale industrialisation took place in and around Glasgow during the Industrial Revolution. Coal from the Lanark coalfield was the fuel behind the industrial growth. Iron and steelworks used local coal and iron-ore. The steel was used in the manufacture of railway engines, textile machinery, sewing machines, ships, boilers and (later) cars. Glasgow became a centre of trade, business and education.

Clydeside was best known for shipbuilding. At one time a third of all ships built in Britain were launched on the Clyde. From Glasgow city centre to the sea, over thirty kilometres of riverside were lined with shipyards. At Clydebank, the world's largest passenger ships were built: the *Queen Elizabeth*, the *Queen Mary* and the *QE2*.

Glasgow is no longer one of Europe's chief ports. The inner docks have closed and the port has moved downstream to the wider and deeper estuary. A container terminal has been built at Greenock, but there has been no large-scale port and industrial development. There is a lack of extensive flat land such as is found on Teesside, Servernside and Humberside. Clydeside has not benefited from the growth of European trade owing to its position in the west of Britain.

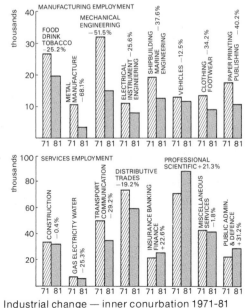

Fig. C Industrial change — inner conurbation 1971-81

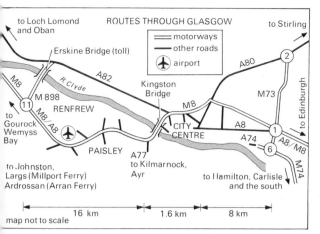

Fig. D Route map produced by Strathclyde Regional Council

	Population	% decline
1961	1 057 679	
1971	897 485	15
1981	765 915	15

Fig. E

Out-migration has been very high and has only recently declined.

In spite of port decline, factory closures, urban decay, housing problems and out-migration, it would be wrong to say that Glasgow's problems are too big to be solved. Clydeside is in a special development area and receives grants from the government. The area is served by new motorways and has good rail and air communications. Scotland's major city and conurbation is modernising and looking to the future.

Clydeside's basic heavy industries have declined rapidly since World War II. Coal and steel output decreased after 1945. By the mid-1980s, the steel industry had almost ceased to exist. Its plants had always lost much more money than the English steelworks. Much of the steel was sent south to England, involving high transport costs. Less and less was being used in Scotland. The shipbuilding and car assembly industries were also declining.

There were still twenty-three shipyards on Clydeside in 1945, but many closed down as orders contracted. The government helped maintain a much-reduced shipbuilding industry. A few yards remain, such as Govan Shipbuilders at Govan and Scotstoun and the Upper Clyde Shipbuilders yards. They are short of orders and their future is doubtful. Heavy engineering firms such as John Brown's have declined as orders have decreased. The threat of short-time working and redundancy dominates the lives of many Clydeside workers.

Clydeside has been short of modern growth industries. The North Sea oil boom provided extra jobs in steel pipe-making. Some oil rigs were made in the shipbuilding yards. The automobile industry has never provided a high percentage of jobs in the region and in 1980 the Talbot factory at Linwood, near Paisley, closed.

Urban problems

Glasgow's population reached its peak in the early twentieth century. It became a 'millionaire' city as people flocked to it in search of work, from the rural areas of Scotland and from Ireland. Close-packed tenements were built. These are housing blocks split into several separate homes. Living conditions in the inner city areas were among the worst in Europe. In 1945, the *population density* in Glasgow was two and a half times that of Birmingham, but has fallen during the last twenty years (E).

QUESTIONS

A1 What do you understand by 'colonial goods'?

2 Why was the Clyde suitable for port growth?

3 What types of engineering grew up in the area?

4 List the basic heavy industry which made Clydeside great.

5 In what ways has Clydeside declined?

6 Study the employment graphs (Fig C):
 (a) How did total manufacturing employment change between 1971 and 1981?
 (b) Using the scale, calculate how many jobs were lost in mechanical engineering between 1971 and 1981.
 (c) Which type of manufacturing industry had the largest percentage decrease between 1971 and 1981?
 (d) Which types of services employment increased between 1971 and 1981?

B1 Why have the upper docks on the Clyde closed?

2 Why has Clydeside been at a disadvantage compared to some English river estuaries?

3 It has been said that giving government money to industry on Clydeside is like supporting a 'lame duck'. What do you think is meant by this? Why do you think aid has been given?

4 Look at Fig D and answer these questions:
 (a) Suggest why the regional council chose to produce a map like this.
 (b) Why is Glasgow no longer the lowest bridging point on the Clyde?
 (c) Briefly state the advantages and disadvantages of routing motorways through a densely built-up area such as Clydeside.

C For one major area of heavy industry in the UK:
 (a) Describe and account for the growth of industry in the area.
 (b) Explain how the economy of the area has changed in recent years.

10.6 GLASGOW

Many areas of Glasgow have been redeveloped since World War II. Rebuilding was necessary because so much of the city was old and housing was poor. Much of the housing consisted of tenements mixed with nineteenth-century industry. These 'twilight' slum areas of Glasgow were vast, and the policy was to knock down whole areas and replace them. These Comprehensive Development Areas (CDAs) have transformed much of inner Glasgow. Areas like Govan and Townhead have been totally changed. New houses, high-rise blocks and open spaces have replaced high-density tenement areas.

GEAR

The GEAR project is one of Europe's most advanced redevelopment schemes. GEAR was started in 1976 to renew the Glasgow East End. This part of the city was the centre of economic activity during the Industrial Revolution. By the 1970s, it was an area of economic decline and urban dereliction. Its population is 45 000, there are 17 000 houses and the area provides for 42 000 people. GEAR aims to make this part of Glasgow a pleasant place to live and work in, not a place to move away from.

Successes so far include the construction of workshop and factory units. A new industrial estate has been built at Cambuslang. Improving the quality of life is an important target. New play areas and sports centres have been provided. Local transport has been improved. The Trans-Clyde railway has new stations at Bridgeton and at Dalmarnock. 'Shoppabus' services have been introduced and many new shops are planned.

Old houses have been modernised and hundreds of new ones built. It is hoped that residents will take part in making the community work. Community groups have started and local meeting places have opened up.

Fig. A A Glasgow tenement area

Fig. B

Fig. C

Fig. D

Fig. E

Fig. F

Fig. G

QUESTIONS

A1 Why was redevelopment necessary in inner Glasgow?

2 What are CDAs?

3 What does GEAR stand for?

4 Write out the six targets and give one example of success for each. Use Figs B–G.

B1 Account for the changes shown in these Glasgow population figures:

	Population	Net out-migration
1972	861 898	34 146
1976	856 012	22 803
1979	794 316	12 762
1981	765 915	11 165

2 How do these figures help to explain the setting up of GEAR project?

3 Population density in inner Glasgow before redevelopment was about 1000 persons per hectare. After complete redevelopment, such as in the CDAs and parts of the GEAR area, density fell to 350 persons per hectare. Suggest reasons for this.

4 The following environmental targets were published in the GEAR *Strategy and Programme* (Scottish Development Agency, 1980).

Implement additional projects as follows:	No. of projects
General landscaping works	25
Preliminary backcourt improvements	7
Treatment to buildings	10
Industrial improvement areas	6
Stream clearance	1
TOTAL	49

Suggest how the environment might be improved by each project.

10.7 CUMBERNAULD NEW TOWN

The inner city redevelopments in Glasgow have provided new homes for about 40 per cent of the population needing housing. The remaining 60 per cent have had to move out of the city. Many are now living in the outer suburbs in the new housing estates. More have moved away as part of planned overspill movements. These movements have taken Glaswegians as far afield as north-east Scotland, the Fort William area and Edinburgh. By far the largest overspill has been to Scotland's five new towns: Cumbernauld, East Kilbride, Irvine, Livingstone and Glenrothes. Cumbernauld and East Kilbride are the newest in the Clydeside region and the majority of people now living there are Glaswegians. In 1981, 68 per cent of Cumbernauld's population was from Glasgow.

Cumbernauld new town was designated in 1955. The population was 3000 at that time, and had reached 50 700 by 1981. The target is 70 000. Cumbernauld is thirty minutes by car to central Glasgow and forty-five minutes to Edinburgh.

Housing districts are separated from industry and recreation, and there are safe pedestrian ways and

Fig. B Cumbernauld town centre

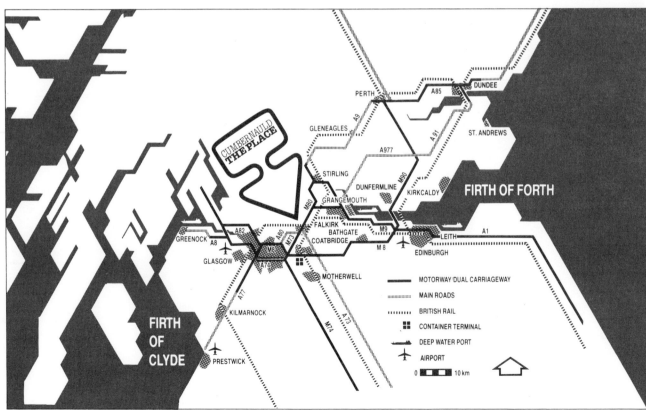

Fig. A The location of Cumbernauld

176

Fig. C Corporation housing in Cumbernauld

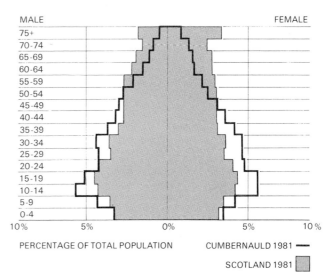

PERCENTAGE OF TOTAL POPULATION   CUMBERNAULD 1981 —

SCOTLAND 1981 ▨

play areas. Standards of landscaping are high.

There is one corner shop to every 400 houses. The main undercover shopping centre is linked with bus and car access.

The town centre has shops, library, health centre, cinema and indoor recreation complex (including an Olympic-size swimming pool).

There are three categories of roads: (i) the urban motorway; (ii) the fast distributor roads; (iii) the feeder roads which serve the housing areas.

Over 200 companies (10 per cent from overseas, 15 per cent from Glasgow, 40 per cent from England) have established themselves in industrial estates on the edge of the town. Grant incentives are offered to firms wishing to locate in Cumbernauld.

Cumbernauld new town was set up with money from central and local government and private sources.

QUESTIONS

A1 Define overspill. Where have Glaswegians moved to?

2 Answer the following questions, using Fig A:
 (i) Which motorway links Cumbernauld to Stirling?
 (ii) Which two motorways would you travel on to reach England?
 (iii) How far in kilometres is it from Cumbernauld to central Glasgow?
 (iv) How far is it to the railway container terminal?
 (v) Where are the two newest airports?
 (vi) Describe the situation of Cumbernauld.

3 How long does it take to drive from Cumbernauld to central Glasgow? Which roads are used?

B1 Study the age–sex pyramids for Cumbernauld and Scotland, 1981.

(a) Which age groups living in the new town exceed 5 per cent of the population?

(b) Compare the Cumbernauld pyramid with that of Scotland under the following headings: (i) working people 20–50 years; (ii) teenagers; (iii) children under 5 years. (Example: People aged 60 and over — There are few old people in the new town compared with Scotland as a whole.)

2 In 1981, 58.8 per cent of Scotland's households had no children. In Cumbernauld, only 32.4 per cent had no children. Suggest why the household structure is so different.

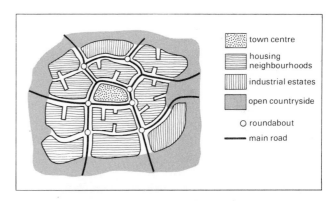

town centre

housing neighbourhoods

industrial estates

open countryside

O roundabout

— main road

C (a) Study the figure above. Give three ways in which Cumbernauld resembles the model.

(b) Explain why new towns were founded in Scotland after 1945.

(c) The following policies have been used to help solve the inner city housing problems of Glasgow: (i) overspill agreements; (ii) urban renewal; (iii) outer city housing schemes.
 Describe two of these policies and explain how they have helped solve housing problems in inner Glasgow.

177

10.8 LONDON: SITE AND GROWTH

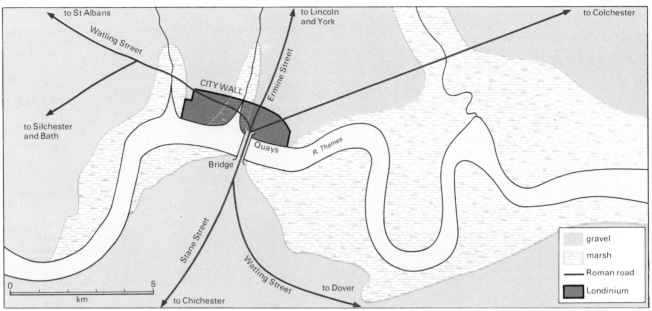

Fig. A The site of Roman London

London is one of the most important cities in the world. It dominates southern England and its influences spread throughout Britain. This vast conurbation of 6.7 million people has a long history covering almost two thousand years. Throughout this time London has grown, swallowing up surrounding settlements to become a conurbation, with several distinct centres within the built-up area.

The Romans in their search for a suitable place to bridge the Thames chose a place which was not marshy and where the river narrowed. They built a fortified settlement which became a seaport and route centre. A town grew, which the Romans called Londinium. Londinium became the capital of Roman Britain, with a population of up to 25 000. During the Middle Ages, London grew as trade developed. By 1700, the city's population had reached half a million. As the British Empire expanded, London became the greatest seaport in the world, linking Britain with its colonies. Industries developed, processing raw materials such as sugar, tobacco and flour. London became an important commercial, banking and insurance centre.

By 1888, London had grown so large that a special county had to be created to control it. The County of London was replaced in 1964 by Greater London, at which time over eight million people lived in the conurbation. Between 1801 and 1951, the population increased by seven times. London was growing faster than the rest of Britain. The causes were:

1 In common with the rest of Britain, there was a high rate of natural increase in London.
2 People moved into London seeking work in the capital's increasingly wide range of industry.
3 There was a great development in government employment, in offices and services.
4 London's growing population was a market for more industry and more services.

A point was reached when London became too large. The rapid spread of the city during the 1920s and 1930s caused great concern. Vast suburbs of houses and gardens sprawled across the countryside surrounding the capital. People were able to travel further to work because of the development of suburban rail and bus services and the private car. During the 1920s and 1930s, the built-up area of London increased by over three times. Under the Greater London Plan of 1944, the outward growth was to be halted by the establishment of a green belt of countryside around the city in which building was to be strictly controlled. A ring of new towns were to be built beyond the green belt to take the overspill of population. From 1952, overspill was directed to expanded towns beyond the new towns.

Three new cities were proposed in the outer south-east region and there was to be major growth at six other towns. The Strategic Plan for the South-East of 1970 followed broadly the same proposals. In 1978, the plan was reviewed because of:

1 The reduction in the growth of population.

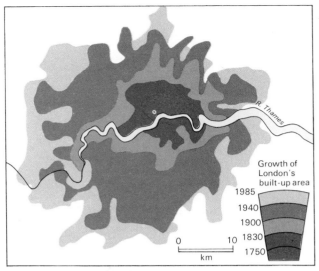

Fig. B The growth of London

Growth of London's built-up area

1985
1940
1900
1830
1750

0   10
km

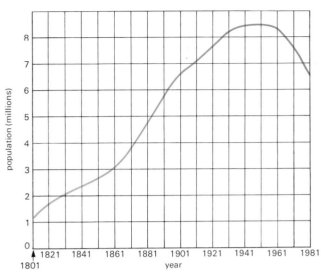

Fig. D London's population 1801-1981

0   10
km

	%		%
1 City	+32	18 Brent	−10
2 Islington	−20	19 Harrow	−3
3 Hackney	−18	20 Barnet	−5
4 Tower Hamlets	−15	21 Enfield	−4
5 Southwark	−20	22 Redbridge	−6
6 Lambeth	−20	23 Barking	−8
7 Westminster	−23	24 Havering	−4
8 Camden	−18	25 Bexley	−1
9 Harringay	−15	26 Bromley	−4
10 Waltham Forest	−9	27 Croydon	−6
11 Newham	−11	28 Merton	−8
12 Greenwich	−2	29 Sutton	−1
13 Lewisham	−14	30 Kingston	−5
14 Wandsworth	−16	31 Richmond	−10
15 Kensington & Chelsea	−29	32 Hounslow	−4
16 Hammersmith	−21	33 Hillingdon	−3
17 Ealing	−7		

Fig. C Greater London population change 1971-1981

2 The worsening economic recession at the time.

3 The increasing problems of Inner London.

The revised strategic plan emphasised growth in Inner London. In 1980, part of London's docklands was designated an enterprise zone and in 1981 the London Docklands Development Corporation was set up to encourage development in the area.

London's problems had changed rapidly from those of controlling growth to those of arresting decline. Figure D shows that the population of London has declined since 1961. People had become dissatisfied with life in London:

1 Housing was poor in some areas and expensive everywhere. House prices in London were almost twice the national average.

2 Land for new development was scarce and rates and rents were high.

3 There was increasing traffic congestion.

The inner boroughs of London have lost population more than the outer boroughs (Fig C, and Question B3 on p. 115).

The new towns and regional development policy had worked quite well; millions of people and thousands of factories and offices had moved out of London. Now, government policy has changed. Priority is being given to the revival of Inner London as a place to live and work, and overspill and decentralisation are receiving less emphasis.

QUESTIONS

A1 Why did the Romans choose the site of Londinium?

2 Why did London grow so rapidly after 1801?

3 Why did the built-up area of London increase so greatly during the 1920s and 1930s?

4 What is the green belt?

B1 Describe and account for the changes in population shown on Fig D.

2 Describe the development of planning policies for London and the south-east region.

3 Suggest why government policy on London's growth has changed since 1970.

C Using selected examples from the United Kingdom, discuss population overspill movements. Why are such movements likely to decline in the future?

179

10.9 LONDON: INDUSTRY

	% of UK total in south-east
Population (total for England)	30
All manufacturing industry	26
Computers	55
All service industry	38
Insurance, banking and finance	54
Unemployment (total for England)	22

Fig. A

Greater London (with the south-east of England) is Britain's leading industrial region. Figure A shows the dominance of certain types of employment. Reasons for the presence of so much industry are:

1 The region is by far the largest market in Britain. The region covers only 12 per cent of the nation's area but contains 30 per cent of the total population.

2 The region is the most prosperous in Britain. Average wages are 7 per cent above the national average.

3 The region has a very wide range of industry but little traditional heavy industry (coalmining, iron and steel, shipbuilding) which has declined this century.

4 Good communications link the region with the rest of Britain by road, rail and air. 80 per cent of Britain's population lies within 300 kilometres of London.

5 London is well-placed for export markets, especially the EEC.

6 London is the centre of government, finance and insurance.

Manufacturing industry

A quarter of a million people in London work in manufacturing industry. There are four main manufacturing areas:

1 The *East End:* This is an area of long-established industries including clothing, leather goods, furniture and printing. The companies are small. Most of the workshops are converted houses. This district is a survival from Victorian times when a vast pool of skilled workers lived in the area. Recently, it has faced serious decline.

2 *Thames-side:* Large factories using imported raw materials developed along the Thames (port industries), many with their own wharves and jetties. Flour-milling, margarine manufacture, sugar-refining and saw-milling were all important within Greater London. Ford's car factory at Dagenham has its own large wharf handling ships of up to 10 000 tonnes. Further downriver are the paper, cement and oil-refining and storage plants of the estuary.

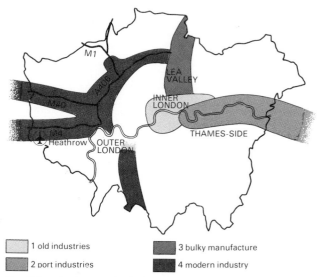

1 old industries
2 port industries
3 bulky manufacture
4 modern industry

Fig. B London's manufacturing zones

3 *The Lea Valley:* The Lea Navigation Canal allows barges and lighters of up to 150 tonnes to carry bulky raw materials such as coal, timber and steel to the factories which use them. They are used by furniture, chemical, metal and engineering factories attracted by the flat open sites provided by the flood plain of the river Lea. The A10 and A406 provide good road access.

4 *Outer London:* Modern industry needs large sites with good road access. A range of light engineering factories has been built along the main roads radiating out of London (Fig B). Several industrial estates have been built at the most accessible sites such as Park Royal. North and west London have attracted most of the modern industry because of the easy access to the rest of Britain and to Heathrow Airport. Electrical, electronic, plastics and food and

Fig. C The M4 motorway, West London

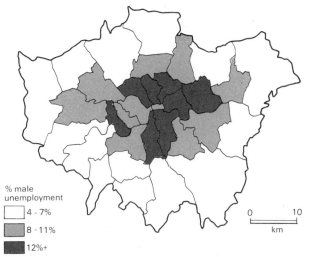

% male unemployment
- 4 - 7%
- 8 - 11%
- 12%+

0   10
km

Fig. D Male unemployment in London

drink factories dominate. These industries are footloose and have located throughout the outer suburbs.

The decline of London's manufacturing industry:
London's importance as a centre of manufacturing industry is rapidly declining. Between 1961 and 1981, the number of workers was halved. 700 000 jobs were lost. This reflected the decline of manufacturing throughout Britain, but no area suffered as badly as London. After a century of prosperity and growth, London's industrial sector has collapsed within twenty years. The reasons are:
1 Industrial land in London costs four times the national average.
2 Increasing traffic congestion.
3 Government regional policy would not allow expansion of factories within London.
4 The population of Inner London dropped by 30 per cent between 1961 and 1981, causing labour shortages in the East End.
5 The old congested London factories have been closed and replaced by modern buildings outside London in new towns and expanded towns.
6 The decline and closure of the Upper Docks.

Service industry

2.75 million people in London work in service industry. This high proportion is due partly to the need to provide services for London's population — education, health, transport, shopping — but mainly to London's role as the capital city of Britain. Central London is the major area of services.
1 The *West End* has a wide range of offices employing 400 000 people including national government departments in Westminster which alone employ 130 000. Publishing, entertainment, airline and advertising offices are important. The headquarters of hundreds of national and inter-

national companies are also in the West End.
2 300 000 people work in the square mile of the *City of London* in finance, banking, insurance and trading. The City is a financial centre of world importance with the Stock Exchange second only to New York's Wall Street.

	% of total
Primary industry	0.2
Manufacturing industry	27
Of which:	
Electrical engineering	4.1
Paper, printing and publishing	4
Mechanical engineering	3.2
Food, drink and tobacco	2.6
Clothing, footwear and leather	2.5
Chemicals	2
Vehicles	1.6
Timber, furniture	1.3
Metal manufacture	0.5
Textiles	0.4
Other manufacturing industry	4.7
Service industry	72.8
Of which:	
Distributive trades	13.6
Professional and scientific services	12.6
Transport and communication	10.5
Other service industry	36.7

Fig. E Greater London: employment structure

QUESTIONS

A1 Why has industry developed in London?
  2 Where are the four main areas of manufacturing in London and which industries are associated with each?
  3 Why has manufacturing industry in London declined since 1960?
  4 Where are the main centres of office employment in Greater London?

B1 Account for the growth of industry (i) in the East End; (ii) on Thames-side; (ii) in the Lea Valley; (iv) in Outer London.
  2 Fig E shows the employment structure of Greater London.
  (a) Construct a pie graph to illustrate these statistics.
  (b) Refer to Fig C (page 52), which shows the employment structure of Britain. Calculate location quotients for the following occupations: (i) primary industry; (ii) engineering and vehicles; (iii) metal manufacture; (iv) distributive trades; (v) transport and communications. Comment on your results.

10.10 THE PORT OF LONDON

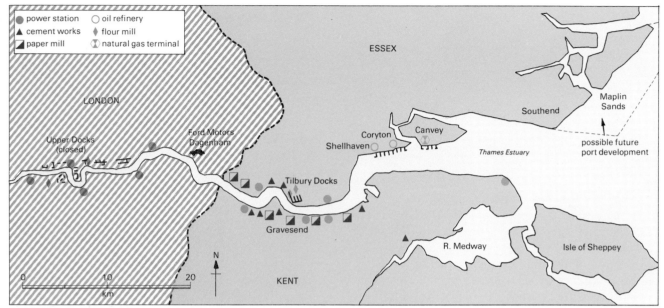

Fig. A The Port of London

For seventeen centuries, the Port of London consisted of quays and wharves along the banks of the river Thames downstream from London Bridge. This was the Pool of London, which by the eighteenth century was seriously congested. Tidal currents made unloading large ships difficult and there was much stealing from vessels. The answer to these problems was to build docks below the Pool of London where the marshland was easily excavated. Lock gates allowed ships to enter at high tide and maintained deep water at all times. Ships could be unloaded at the dockside. A series of docks was built during the nineteenth century as London became the most important port in the world. Britain's overseas empire brought trade and wealth to the dock owners. In 1908, the docks and the river were taken over by the Port of London Authority, a government body.

Since the 1960s the dock systems have become unsuitable for modern shipping because:

1 Container traffic needed special handling facilities. Most of the old docks were too small, and freight-handling facilities were outdated.

2 Cargo ships had increased in size; only the Royal Docks were able to handle ships larger than 10 000 tonnes.

3 General cargo traffic declined and was replaced by specialised ships needing new handling methods.

4 The docks were so far from the open sea that ships wasted time using them. Shipowners increasingly demanded fast turnrounds in port.

The Port of London Authority decided not to invest large amounts in the Upper Docks but to concentrate on enlarging the docks downriver at Tilbury in Essex. At Tilbury, the Thames is wide and deep, allowing large ships to enter the docks.

Between 1967 and 1981, the Upper Docks were run down. By 1982, only a few specialised berths, such as the bulk wine terminal in Millwall Docks, remained open. The closures were opposed by the dockers who said that investment in specialised facilities would have kept most of the Upper Docks open. Between 1970 and 1982, the number of dockers employed by the PLA fell from 18 000 to 3000.

Tilbury

By 1983, the PLA's activities were almost completely concentrated at Tilbury. The PLA built the large dock extension during the 1960s, and began the development of the large specialist facilities needed by modern shipping:

1 **Containers:** The first container berth at Tilbury was opened in 1968. Six berths were built around the dock extension and a Freightliner rail terminal was opened.

2 **Grain:** The grain terminal can accept bulk carriers of up to 85 000 tonnes at its deepwater jetty. The terminal is automated and can discharge the bulk carriers at a rate of up to 2000 tonnes per hour by suction pumps. Four flour mills have been built beside the terminal and flour is distributed to other

Fig. B Tilbury Docks

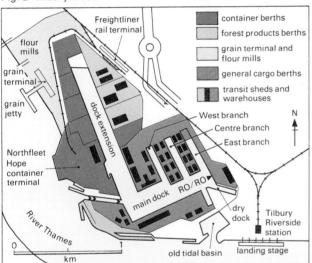

Fig. C Tilbury Docks

ports in Britain.

3 **Forest products:** Timber, plywood, newsprint, pulp and paper are handled at the four specialist berths opened since 1966. All four berths are highly mechanised and have a large area of covered storage.

4 **Roll on–roll off** berths have been built and the general cargo berths have been mechanised and modernised to handle ro–ro ships.

The Port of London provides a good example of the 'Anyport' model (page 100) with the movement of port activities downriver. Plans exist for a new 'super port' at Maplin Sands where the Thames meets the North Sea.

Despite the impressive developments at Tilbury, most of London's annual trade of 40 million tonnes is handled at the dozens of privately owned wharves and jetties. Oil is still the most important import and export of the Port of London. Two refineries at Coryton and Shell Haven import 13 million tonnes of crude oil a year. Cement works, power stations, chemical plants, paper mills and margarine works all have their own berths along the river.

Despite the closure of the Upper Docks and the reduction in manpower, the new methods are so efficient that there has been little decline in trade. London remains Britain's leading port and its new facilities at Tilbury rival anything in Britain. Over the last two decades, London has faced fierce competition from other ports in southern and eastern England including Felixstowe, Harwich, Dover and Southampton. There is competition from European ports, especially Rotterdam. These ports have been able to build new facilities and were not hindered by the legacy of large, outdated dock systems, but London is favoured by its geography.

QUESTIONS

A1 Describe the early development of the Port of London.

2 Why was it necessary to build enclosed docks?

3 How has the port changed since 1960?

4 Where are Tilbury Docks? How far are they from Tower Bridge?

B1 Why have the Upper Docks closed?

2 Study the map and aerial photograph of Tilbury Docks (Figs B and C).

   (a) In which direction was the camera pointing?

   (b) How many entrances are there to the docks?

   (c) Why is a lock necessary?

   (d) How does the dock extension differ from the older docks?

   (e) Why have two specialised berths been built out into the river?

3 Make a sketch from the aerial photograph and label the features lettered A to M. Use Fig C to help you.

10.11 LONDON'S DOCKLANDS

Fig. A The Royal Docks in the past

Fig. B The Royal Docks in the 1980s

For twelve kilometres east' of Tower Bridge lie London's docklands, twenty years ago the heart of the Port of London. Most of the docks are empty, and Commercial Road and other once-busy streets are now deserted. Vandalism·is common, and there is evidence of neglect and decline.

The population of the docklands has dropped dramatically in recent decades; the boroughs of Tower Hamlets and Southwark had only 350 000 inhabitants in 1981 compared with 570 000 in 1951. Wealthier people have moved out. Only 10 per cent of the housing in the docklands is owner-occupied compared with 44 per cent in the city as a whole. Unemployment rates of over 25 per cent are found in the area.

At the beginning of the 1980s, the docklands

showed all the symptoms of inner-city decay. Yet the closure of the docks has presented a great opportunity for revitalising the area. London's docklands cover over 2000 hectares of land, offering potential for redevelopment. The London Docklands Development Corporation was set up in 1981 to recreate a prosperous region in the heart of London, generating new wealth and employment to replace the port activities. The urban environment, services and communications were to be improved. The LDDC is funded by the government and acts like a new town development corporation. Part of the area, the Isle of Dogs, has been designated an enterprise zone. This is an area which can receive government money for redevelopment.

One of the earliest redevelopment schemes in-

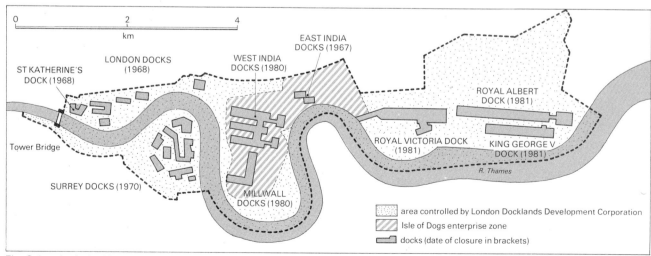

Fig. C London's docklands

Fig. D New housing in dockland

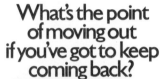

Fig. E

volved the St Katharine's Dock area. Here, a ten-hectare site, developed privately, includes: an 826-bedroom hotel; warehouses transformed into a World Trade Centre; an old brewery converted into a public house and restaurant; shops, offices, and apartments housing 900 people. The old dock is now a yacht marina and maritime museum. Jobs have been created for 1700 people.

Elsewhere in the docklands development plans include:

Housing A wide range of housing schemes is proposed throughout docklands, but most will be small, inexpensive homes. If too many wealthy people were attracted by expensive homes, prices would rise and those living in the area would be forced to find homes elsewhere. Six hundred houses have been built near Royal Albert Dock, 600 at Limehouse Basin and 250 at the Surrey Docks.

Employment Offices and factories are being encouraged to set up in the docklands. Some of the old docks, such as the London Docks where printing and office development has taken place, have been filled in. Other docks, such as the Royal Victoria and Millwall Dock, will stay open for commerce and pleasure. Small factory units, offices and shops have been built around the West India Docks which is the site of the new Billingsgate Fish Market.

Transport One of the major problems facing the redevelopment of the area is poor transport links. Road improvements under way include the Docklands Relief Road and the East London River Crossing, a new suspension bridge. Plans for the extension of London's underground rail network into the docklands have been scrapped, but support exists for a light rapid transit system similar to the Tyne and Wear Metro. One of the most remarkable transport schemes involves the proposed construction of an airport at the Royal Docks. Quiet, short-take-off-and-landing (STOL) aircraft carrying up to fifty passengers could operate from runways only 700 metres long. Over one million passengers a year could be flown to destinations within 700 kilometres. An airport here would be more easily reached from central London than Heathrow and Gatwick.

Success or failure of the docklands development will depend upon investment by the government and private enterprise. The scheme marks a reversal of the previous policy of overspill and decentralisation. The LDDC realises that it is in direct competition with the new towns and expanded towns, as its advertisements make clear: 'What's the point of moving out if you've got to keep coming back? Why move to the middle of nowhere, when you can move to the middle of London?'

QUESTIONS

A1 List the problems facing London's docklands.
 2 What do the initials LDDC stand for?
 3 What is the LDDC's purpose?
 4 Describe the St Katharine's Dock redevelopment.
B1 Account for the problems facing London's docklands.
 2 Why are most of the homes to be built in the docklands planned to be small and inexpensive?
 3 Study Fig E. What advantages do London's docklands have to attract industry?
 4 (a) Design another advertisement to attract people to live in the docklands.
   (b) Design an advertisement for Milton Keynes which is intended to overcome competition from the LDDC advertisement.
C Discuss the measures being taken to revitalise London's docklands.

10.12 THE CAPITAL CITY

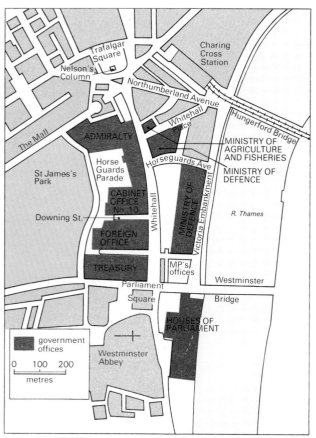

Fig. A Whitehall

Fig. B

London is the centre of the government of the United Kingdom. The Houses of Parliament are in the district of Westminster and the offices of government departments line Whitehall. In and around Westminster are the embassies of foreign nations, the major law courts of England and the police headquarters at New Scotland Yard: 150 000 people in London are employed in national government jobs.

London's function as capital involves more than acting as the seat of government. It is the leading entertainment and musical centre of Britain and has the major sports centres: Wembley, Twickenham, Lord's and the Oval, Crystal Palace and Wimbledon.

The West End is one of the world's best-known shopping areas, with Oxford Street, Regent Street and New Bond Street.

London's entertainment and shopping facilities explain why the city is Britain's major tourist attraction. Millions of tourists visit London each year from all over the world. 200 000 people are employed in hotels, boarding houses and restaurants catering largely for tourists.

The City of London

The City of London is the most important business and financial centre in Britain and one of the most important in the world. 300 000 people work in the offices of the City. It was because of its links with the Port of London that the City became such an important centre. Out of the shipping and trading interests grew finance, insurance and banking. Some of the City's services are:

1 The Bank of England, which controls the issue of banknotes in England and is where the government banks its money.

2 The Stock Exchange, the centre for the buying and selling of stocks and shares.

3 Important shipping, finance and insurance companies include Lloyd's of London.

4 Most of Britain's daily newspapers, which are written and published in Fleet Street, just to the west of the City.

The City of London covers only 2½ square kilometres and only 5800 people live there. Every weekday, hundreds of thousands of people travel into the City to work.

London's transport

London has an impressive system of roads, surface and underground railways which face two serious problems: congestion and commuting.

During the 1960s, it seemed that London's road system would be choked by the amount of traffic using it. The increase in traffic was due mainly to the growth in car ownership. The Greater London Council's answer was to propose a system of urban motorways called ringways, which would have forced 50 000 people to move because of house demolition. Only the M25 has gone ahead.

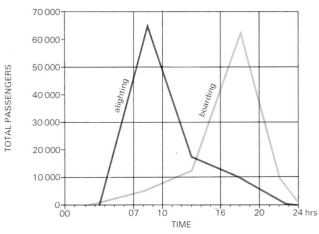

Fig. E Passengers using Waterloo station

Fig. C The Westway urban motorway

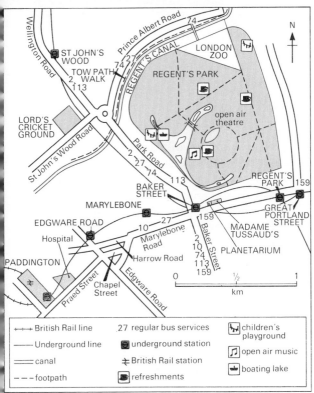

Fig. D

QUESTIONS

A1 On which street in Westminster are the offices of many government departments?

2 How many people are employed in national government administration in London?

3 What are the functions of the City of London?

4 What is the 'rush hour'? Why does it cause problems for London's transport?

B1 Why did the City of London become one of the world's most important business and finance centres?

2 Figure D is like a map provided by London Transport for visitors. Use it to answer the following questions:

(a) You have arrived at Paddington Station (British Rail). You are going to see a Test Match at Lord's Cricket Ground. You have been told to take the underground to Baker Street. What bus must you catch from Baker Street to the cricket ground?

(b) How far is it to walk from Baker Street to Lord's?

(c) Would it be worthwhile taking the underground from Baker Street? If you did so, where would you get off?

(d) From Lord's, you decide to go to the Regent's Park Zoo. Which bus should you catch?

(e) Which canal do you follow on your way to the zoo? Could you have walked along the canal?

(f) After visiting the zoo, you walk south through Regent's Park. How many refreshment places are there in the Park? What other forms of entertainment are there in the park?

(g) You end up at Great Portland Street station. Describe carefully your walk back to Paddington. What interesting places do you pass?

C What are the difficulties facing London's transport system? Discuss some possible solutions.

187

10.13 THE SPREAD OF LONDON

London's influence is felt far beyond the limits of the conurbation. Planners have defined an area called Metropolitan London or the Outer Metropolitan Area (OMA), stretching from the Cambridgeshire border in the north almost to the Sussex coast, and from Reading in the west to the coast of Essex. This recognises that London has leap-frogged the green belt.

The decline of population and employment in the capital has not spread to the south-east, which has taken many of the people and companies moving out of London. Figure B shows the population growth of the counties of south-east England between 1971 and 1981. Increases ranged from 3.2 per cent in Hertfordshire to 18.8 per cent in Buckinghamshire, against an average increase for England of only 0.4 per cent. This increase was due partly to government policy, with the new towns and expanded towns showing rapid growth. The growth of the region was due also to its attractiveness to people wishing to leave London or seeking work from elsewhere. Retired people are drawn to the south coast.

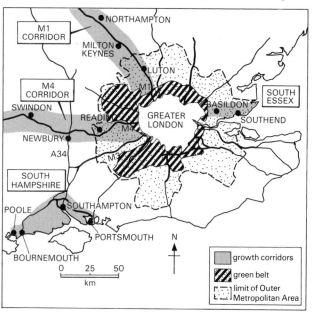

Fig. A The Outer Metropolitan Area

The corridors of growth

Urban development has happened especially quickly in certain areas which can be called corridors of growth.

The western corridor. This is the most important, and has developed along the route of the M4. From Heathrow Airport in the east to Bristol in the west, it has been described as 'England's new industrial axis'. At or near each junction of the M4 you will see industrial estates, warehouses and office complexes. The three main centres are Reading, Newbury and Swindon.

Reading (population 132 000) has established industries based on agriculture: biscuits, brewing and farm machinery. Its recent growth has been due to electrical engineering, electronics, computers, plastics and office employment.

Newbury (population 40 000) was a small market town until the M4 was built. It has seen rapid growth in light engineering, especially computers and microprocessors.

Swindon (population 130 000) grew as a railway engineering town. Swindon has doubled in size since 1945. Its success is based on its accessibility. Early post-war growth was based on engineering, including car components and electrical goods. Recently, pharmaceuticals, electronics and distribution have become important. Several large office complexes have also been developed.

The M1 corridor. The main centres are Luton, Milton Keynes and Northampton.

Luton (population 164 000) has also doubled in size since 1945. Its growth is based on car assembly (Vauxhall), engineering and clothing. A wide range of light industry has become established. Luton has an airport catering mainly for holiday flights.

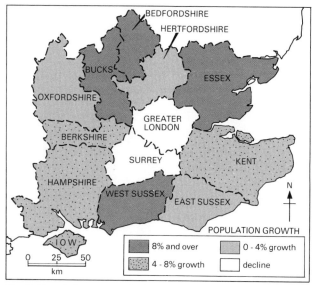

Fig. B Population growth in the south-east

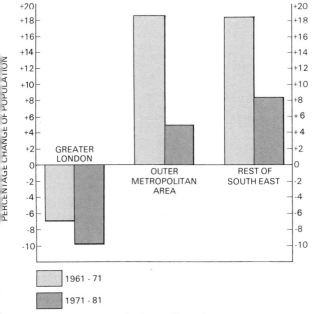

Fig. C Population change in the south-east

Legend:
- 1961 - 71
- 1971 - 81

Milton Keynes (population 124 000) is a new town which has attracted an impressive array of light manufacturing, distributive and office employment.

Northampton (population 157 000) became a new town in 1968 but is a long-established county town. Its traditional industry of shoemaking has declined but there has been rapid growth in brewing, chemicals, plastics and office employment.

South Essex corridor. Proposals for airport and seaport development at Maplin Sands east of Southend would turn this into England's leading growth corridor. Much growth has already occurred. The two main centres are Basildon and Southend-on-Sea.

Basildon (population 152 000), established as a new town in 1949, has already exceeded its target population. The town's industries include tractor assembly, chemicals and cigarettes.

Southend-on-Sea (population 157 000) grew as a seaside resort for day trippers travelling by rail from London. There has been remarkable growth in office employment and light industry. Government offices decentralised to Southend include HM Customs and Excise and the VAT centre.

South Hampshire and Dorset. Over a million people live in the urban area stretching 80 km from Portsmouth to Poole. The three major centres, Portsmouth, Southampton and Bournemouth/Poole, all showed a decline in population between 1971 and 1981, but major growth has occurred between them, especially at Fareham, the New Forest and Christchurch.

Portsmouth (population 180 000) developed as a naval base and has faced large job losses from the rundown of the Royal Navy. Light engineering and food processing industries have developed recently.

Southampton (population 204 000): recent development dates from 1840 when the railway from London was completed. With the decline of ocean passenger services it has developed a large deepwater container terminal. Southampton's industries include van assembly, shipbuilding, oil refining, petrochemicals and plastics.

Bournemouth (population 145 000) and *Poole* (population 119 000): Bournemouth is a fashionable resort. Many retired people have moved there. Poole is a small port. Its established industries, including flour-milling and pottery, have been supplemented by an increase in office employment.

Outside the main growth corridors, towns in south-east England are of three main types: seaside resorts, seaports and inland market towns. Many have seen growth based upon the decentralisation of industry within the region. The fact that many light industries chose to locate in them reflects the attraction of living in small, established communities. Towns such as Colchester, Chelmsford, Canterbury, Winchester and Banbury have recorded rapid growth.

QUESTIONS

A1 What is the Outer Metropolitan Area?

2 What is a 'corridor of growth'? List the four main corridors of growth in south-east England.

3 Design an advertisement to attract companies to Reading.

4 What type of industry has developed in the corridors of growth?

5 Why is industry attracted to the smaller towns of south-east England?

B1 Why have the four corridors of growth attracted people and employment?

2 Why is the Outer Metropolitan Area a more correct limit for the London conurbation than the boundary of the GLC?

3 Study the graph of population change in south-east England (Fig C):
   (a) Which area experienced the highest percentage population growth (i) between 1961 and 1971, (ii) between 1971 and 1981?
   (b) Account for the changes during the two ten-year periods.
   (c) Attempt to predict the population change within the three areas between 1981 and 1991.

C Describe and account for the changing population and employment distribution of south-east England, including London.

11.1 THE LAKE DISTRICT

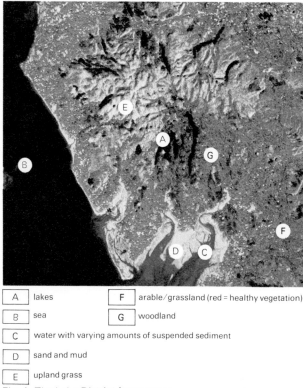

A	lakes	F	arable/grassland (red = healthy vegetation)
B	sea	G	woodland
C	water with varying amounts of suspended sediment		
D	sand and mud		
E	upland grass		

Fig. A The Lake District from space

The Lake District National Park is the largest of ten national parks in England and Wales. It was established to conserve the natural beauty of this glaciated highland region for public enjoyment. The national park is administered by the Lake District Special Planning Board which controls development and maintains the tourist environment.

The Lake District is a unique upland area. The most recent glaciation (ending about 10 000 years ago) left U-shaped valleys, hanging valleys, corries, tarns and ribbon lakes. Numerous streams (becks) flow over rocky terrain which is often scree-covered at the foot of the steepest slopes. The three major rock types give a variety of scenery. Figure C shows the more rugged scenery of the Borrowdale volcanic rocks. The Skiddaw slates produce more rounded mountains such as Skiddaw. The less-resistant Silurian shales form more gentle hills. The Lake District is an *eroded dome* and rivers and lakes have developed in a *radial* pattern.

The economy of the national park is dominated by tourism, hill farming, forestry and water provision. There was once mining for gold, silver and lead but today only slate is quarried near Coniston and granite at Shap Fell.

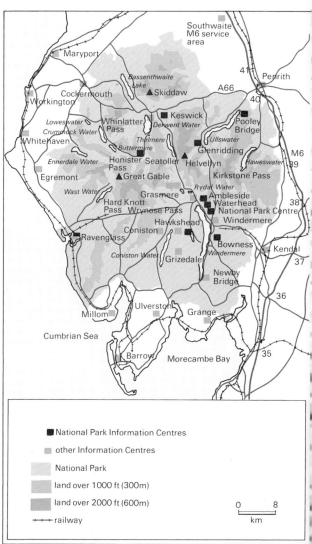

Fig. B The Lake District

Fig. C The rugged scenery of the Borrowdale volcanic rocks

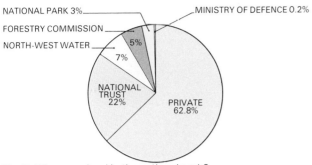

Fig. D Who owns land in the national park?

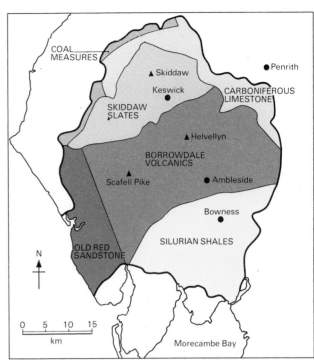

Fig. E Geology of the Lake District

QUESTIONS

A1 Study the false-colour image (Fig A). Identify the major lakes and Morecambe Bay.

  (a) Why does the shape of Morecambe Bay differ from the shape shown on Fig B?

  (b) What type of vegetation covers most of the central Lake District?

  (c) Describe the land-use in the southern part of the national park.

  (d) On which type of rock (see Fig E) is most of the woodland and farmland?

2 What is meant by a radial pattern of drainage? Draw a map to show the boundary of the national park and the ten major lakes. Label Scafell Pikes (the highest mountain — see atlas for height).

3 Name the three major rocks of the Lake District and briefly state the type of scenery found in each geological area.

4 Describe the type of scenery shown in Fig C.

5 Which groups of people own land in the Lake District?

B1 (a) In what ways does Fig A help us understand the nature of the Lake District environment?

  (b) What advantages does this type of image have over a normal satellite photograph?

2 Study the climatic data for the Lake District and compare it with Brighton.

  (a) Compare the mean temperatures for January and July.

  (b) Suggest why the January temperature for Keswick is as high as 3.5°C.

  (c) What reasons are there for the relatively low July temperature in Keswick?

  (d) Compare rainfall totals and the distribution of rainfall.

  (e) How much less sunshine does Keswick have compared with Brighton? Give the answer in total hours and as a percentage.

  (f) What are the climatic disadvantages of the Lake District for tourists?

  (g) When would you choose to go on holiday to the Lake District and to Brighton?

KESWICK (Height 77 metres)	Jan	Feb	Mar	Apr	May	June	July	Aug	Sept	Oct	Nov	Dec	Annual mean
Temperature °C													
Daily mean	3.5	3.6	5.6	7.9	10.9	13.7	15.1	14.7	13.0	10.3	6.5	4.7	9.1
Average rainfall (mm)													
Monthly total	151	109	95	95	89	87	102	131	158	153	163	163	1496
Average sunshine (hours)													
Monthly total	33.2	56.9	103.3	139.5	185.7	182.4	147.8	135.5	100.1	74.5	41.4	30.3	1230.6

BRIGHTON (Height 10 metres)	Jan	Feb	Mar	Apr	May	June	July	Aug	Sept	Oct	Nov	Dec	Annual mean
Temperature °C													
Daily mean	4.5	4.5	6.3	9.1	11.9	14.9	16.7	16.9	15.5	12.4	8.3	5.9	10.6
Average rainfall (mm)													
Monthly total	71	51	48	42	43	45	54	69	62	67	89	71	712
Average sunshine (hours)													
Monthly total	62.6	80.5	133.4	179.0	224.7	234.6	213.1	203.0	161.0	126.9	72.8	55.9	1747.5

11.2 THE LAKE DISTRICT: FARMING

Fig. A Upper Longsleddale

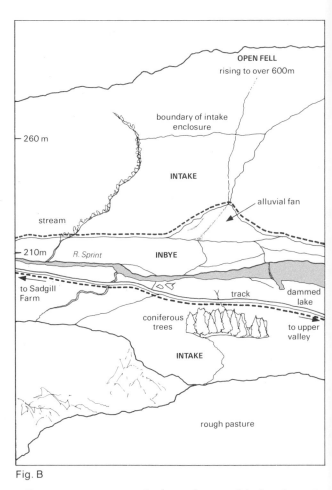

Fig. B

Hill farming of sheep and cattle is traditional in the national park. Under 10 per cent of the land is used to grow crops of grass, clover, oats and root crops. This *improved* farmland is in the valley bottoms where the small farmsteads are located. Most of the farms are old and the stone buildings may date from the seventeenth and eighteenth centuries. Farming is difficult because of the harshness of the environment. Considerable financial help is given to farmers in the form of subsidies to maintain hill farming.

The photograph and field sketch (Figs A and B) show part of Upper Longsleddale in the south-east corner of the national park. The glaciated valley is steep-sided and flat-bottomed. The river Sprint has its headwaters high on the open *fells* and flows south-east towards Kendal where it meets the river Kent. Both rivers are part of the radial drainage pattern. Numerous small streams (becks) meet the river Sprint. A large-scale Ordnance Survey map shows a high *stream density*, with up to ten tributaries per kilometre stretch of river.

Permanent pasture is the only possible land-use in these wet conditions. The high fells receive up to 3000 millimetres of rain per year and the valley totals can be up to 2000 millimetres. There are low sunshine totals and the north-east facing side of the valley is in shade as the sun sinks in the west. Valley fogs and mists are common and on clear winter nights severe frosts result as cold air sinks down the valley sides. The soils on the valley sides are thin and there are many rock outcrops and screes (loose rock fragments at the base of the slope). There are deeper soils in the valley bottom but these may be flooded and remain waterlogged. They are acid and require *liming* to encourage better grass growth.

The highest farm in the Sprint valley is Sadgill (Fig C). There is a little improved pasture upstream, then a large area of wet, windswept fell rising to over 830 metres in places. The term *inbye* (or *inland*) is given to the improved valley bottom pasture. The *intake* (or *allotment*) is enclosed land on the slopes above the valley floor. Above the intake, the open fell is not divided into fields.

Farming in Upper Longsleddale is typical of the Lakeland valleys. The inbye is used to grow grass for hay or silage, and animals are grazed there. The intake and open fells are used as *rough grazing* for sheep. Beef cattle are sometimes allowed in parts of the intake. The sheep are hardy breeds such as *Swaledale* and *Herdwick*. They are brought to the valley farms only for lambing, shearing and dipping. The beef cattle include Hereford–Friesian cross-breeds, Aberdeen Angus–Friesian crosses and Galloways. The sheep and cattle provide the main farming income. Farms are either owner-occupied or rented. The *tenants* may rent from larger landowners such as the National Trust. The average Lake District

Fig. C Sadgill Farm

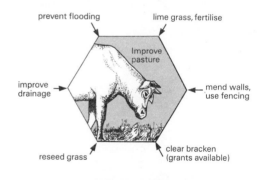

IMPROVING HILL FARMING

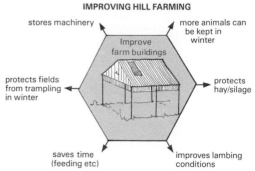

Fig. D Improving hill farming

farm is between forty and eighty hectares but these figures exclude the areas of open fell. Farmers have rights to pasture a certain number of animals on the fells.

Change

Figure D shows some recent improvements to the hill farming economy. The national park area has lost farms since World War II. Between 1940 and 1965, the number of farms decreased by 37 per cent and the decline continued into the 1970s. Fewer men are now employed on fewer farms. Figure E illustrates

	1937	1976
Overall employment	20	60
Farm area (hectares)	1225	264
Cattle	200	500
Hill sheep	1000	—
Cross-bred sheep	—	300
Milk (gallons)	40 000	150 000
Forest area (hectares)	525	2712
Wood (tonnes)	50	7000

Fig. E   (The Forestry Commission)

changes in the Grizedale area to the west of Lake Windermere. Here, the Forestry Commission started planting coniferous trees in 1937, which led to a 75 per cent reduction in the area under hill-farming by 1976. However, farming yields have risen and wood offers an alternative crop from land which might otherwise be unproductive because of the nature of soil and climate.

QUESTIONS

A1 Why is the natural environment such a harsh one for farming?

2 How are the inbye, intake and open fell used by farmers?

3 Study Fig D. (i) How can Lake District pasture be improved? (ii) What are the possible benefits of improving farm buildings?

B1 On a simple cross-section of a typical Lake District valley, label: wet/windswept fell, drier sheltered valley, intake, inbye, farmhouse, river. Base your vertical scale on the heights for Upper Longsleddale: 1cm to represent 100 metres.

2 Describe the system of farming found in the Lake District.

3 What are the problems facing a Lake District farmer?

4 Suggest ways of maintaining and improving the traditional system of hill farming in the Lake District.

5 Study Fig E. Summarise the major changes in the Grizedale area between 1937 and 1976.

11.3 THE LAKE DISTRICT: CONSERVATION

The Lake District receives millions of visitors every year. As a result there are many pressures on natural and man-made resources. Visitors' activities in the park often *conflict* with the way of life of people who live and work there (Fig A). The main work of conservation is to control pressure and conflict arising from over-use and to protect the environment from damage.

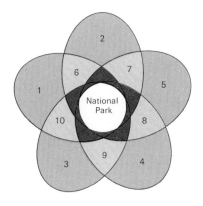

1 Geology, landforms, soils, climate
2 Vegetation, animals, birds
3 Farming, mining and quarrying, settlements, roads
4 Population, employment, cultural activities, sport
5 Visitors, types of recreation, accommodation, services
6 Habitats
7 Enjoyment
8 Tourism
9 Development
10 Land use

Fig. A

Fig. B Wastwater screes

Fig. C Access: for whom?

Narrow winding roads become congested, and car parking areas are often filled to capacity. Walkers and day trippers sometimes damage farm fences and frighten livestock. Litter is unsightly and can be dangerous to sheep and cattle. Continuous trampling of paths can wear them away, and *footpath erosion* is a problem. In severe cases, paths have turned into gulleys. This occurs when visitors take the direct route between a car park and an amenity such as a lake shore. Damp areas are trampled into boggy expanses and vegetation may be completely worn down (*degraded*). Wastwater in the west has fewer visitors than the more accessible lakes, but there are problems of lake-shore accessibility. Access points must be clearly marked and car parking must be made available. At the same time, fields have to be protected.

Special measures are needed to conserve the area as a whole. The Lake District Special Planning Board

advises landowners on developments and there are strict planning controls on new buildings. They have to fit in with existing architectural styles. Landowners must make special efforts to blend their developments with the landscape. The Forestry Com-

Fencing off gullied slopes
Marking main paths
Keep Out signs
Educating the public
Providing visitor centres
Providing public transport
Reseeding eroded paths
Resiting car parks
Patrolling wardens
Building new roads
Directing visitors
Discouraging cars

Fig. D Solutions to the problems

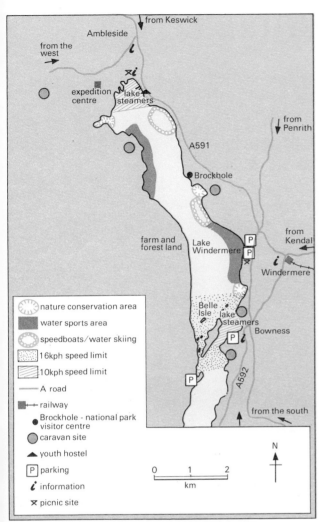

Fig. E Windermere: lake zones and lakeside amenities

mission *integrates* its forests with the shape of the land. Plantations have wavy edges, deciduous trees are left along the rivers and streams and are planted along roads.

Conservation v tourists

The development of a *tourist environment* will to some extent conflict with the efforts to conserve the national park. The aim has been to secure a balance between different interests. For example, there is a conflict of land use at Lake Thirlmere which is a reservoir. It centres on the extent to which visitors can be allowed to use the lake shore and the lake for water sports. Another issue is whether hill-walkers should be directed to marked footpaths.

Lake Windermere illustrates how a range of tourist activities can exist alongside the traditional way of life. It is the first lake visitors see as they approach the Lake District from the industrial districts of England. It is the longest lake, and its surroundings are easily accessible on foot, by car and boat. A wide range of activities is permitted on the lake, but there are speed

limits and conservation areas. All types of lake craft use Lake Windermere. In a survey at the end of 1970s, 27 per cent of craft had no engine and 30 per cent were speedboats, the majority of which had engines over fifty horsepower. Zoning of the lake has been necessary to reduce accidents.

QUESTIONS

A1 Study Fig A. Write a sentence explaining each of the overlapping areas 6 to 10.

2 Why are there conflicts and pressures in the national park?

3 Make a list of some of the problems found in the national park. For each problem suggest one solution. Example: Damage to fences — provide stiles.

4 Study Fig B. Describe the landscape. What is the problem of access to the lake shore?

5 Which of the following development plans do you think the National Park Planning Board would give permission for? Give reasons for your answers.

(a) Farmer Kemp wants to paint his new barns bright red.

(b) A property developer wishes to build a high-rise hotel on the north shore of Windermere.

(c) The Forestry Commission wants to develop small picnic areas in their forests.

(d) A water-ski club wants to use the area of Wastwater shown in Fig B.

(e) Farmer Case wants to put up a sign such as the one in Fig C.

(f) A Lakeside steamer company wants to build landing jetties on the west side of Lake Windermere.

6 As well as the Country Code there is also a Water Sports Code. Suggest some of the rules that could be included in a Water Code for Lake Windermere.

B1 What do you understand by: footpath erosion; degradation of vegetation; planning controls; conflict of use?

2 With reference to Lake Windermere, discuss what you understand by a tourist environment. How have some of the conflicts of lake and lakeside uses been solved?

C For a national park that you have studied:

(a) Name the national park and describe the principal features which attract visitors.

(b) State the main areas from which visitors come and the transport routes they use.

(c) Describe and explain any conflicts in land use that exist there.

(d) Are national parks successful in conserving the country's most attractive landscapes?

11.4 THE PEMBROKESHIRE COAST NATIONAL PARK

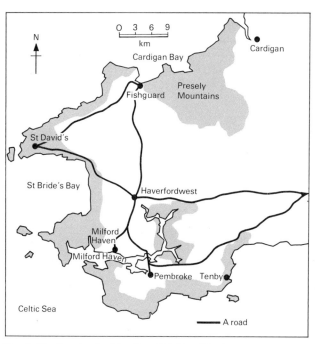

Fig. A The Pembrokeshire Coast National Park

Fig. B Martin's Haven

The county of Pembrokeshire became a part of the new county of Dyfed in 1974. The name is preserved in the Pembrokeshire Coast National Park, which is unique among national parks in three ways:
1 It is the only national park without a large area of mountainous moorland country as its main visitor attraction and qualification for national park status.
2 It is the only park to be divided into separate areas.
3 It is the most densely populated national park.

The main attraction of the Pembrokeshire Coast National Park is its 420 kilometres of varied coastline on the mainland and offshore islands. There are broad bays, beaches of sand and pebbles, narrow inlets, rugged cliffs and stacks. The succession of bays and headlands is explained by the rock outcrops. The headlands are formed from resistant igneous rocks and sandstones. The bays have developed in softer rocks such as the coal measures or where the rocks have been weakened by faulting. Post-glacial rises in sea level have flooded former river estuaries to form rias. The wooded shores and upper reaches of the Milford Haven ria form a separate part of the national park. In the north, the broad moorland of the Presely Hills rises to over 300 metres.

The Pembrokeshire Coast National Park is not an open-air museum, nor is it a playground for tourists. It is an area of national importance in environmental quality. Its governing body, the National Park Authority, is charged by parliament with two main duties:
1 To preserve the natural beauty of the park.
2 To promote its enjoyment by the public.

The well-being of local people must be safeguarded: 20 000 live in the national park. Tenby, with a population of over 7000, is the largest town in any national park.

Employment in the park

Farming: 1800 people work full-time on farms in the park, about 45 per cent of the area's workforce. Arable farming, mainly cereals, is dominant in the coastal areas, which have a mild, moist climate. The warm waters of the North Atlantic Drift help create an average January temperature of over seven degrees centigrade. The area has one of the longest growing seasons in Britain. Early potatoes · and flowers are grown along the sheltered southern coast. Annual rainfall totals increase from the 875 millimetres of the coastal areas to over 2000 millimetres on the hills. Livestock farming is dominant inland, with sheep on the steeper slopes and poorer quality grazings. Beef cattle and dairying are important on better-quality land.

Forestry: About 3 per cent of the total area of the park is forested. Coniferous plantations are found mainly on the Presely Hills and along parts of the south coast. The loss of moorland on the Presely Hills has been made worse by the concentration on single species of conifer. About thirty people are employed in the park's forests.

Mining and quarrying: Mineral extraction has existed in the area of the park since prehistoric times. Coal and slate were mined until fairly recently. Granite, limestone and gravel are still quarried in several places. The main use of these minerals is roadstone and aggregate.

Manufacturing: Only 10 per cent of the park's workforce is employed in manufacturing, mainly agricultural processing and craft industries. Milford Haven provides a deepwater port for the oil industry, and some of the oil installations have been built within the national park.

Fig. C The sands at Tenby

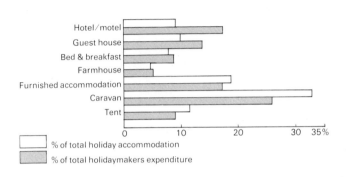

Fig. D Holiday accommodation in the national park

QUESTIONS

A1 Why is the Pembrokeshire Coast National Park unique?
2 What are the duties of the National Park Authority?
3 What types of farming occur in the park?
4 Describe the industries of the park.
B1 Describe and account for the coastal scenery of the park. Use a geology map from your atlas to help you.
2 The table below shows the crops grown in the park:

	Percentage of total area under crops
grass	65
cereals	16
rough grazing	15
early potatoes	3
fodder roots	1

(a) Construct a pie graph to illustrate these statistics.
(b) Explain the relative importance of the various crops.
3 How does land-use in the Pembrokeshire Coast National Park compare with that in the Lake District National Park? (See pages 190–195.)

4 Here is the employment structure of the park:

agriculture 45%   services 33%   quarrying 3%
construction 9%   manufacturing 10%

(a) Construct a bar graph to illustrate these statistics.
(b) The statistics are for full-time employment. How important do you think part-time employment is in the park? How would the amount of part-time work available vary throughout the year? What sort of part-time jobs might be available?
5 Study Fig D, which shows holiday accommodation in the Pembrokeshire Coast National Park.
(a) What percentage of holidaymakers is using a caravan or tent?
(b) What percentage is staying at hotels or guest houses?
(c) Suggest why more holidaymakers staying in hotels or guest houses would benefit the local economy more than campers.
(d) Are there environmental reasons why the number of caravanners and campers should be limited?
(e) What would be the best policy for future holiday accommodation for the local people and holidaymakers?

11.5 THE PEMBROKESHIRE COAST PRESSURES ON THE PARK

Fig. A Milford Haven

Fig. B Tenby Harbour

The arrival of the oil industry at Milford Haven illustrates a problem facing our national parks. The building of oil refineries, oil depots and a power station within or close to a park is not in line with the aims of conservation, but the government overruled the National Park Authority's objections on the grounds that it was in the national economic interest to develop the deepwater harbour offered by Milford Haven. At that time, multinational oil companies were considering several sites in western Europe and the government was anxious to secure one for Britain.

Great efforts have been made to reduce the effect of the oil industry on the environment. At the Amoco/Murco refinery, the following measures have been taken:

1 The oil tanks have been sunk below ground level.
2 The tops of the oil tanks have been painted to blend into the landscape.
3 Earth embankments and traditional Pembrokeshire stone walls were built, and 60 000 trees and shrubs planted, to help reduce the refinery's visual impact.
4 Silencers and mufflers have been fitted to the refinery machinery to reduce noise levels.
5 All the water used in the refinery, plus tanker ballast water, is processed before being pumped into the Haven. The water outlet is monitored to ensure that the oil content of the water is below 25 parts per million.
6 Sulphur is recovered from the waste before it is emitted from the chimney stacks. This reduces discharge of sulphur dioxide into the atmosphere.

Eleven per cent of the total cost of the refinery was made up of the environmental measures. However, the refinery is a dominant feature and affects enjoyment of the landscape. Two chimney stacks are over 110 metres high and air and water pollution are caused. Although the number of oil spills is low, those which have occurred resulted in fouled beaches, dead and injured seabirds, seriously injured seal pups and pollution of the water.

There are many other pressures on the park. Farming, quarrying, the demands of the armed forces

	Percentage of total visitors
South Wales	16
South-east England	20
West Midlands	20
East Midlands	9
South-west England	6
Mid Wales	2
North Wales	2
East Anglia	2
North-west England	14
North-east England, Yorkshire and Humberside	6
Scotland	2
Northern Ireland	1

Fig. C Origin of visitors to the park

and the need to provide improved roads and services for local inhabitants all have an effect. Tourism, the park's major activity, creates problems of its own.

Tourism

Each year one hundred thousand people visit the Pembrokeshire Coast National Park on day trips. Six hundred thousand visitors holiday within the park. The average length of stay is twelve nights. Most visits occur in July and August, during the school holidays. Figure C shows the origins of the visitors. The tourists are attracted for a variety of reasons. The National Park Authority describes the Park's attractions as 'Superb and varied landscapes and mild climate . . . the splendid scenery, fine beaches and clear waters of the coast . . .'

A survey of visitors revealed the following reasons for their visits:

Reasons for visit	Percentage of total
Beach	38
General sightseeing	17
Coastal scenery	17
Shopping	7
Inland scenery	7
Walking	4
Sailing	4
Other water sports	3
Other reasons	3
Total	100

Fig. D Reasons for visiting the park

The main form of tourist accommodation is caravans. There are over five thousand in the park. The caravans cause problems: road congestion and visual impact. Strict planning controls have operated since 1970 to prevent the spread of caravans: similar controls apply to tents. There is a danger that too much tourist development will lead to a reduction in the area's attractions. Figure E shows the main leisure

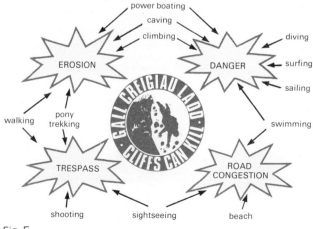

Fig. E

activities and the problems they may cause. The National Park Authority's role is to balance the public's desire to enjoy the area with the need to conserve the natural beauty of the park. The Authority's task is made more difficult by the willingness of government to sacrifice the park's natural assets to the demands of industry.

QUESTIONS

A1 What effects do the Milford Haven oil refineries have on the environment?

 2 (a) How many people visit the national park on day trips each year?

   (b) How many people holiday each year in the national park?

   (c) When do most people visit the park?

 3 (a) What reasons do people have for visiting the park?

   (b) Construct a pie graph from the figures in Fig D.

 4 What problems can be caused by (i) pony trekking; (ii) swimming; (iii) power-boating; (iv) sightseeing?

B1 (a) Why have oil installations been built within the park?

   (b) What oil installations have been built within the park? (See page 62.)

   (c) Describe the efforts made to reduce their environmental impact.

 2 Figure F shows the regions of Britain included in Fig C.

Fig. F

   (a) Make a copy of this map and draw flow lines from the national park to each region. The flow lines should be proportional to the percentage of visitors from each region. A possible scale is 1 mm = 2 per cent.

   (b) Account for the flows revealed by the map. Why do visitors from Mid and North Wales constitute such a small percentage of the total?

 3 Discuss the conflicting pressures upon the Pembrokeshire Coast National Park. What is the role of the National Park Authority?

12.1 THE SCOTTISH HIGHLANDS

The satellite photograph of northern Scotland shows a rugged and mountainous landscape. Most of the land is over 200 metres above sea level. The Grampians and the Cairngorms are the most extensive mountain areas, with peaks rising to over 1200 metres. The highest mountain is Ben Nevis (1343 m). North of Glen Mor, a valley formed along a major fault, are the North-west Highlands.

The rocks are among the oldest in Britain, and the soils that develop on them are acid, thin and infertile. In the Cairngorms and the Aberdeen area, there are granites. Elsewhere there are schists and gneisses, hard metamorphic rocks. Only around the north-east coast and the Moray Firth are younger rocks found. These old red sandstones weather to provide more fertile soils. This coastal strip is the lowest-lying in the region and has the greatest farming potential (Fig H).

A reason for the barren nature of much of the Highlands is the influence of the Ice Age. There was still ice in parts of northern Scotland 10 000 years ago. Its effect was to remove the topsoil and erode the ancient rocks. The mountains have been moulded into U-shaped valleys, hanging valleys, arêtes and corries. Glaciated areas have never been used productively, but are important today as a scenic recreation resource and wildlife habitat.

The valleys which criss-cross the Highlands are usually straight as they follow lines of faults. They are deep and many contain ribbon lakes such as Loch Ness, Loch Shin and Loch Garry. The west coast is a fiord coast of sea-lochs where the glaciated valleys have been drowned. The satellite photograph shows them penetrating the western Highlands. Among the largest are Loch Linnhe, Loch Fyne, Loch Broom and Loch Torridon.

The high relief influences climate and the day-to-day weather. The mountains receive a high rainfall. In winter, snowfall can be heavy. The east coast is in the rain shadow of the western hills and is protected from the wettest weather:

west: Fort William, rainfall total 2006 mm/yr
east: Inverness, rainfall, total 730 mm/yr

Temperatures in the coastal areas are mild in

Fig. A The native Scots Pine — wood for fuel and building

Fig. B The mountains and lochs — large sheep rearing estates

Fig. F Crofting — living conditions were basic

Fig. E Whisky distilling: an old tradition

Fig. D Inshore and distant fishing

Fig. C Cattle sale: an important event in the crofting calendar

winter (Fort William and Inverness, January, 3.9°C mean). In the Western Isles the winters are even milder because of the influence of the warm North Atlantic Drift. Here, winter temperatures are similar to those on the south coast of England.

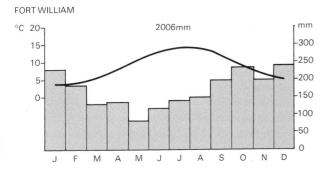

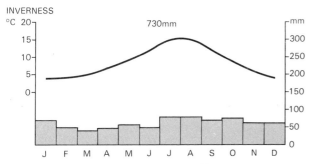

Fig. G Climate graphs for Fort William and Inverness

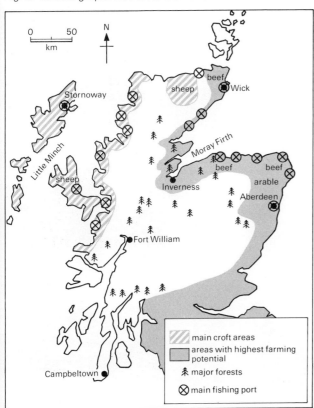

Fig. H

Temperatures in the mountain areas are lower than in the coastal lowlands. The *chill factor* of strong winds in the uplands makes temperatures feel lower than they are, and threatens unprepared walkers and climbers with exposure which can lead to death.

The combination of relief, geology, climate and the effects of the Ice Age gives a harsh environment. Except for the north-east coastal area, soils are poor. They are wet, and the rainwater washes out (*leaches*) the minerals needed for plant growth, leaving them infertile. There are large areas of peat throughout the mountains. The natural vegetation is a mixture of Scots pine and birch forest with Arctic Alpine plants in the highest places. Centuries of clearing and grazing have left thousands of hectares of moorland made up of coarse grasses, heathers and mosses. Most of the natural forests have gone.

The photographs (Figs A to F) summarise the old way of life in the Highlands. The population density has always been low (under fifteen inhabitants per square kilometre except for the eastern coastal areas). The economy has been simple, based on the land and the sea. There are still about 15 000 crofts which consist of small rented farms usually less than four hectares in size. Tweeds are still woven from local wool in the Outer Hebrides (Lewis and Harris). Peat is still used as fuel, and can be seen stacked outside single-storey crofthouses.

QUESTIONS

A1 Use an atlas map to identify the following on the satellite photograph. The Cairngorm Mountains, Loch Linnhe, Glen Mor (fault guided valley containing Loch Ness).

2 Find in your atlas the three freshwater lochs and the four sea-lochs named in the text.

3 Name one igneous, metamorphic and sedimentary rock found in the Highlands.

B1 Look at the climate graphs and compare them, using the table below:

	Fort William	Inverness
January temperature		
July temperature		
temperature range		
wettest season		
driest season		
total rainfall		

Explain the differences between the two climates.

2 Explain why the soils are generally poor in the Highlands.

C Write about the harsh environment of the Highlands of Scotland under the following headings: Relief; Geology; Rainfall; Temperature; Soil.

12.2 THE HIGHLANDS: DEVELOPMENT

The Highlands and Islands Development Board (HIDB) was set up in 1965 to improve economic and social conditions in the Highlands and Islands of Scotland.

The Board receives grants from the government, and helps to finance new developments in manufacturing and processing industries, crafts, tourism, services, agriculture and fisheries. The HIDB works alongside the government regional development programmes. The local authorities (Highland and Grampian Regional Councils) are concerned with attracting business as well, and work to improve housing, roads and other services. The EEC Regional Fund is increasingly providing finance for projects which will improve the accessibility of remote areas and bring employment and new business ventures.

The big projects

Regional development in the Highlands included the building of the experimental fast-breeder nuclear reactor at Dounreay on the north coast near Thurso. Later, an advanced gas-cooled reactor was built. Next came the pulp and paper mill at Corpach, Fort William, and the British Aluminium smelter at Invergordon. The 1970s were dominated by oil and gas developments. Oil platforms were built at Loch Kishorn on the west coast. Two oil-rig construction yards were sited in the deep, sheltered waters of the Moray and Cromarty Firth area, and an oil terminal nearby at Nigg Bay was opened in the 1980s.

Other big projects in the north of Scotland are the oil and gas plants at Cruden Bay near Peterhead and the oil terminals at Flotta, Orkney, and Sullom Voe in Shetland. An oil/gas-fired power station has been built at Peterhead. Some of the hydro-electric power stations in the Highlands can be classed as big projects. The pumped-storage Cruachan station was opened in 1968 and in 1975 the 400-megawatt Foyers pumped-storage scheme was opened on the east shore of Loch Ness.

Some of the large industrial projects have not been totally successful. In 1980 the Corpach pulp mill closed (paper manufacturing continued); two years later, the British Aluminium smelter at Invergordon closed.

When the aluminium works closed, unemployment in the Dingwall/Invergordon area rose to 25 per cent. British Rail lost passenger and freight revenue (alu-

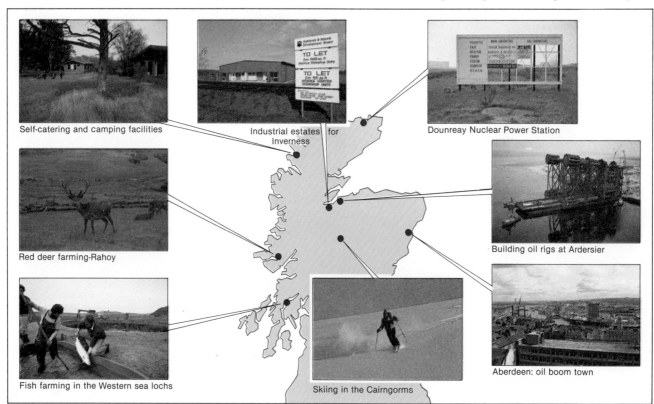

Self-catering and camping facilities

Industrial estates for Inverness

Dounreay Nuclear Power Station

Red deer farming-Rahoy

Building oil rigs at Ardersier

Fish farming in the Western sea lochs

Skiing in the Cairngorms

Aberdeen: oil boom town

Fig. A The new developments

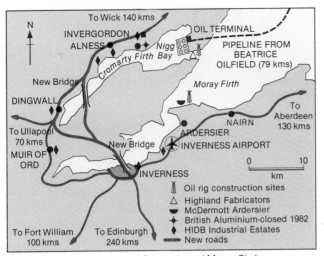

Fig. B Developments around Cromarty and Moray Firths

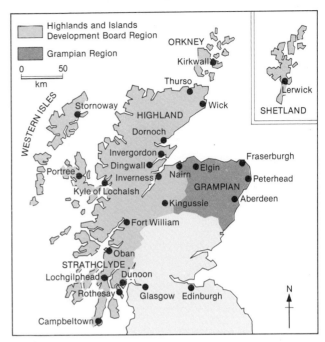

Fig. C

minium was transported from Invergordon by rail). Some electricity power stations lost their biggest market and were threatened with closure. Britain was faced with importing aluminium worth £85 million.

Today there is more emphasis on smaller factories and the development of small-scale crafts. The growth of the primary sector such as fish farming and red deer estates is encouraged.

Aberdeen — boom city

Aberdeen has experienced non-stop growth since the 1960s, when it developed as the main centre for North Sea oil operations. It is a supply and repair centre for equipment and an administrative and control base.

People have moved to Aberdeen and its surrounding area to work in the oil industry. It is the fastest-growing area in the whole of Scotland. Foreign companies, American, French and Italian, work from Aberdeen, and traffic at the city's airport has increased faster than at any other in the United Kingdom. Long-range Chinook helicopters that carry over forty passengers operate from Aberdeen to the most distant oilfields.

Growth has led to conflict. The 'oilies', as they are called, have brought money but they have pushed up house prices, which are now among the highest in Britain. New houses have been built on the outskirts of the city. Some of the best farmland in the Highland area is threatened with development. Prices in hotels and restaurants have risen and the local people have suffered as a result.

Aberdeen is an old-established city and had a range of industry before the oil boom. Textiles, paper-making and fishing are still important. The city has to plan for when the oil stops flowing. The fast growth could easily be reversed.

QUESTIONS

A1 List the new developments in the Highlands. Underline those that can be called 'big projects'.

2 Why was the Moray Firth and Cromarty Firth area chosen for oil rig construction and other oil developments?

B1 If a big project like an aluminium smelter closes, there are many 'knock-on' effects. Explain how these can spread beyond the factory area.

2 How do you explain the following population statistics:

	1971	1981
Inverness	34 839	39 373
Dingwall	4 232	4 815
Invergordon	2 350	4 050
Nairn	5 326	7 721

3 What type of problems have arisen because of Aberdeen's fast growth?

4 What could happen to Aberdeen if the oil ran out?

5	**POPULATION**	
	HIDB Area	**Shetland Islands**
1921	371 372	25 520
1951	316 471	19 352
1971	307 103	17 329
1981	352 572	26 716

(a) Construct a line graph to illustrate the HIDB area figures.

(b) Comment upon the statistics.

203

12.3 THE HIGHLANDS: PROSPECTS

Fig. A A crofting township, Barra

The area covered by the HIDB lost population every decade between 1851 and 1961. Young people moved away to seek work in the industrial areas of lowland Scotland and England. Many emigrated to North America, Australia and New Zealand. There were few incentives to stay in the scattered farming and fishing communities.

Since 1966, the population has increased slowly, helped by many types of development in the area. Big projects such as oil, aluminium and paper offered large numbers of jobs, although many were lost when the industries cut back or closed. Smaller developments appear to offer a more secure future for the Highlands and Islands.

Transport

Communications have been improved. Subsidised ferry services operate to and from the islands. Roads have been rebuilt, and the A9 now gives an efficient north–south link. Air links have developed between the mainland and islands. Loganair and Air Ecosse operate 'short hop' routes with aircraft which can operate from short runways.

The railway network is limited and has seen few improvements. Railways are not economic in remote areas and there has been discussion about the closure of Highland lines. However, they provide a vital link for some areas such as Kyle of Lochalsh.

Industry

Whisky distilling and weaving are well established in the Highlands and Islands. Today, it is the smaller industries like these that encourage people to stay in the region. The annual trade fair at Aviemore displays the work of over 200 Scottish manufacturers. Craft goods such as hand-carved chairs, spinning wheels, leathers and sheepskins have developed from traditional skills. A local firm makes fine bone-china pots in modern Scottish designs; a Shetland knitwear company employs 200, many working at home.

Further examples of industrial success are the shipyard and cheese factory at Campbeltown, the glass factory at Caithness and the telegraph-pole factory at Fearn in Easter Ross. In 1982, 300 000 poles were shipped out of Invergordon to the Mediterranean and Middle East. Forty-seven people are employed, using wood from local forests.

Fishing

This magazine article highlights an example of the growth in the fishing industry. Fish farming is expanding fast. The best prospects seem to be for

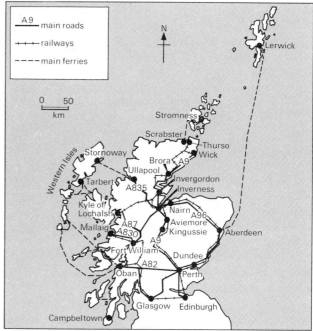

Fig. B Communications in the Highlands

Fig. C Road improvements: the A9

Fig. D 'Loganair Trislander', Barra in the Western Isles

higher-cost fish such as salmon, turbot, eels and shellfish. Scotland is now the most important inshore fishing area in Britain.

The Integrated Development Programme for the Western Isles is an EEC-supported programme which started in 1982. It provided £20 million for the Western Isles, where about 30 000 people live. Population has fallen this century, and there is a high proportion of old people.

The Integrated Development programme (IDP) is one of several EEC programmes for the less-favoured agricultural regions of Europe. Large grants are available for land improvements, drainage, windbreaks, fertilisers and livestock. The fishing industry is being helped with grants for new landing facilities, processing plants and fish farms. It is recognised that primary industries will never be the basis of the local economy, and there is help for the traditional industries of Harris tweed, weaving and knitting. Tourism and other industries are encouraged. Other recent developments in the Western Isles include a steel-building yard at Stornoway. Military activity has increased at Stornoway, where NATO Tornado jets are based.

QUESTIONS

A1 Why did the population of the HIDB area fall every decade between 1851 and 1961?

2 Calculate the percentage fall in the HIDB area population between 1851 (424 000) and 1961 (303 000).

3 Since 1966, the population of the HIDB area has increased about 1 per cent per year. What have been the reasons for this increase?

4 What transport improvements have been made in the region?

5 How do transport improvements help regions like the Highlands and Islands?

6 Give three examples each of large-scale industry and small-scale industry in the Highlands.

Triumph for Wick boat

The 86ft Wick-registered seiner BOY ANDREW landed an amazing £446,500 worth of fish last year. The vessel completed 244 fishing days during 1981 and her catches averaged over 500 boxes a week.

It was the first year under the command of 23-year-old Andrew Bremner who succeeded his father, Norrie Bremner, as skipper.

Although operating from Wick, the boat landed mainly at Peterhead. In January, it had just unloaded 753 boxes there when Skipper Andrew Bremner was asked to report to the Don Fishing Co's head office at Aberdeen to discuss 1982 fishing arrangements. Instead, he received a surprise presentation of an inscribed silver salver to mark his superb performance in 1981. Not bad for his first year as skipper!

BOY ANDREW was launched by the Campbeltown Shipyard in 1979.

Fig. E

B1 Explain the following population figures:

	1921	1951	1971	1981
Shetland	25 520	19 352	17 329	26 716
Skye	11 607	8 632	7 346	8 388
Sutherland	18 856	14 413	13 797	14 425

2 At the beginning of the 1980s, about 15 000 people were employed in the oil industry, many on the construction side. What are the problems associated with the 'big projects' such as oil?

3 Why might small-scale developments offer a more secure future for the area?

4 What do you understand by the Integrated Development Programme for the Western Isles?

5 Between 1971 and 1980, the HIDB helped to create 15 378 jobs in the area. Draw a graph to show the distribution of these jobs and comment on the type of employment created:

farming	894
fisheries	1350
manufacturing and processing	6502
construction	1317
tourism	3719
services	1596

205

12.4 THE HIGHLANDS: TOURISM

There is a wide range of tourist opportunities in the north of Scotland. This region has only 4 per cent of Scotland's population but one-quarter of its tourist accommodation. More than one-third of the visitors are from overseas. The landscape is the basic asset for tourism. Many of the visitors are 'active': they take part in angling, pony-trekking, sailing, cruising, climbing, hill-walking and skiing. Others view the scenery from coaches and cars.

Conservation

There is considerable pressure from tourists in some areas, but this is less of a problem in parts of the region that are remote and difficult to visit. However, more and more visitors will spend holidays in the region as communications improve. Already, 600 000

annually make the crossing to the Isle of Skye. Tourist activity sometimes has to be limited. The Forestry Commission provides nature trails and marked paths. At the Beinn Eighe Nature Reserve, the Nature Conservancy protects over 4000 hectares of mountain and moorland. Arctic/alpine plants grow in the mountains, ancient pinewoods survive, and the area contains pine marten, fox, badger, golden eagle and wild cat.

To the west, in the Loch Torridon area, are some of Scotland's finest mountains. They are made of the oldest sedimentary rocks in the British Isles, Torridonian sandstone. The National Trust for Scotland owns much of Torridon and the land is protected. Tourist development here is concerned with activities that do not affect the landscape or wildlife. There are no large caravan sites or holiday camps. The small settlements around the loch do not have amusement arcades or bingo. New buildings are few, and have to fit in with local buildings. In recent years, old crofts have been converted into holiday homes. Tourist development and conservation are closely linked. The Countryside Commission for Scotland oversees the National Scenic Areas which have similar aims to the National Parks of England and Wales. There are also country parks.

The Spey Valley and Cairngorms

This area has high-density tourist development. It is one of the easiest areas to reach from the south. About 10 000 tourist beds are available in excellent hotels. Aviemore has been developed as an all-year-round centre, with ice-skating, squash, table-tennis, billiards, a heated swimming pool, a dry ski-slope and go-karting.

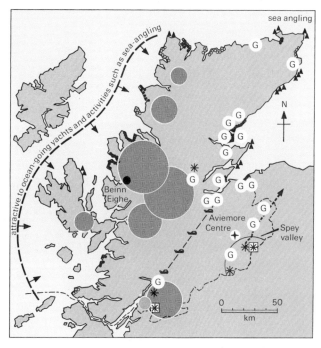

Fig. A Recreational resources in the Highland Region

* potential ski areas (under investigation)

○ proposed major water-based recreation centre

● principal mountain areas for walking/climbing

- - - ▶ long-distance footpaths

•••• coastlines with good beaches under high recreational use

○○○○○ similar coastlines under lower recreational use

Ⓖ 18-hole golf course

▲▲ attractive cliff coastlines

pleasure cruising

Fig. B Beinn Eighe nature reserve

Fig. C

Fig. D

Fig. E

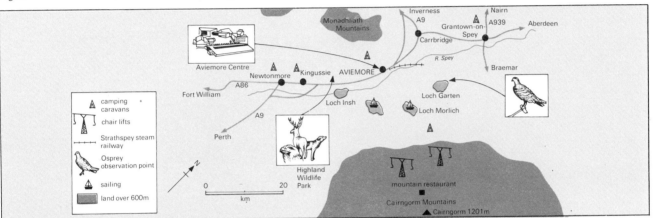

Fig. F Recreation in the Spey Valley

The Nature Conservancy Council regard the Cairngorm mountains as 'the most important area in Britain for nature conservation'. Here, tourist development is in conflict with the natural environment. Up to 5000 skiers a day use the Cairngorm slopes in the snow season, and it is the most developed winter sports area in Britain. The slopes are steep and face north, and snow remains until late spring. The immediate mountain area has suffered erosion from skiing and walking, and soil and vegetation on the ski slopes is being worn away. There were plans in the early 1980s to open up a new skiing area to the south-west of Cairngorm in Lurcher's Gulley but there was such an outcry from conservationists that a public enquiry had to be held. The view was taken that one of Britain's few remaining wilderness areas was being sacrificed to commercial interests.

QUESTIONS

A1 The Highland Region attracts visitors who tour in cars and coaches. What in particular attracts this type of tourist?

2 Why do you think the Spey Valley area has become the leading tourist area in the Highlands?

3 What do you understand by 'tourist pressure' on an area?

4 Which institutions are trying to conserve the natural environment?

5 Why did proposals to extend skiing areas in the Cairngorms bring a lot of opposition?

B1 Find the Loch Torridon/Beinn Eighe area in your atlas. Loch Torridon is a fiord. Describe the shape of the coast in this area. Name a nearby fiord.

2 Suggest why this area has no large seaports despite the deep, sheltered fiords.

3 Comment on the following figures:

region	National Nature Reserves	other conservation areas	sites of special scientific interest
Highland	number: 21 area: 53 163 ha.	80 213 079	122 79 079

12.5 MID WALES

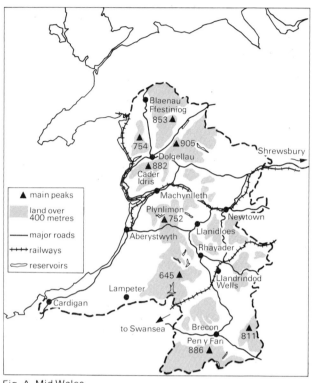

Fig. A Mid Wales

Much of Mid Wales is remote upland where the Welsh language is still spoken. Over 60 per cent of the population of Gwynedd speaks Welsh and this rises to over 80 per cent in some districts.

Mid Wales has suffered rural depopulation for over a century (Fig B). The out-migration has been caused by limited economic opportunities.

	1901	1931	1961	1971	1981
Cardigan	61	55	54	52	55
Merioneth	49	43	34	31	30
Brecon	54	58	40	37	40
Montgomery	55	49	44	43	48
Radnor	23	21	19	18	21
	242	226	190	180	194

Fig. B   (Figures in thousands)

Agriculture

More people in Mid Wales are employed in agriculture (14 per cent of the workforce) than in any other British region, yet few regions are less suited to agriculture. Over much of the upland interior, soils are peaty and acidic. Rainfall totals are high at over 2500 millimetres a year. This moorland is one of the most sparsely populated areas of Britain.

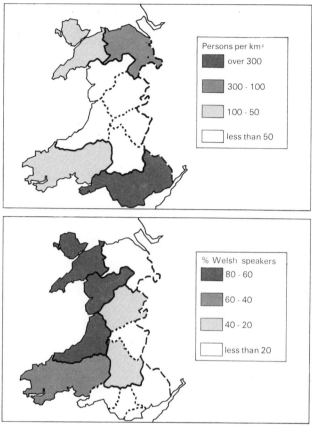

Fig. C Population of Mid Wales

Fig. D Welsh water

Extensive sheep and cattle-rearing is the main form of farming. Farm incomes are low and many of the farms are too small to provide enough work even for one person. In the Upper Severn valley and the coastal lowlands, intensive dairy-farming is practised. Forestry has replaced farming in some of the upland areas below 500 metres.

Water supply

Heavy rainfall, combined with low demand for water has made Mid Wales one of Britain's most important water-supply areas. There has been a great deal of controversy over the flooding of Welsh valleys to supply the water demand of English cities.

The reservoirs have given a limited amount of income and employment, but have stimulated tourism. However, there are problems:

1 Farms and villages have been submerged. For example, Lake Vyrnwy (opened in 1891 to supply water to Liverpool) drowned the village of Llanwddyn, and villagers were forced to move to a new settlement downstream.

2 In an area of mountainous country, flat valley floors suitable for farming are rare and of great value. These valley floors have been flooded.

3 The reservoirs have cut roads and separated neighbouring villages.

4 The reservoirs attract tourists and sportsmen who create congestion on the roads and destroy the peace and beauty of isolated areas.

The Welsh National Party, Plaid Cymru, has demanded that English Water Authorities should pay more for using Welsh water.

Electricity

The high rainfall and deep, narrow glaciated valleys of Mid Wales have encouraged hydro-electric schemes. Developments have been limited because water-catchment areas are small and there is little local demand for electricity. There are small stations at Rheidol (56 mw) and Maentwrog (24 mw). A large pumped-storage HEP station has been built at Ffestiniog (360 mw) and the new Dinorwic scheme lies just outside the region in Snowdonia. A magnox nuclear power station (390 mw) was opened at Trawsfyndd in 1965. It is Britain's only inland nuclear station, and for cooling purposes uses the lake originally created for the nearby Maentwrog HEP scheme.

Industry

Until recently, there was little industry in Mid Wales. The market towns had a limited range of agricultural processing industries: dairies, woollens, breweries, saw-mills. Extensive mineral workings existed in the Brecon Beacons (limestone) and Blaenau Ffestiniog (slate). Most of the quarries have now closed.

The exodus of people from Mid Wales has created several problems:

1 The population decline has led to a reduction in the level of services over much of the area. Schools, chapels and public houses close, public transport services decline.

Fig. E Lake Vyrnwy

2 Rural depopulation is selective. It is usually the younger, more able people that leave. The population structure of the area changes, with fewer younger people and an increasing proportion of the elderly, who most need the declining services.

A 'vicious circle' of decline occurs:

Loss of shops and services makes people move away. *This leads to*: Falling population, which makes the provision of services unecomonic. *This leads to*: The closure of more shops and services. *This leads to*: The departure of more people — and so on.

The problem is to break the circle and stop the decline.

QUESTIONS

A1 What problems face agriculture in Mid Wales?

  2 List the major reservoirs in Mid Wales and the cities which they supply with water.

  3 What advantages and disadvantages do reservoirs have for Mid Wales?

  4 Why has hydro-electric development in Mid Wales been limited?

  5 What industry developed in Mid Wales?

B1 Study Fig B:

  Draw line graphs to show the population change in the five districts. Summarise the main points shown by your graphs.

  2 Account for the fact that the population of Mid Wales has declined by 20 per cent since 1901.

  3 What are the effects of rural depopulation?

  4 What measures could be taken to halt out-migration?

12.6 MID WALES: CHANGES

The Development Board for Rural Wales was set up by the government in 1977 to try to reverse the population decline of Mid Wales. It is the second specialist development board for a rural area in Great Britain, the first being the Highlands and Islands Development Board for Scotland's north and west. The Development Board for Rural Wales has wide-ranging industrial and social responsibilities.

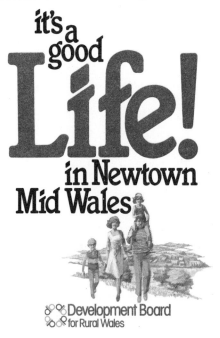

Fig. A

Industrial development

The board has decided to concentrate development at a limited number of centres. There are nine Growth Areas, ten Special Towns and eight Key Towns (Fig B). The largest town, Aberystwyth, has a population of only 11 000. Many of the settlements shown are the size of villages elsewhere in Britain: Rhayader, for example, has a population of 950. In Mid Wales, the settlements can be called towns because, despite their size, they function as towns and provide a range of services for wide rural areas.

The board offers a range of incentives to encourage industry to move to these towns: grants, loans, ready-built factories with rent-free periods, training schemes. Between 1977 and 1983, 263 factories had been opened in Mid Wales providing 6700 new jobs. They include light engineering, electronics, food and drink, clothing and packaging firms. The average is 25 workers per factory; large-scale development would be out of place in this region.

Fig. B Development centres in Mid Wales

Tourism

There are many tourist environments in Mid Wales: rugged highland scenery, broad beaches along Cardigan Bay and a number of resorts such as Aberystwyth, Tywyn and Aberaeron. Ancient towns with castles and historic associations are attractive to visitors, as are the preserved steam railways.

The board has provided grants and loans for many tourist projects including hotel construction and improvement, the development of craft centres and museums, extensions to the light railways and the building of sports and recreation centres.

Fig. C Talyllyn light railway

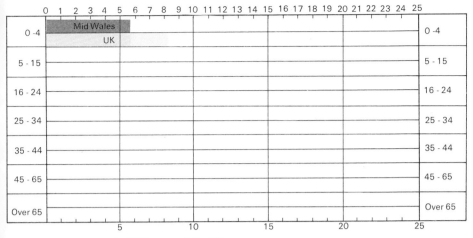

Fig. D Age structure of Mid Wales and the UK

| percentage of total | | |
Age Group	Mid Wales	UK
0- 4	5.6	8.2
5-15	15.4	16.1
16-24	12.3	14.4
25-34	12.6	12.4
35-44	11.8	11.7
45-65	20.6	24
Over 65	21.8	13.2

Social projects

An important cause of out-migration has been the lack of opportunity for recreation and social activities. The board has provided money to help with the construction of several social facilities including community centres, theatres and sports centres.

Newtown

A 1960s plan proposed to build a completely new town in Mid Wales with a population of 70 000 composed largely of overspill from Birmingham. It was withdrawn after it had been exposed as unrealistic, and another scheme adopted, this time based on an existing town — Newtown.

By 1983, the population was 10 000. Over ninety factories had been opened on three industrial estates. Newtown's new industries include electronics, light engineering, plastics, furniture, records and metalworking. The board has built over 1300 homes, a theatre, offices, a sports complex and a new shopping centre.

Manufacturing employment in Mid Wales has increased from 12 per cent of the workforce in 1971 to 15 per cent in 1981. This is still far short of the national average (27.8 per cent), but during this period the percentage of employees engaged in manufacturing has fallen in most regions. More significantly, the population of Mid Wales increased by 8 per cent between 1971 and 1981. This marks a reversal of a century-long decline.

The development board has played an important role, but Mid Wales has benefited mainly from a change in people's attitudes to life and work. The attractions of small-town lifestyle and pleasant scenery have become increasingly strong during the last decade. The revival of Mid Wales has been matched by above-average growth rates in other attractive rural areas of Britain. The revival is fragile, however, and many problems have yet to be resolved.

QUESTIONS

A1 What are the responsibilities of the Development Board for Rural Wales?

2 List the growth areas, special towns and key towns by copying and completing this table:

Growth areas	Special towns	Key towns
Penrhyndeudraeth	Bala	Barmouth

3 How does the board encourage industrial development?

4 What type of industry has been attracted to Mid Wales?

5 What attractions does Mid Wales have for tourists?

B1 Study the table below.

	1971		1978	
	Number	%	Number	%
Primary industry	8 694	17.3	7 331	13.5
Manufacturing	6 111	12.2	8 083	14.9
Services	35 390	?	38 927	?
Total	50 195	100	?	100

(a) Complete the table.

(b) Construct two proportional bar graphs to illustrate these statistics.

(c) Comment upon the changes revealed by the table.

2 How has the policy for the creation of a new town in Mid Wales changed since the 1960s?

3 Describe the activities of the Development Board for Rural Wales. What success has the board had?

4 Study Fig D, which shows the age structure of Mid Wales and the UK. Then:

(a) Complete the graph.

(b) What do the statistics reveal about Mid Wales?

211

12.7 NORTHERN IRELAND

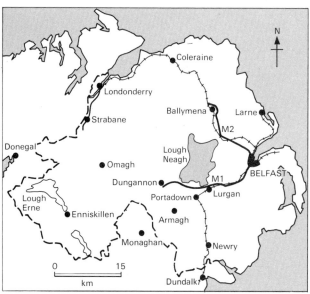

Fig. A Northern Ireland

The news media ensure that we are familiar with violence in Northern Ireland, where 2500 people have been killed in guerrilla warfare since 1969. Politics, religion and economics are all involved, but history and geography lie at the roots of the conflict.

During the seventeenth century, protestant colonists from Scotland and England were encouraged by the English rulers to move to Ireland and settle on land taken from the Irish. Such large numbers of protestants moved into the northern province of Ulster that they became the majority. Their descendants opposed Irish self-government, and when most of Ireland became self-governing in 1921, Northern Ireland was created as a separate country within the United Kingdom. This political creation is dominated by protestants (also known as loyalists and unionists) who wish to remain under British rule. The remaining 35 per cent of the population consists of Roman catholics, many of whom wish for a united Ireland. In the hope of achieving this aim, the Provisional IRA (Irish Republican Army) and other groups decided to fight the British authorities.

Large areas of the city of Belfast are divided by religion. Since the outbreak of warfare, many protestant families living in mainly catholic areas have been forced to leave, and *vice versa*. Most strictly segregated are the inner-city working-class areas. The British Army erected a barricade known as the Peace Line to separate the protestants of the Shankhill Road area from the catholics of the Falls Road. The religious segregation is continued by the

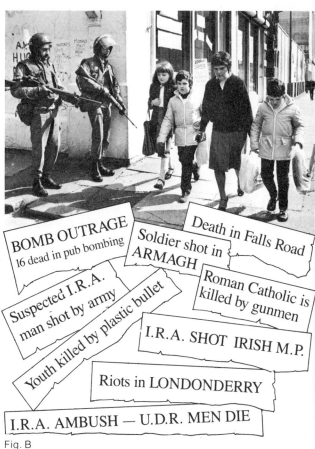

Fig. B

Fig. C An IRA funeral

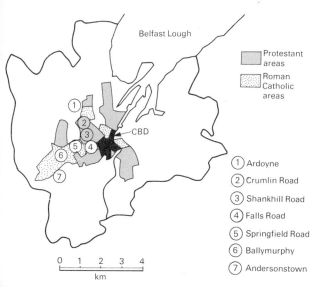

Fig. D Protestant and catholic areas in Belfast

Legend:
- Protestant areas
- Roman Catholic areas

① Ardoyne
② Crumlin Road
③ Shankhill Road
④ Falls Road
⑤ Springfield Road
⑥ Ballymurphy
⑦ Andersonstown

Fig. E

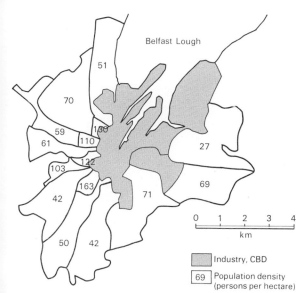

Fig. F Belfast population density

Legend:
- Industry, CBD
- 69 Population density (persons per hectare)

insistence of each group on attending their own schools, churches and community centres.

The unrest and violence in Belfast is not due to political conflict alone. Belfast shares the inner-city problems of other British cities, but in many cases they are worse in Belfast. Thirty per cent of houses lack basic amenities. Unemployment rates in some areas exceed 40 per cent. The congested, decaying slums of the inner city encourage the growth of despair, hatred and violence.

The violence is usually limited to small areas of the cities and the border, and large areas of Northern Ireland remain almost untouched.

QUESTIONS

A1 Why is there a majority of protestants in Northern Ireland but not in the Irish Republic?

2 When was Northern Ireland created?

3 How and why are many housing areas in Belfast segregated?

4 What effects do the problems of Northern Ireland have on the rest of Britain?

B1 What are some of the causes of the conflict in Northern Ireland?

2 Study Fig F and the statistics of population density.

(a) Copy the map and shade in the following areas: (i) Areas with over 100 persons per hectare; (ii) Areas with between 55 and 100 persons per hectare; (iii) Areas with less than 55 persons per hectare.

(b) Comment upon your map.

(c) The average population density for Belfast is 57 persons per hectare. The average for Greater London is 42, Birmingham 40, Liverpool 48, Glasgow 42. What do these figures reveal?

3 Study the table below:

	Roman catholic	Protestant	Total
1971	562 000	965 000	1 527 000
1981	563 500	941 500	1 505 000
Natural increase	+ 78 000	+ 30 000	+ 108 000
	(+ 14%)	(+ 3%)	(+ 7%)
Net emigration	− 76 500	− 53 500	− 130 000
	(− 14%)	(− 6%)	(− 9%)
Population change	+ 1500	− 23 500	− 22 000

(a) Calculate the percentage of the 1971 population of Northern Ireland which was (i) protestant; (ii) Roman catholic. How had the percentages changed by 1981?

(b) Comment on the differences in natural increase and emigration between the two communities.

213

12.8 NORTHERN IRELAND: WORK

Northern Ireland faces several geographical and economic problems:

1 It is in a peripheral location in Britain and Europe.

2 It lacks mineral and power resources.

3 The small population (1 505 000) provides only a small market for the region's products.

4 Trade with Britain is hampered by the sea crossing.

5 Trade with the Irish Republic is limited because of the republic's desire to protect its own industries.

6 Some of its main industries are declining.

Nearly 10 per cent of Northern Ireland's workforce is employed in agriculture, about four times the UK average. There are over 30 000 farms with an average size of 26 hectares (UK average 50 hectares). Since 1960, 20 000 smaller farms have been amalgamated into larger farms. The increasing use of machinery has cut the farm labour force.

Industrial sector	Employment (thousands)	% of total
Primary	58.5	10.1
Manufacturing	130	22.6
Services	389	67.3
Total	577.5	100

Fig. A

The climate of Northern Ireland is mild and wet, more suitable for the growth of grass than arable crops. Livestock is the main farming activity. Most of the region's agricultural output is in the form of livestock products. Dairying is widespread. Beef cattle are concentrated in the south-east where the slightly drier and sunnier climate allows barley and oats to be grown for fodder. Intensive pig and poultry farming takes place; over 20 per cent of the UK's bacon comes from Northern Ireland. Sheep-rearing is restricted to the rough pasture of the uplands.

There are about a thousand fishermen in Northern Ireland. Inshore trawlers operate from the ports of Kilkeel, Portavogie and Ardglass. The main fishing grounds are in the northern Irish Sea. Whiting, cod and herring are the main species caught. Prawns are also important. Almost all the herring and prawns are exported. Five hundred people work in over twenty fish processing factories.

Manufacturing industry

Despite its lack of minerals, Northern Ireland has developed an important manufacturing sector. The major industries are engineering, textiles and food,

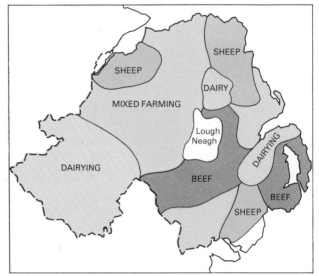

Fig. B Farming regions in Northern Ireland

drink and tobacco (Fig D).

Textiles: The Scottish protestant colonists established the textile industry, based on locally grown flax. Textile mills were built during the nineteenth century, mostly in Belfast but also elsewhere. Today, all the flax is imported. Linen production has declined, due to competition from cheaper man-made fibres. During the 1960s, several artificial-fibre factories were built in Northern Ireland, attracted by government development area incentives. By 1970, there were 10 000 jobs in man-made fibres with famous firms like Courtaulds, ICI and Du Pont. Then factories closed, and by 1983 only 2500 employees were left, making polyester, acrylic fibre and nylon at Antrim and Coleraine. One town alone, Carrickfergus, has lost nearly 5000 jobs in man-made fibres.

Some textile employment remains in linen and woollens, but the industry, one of the few recent growth areas in the region, is now a shadow of its past. The cause is the high cost of transport and energy in Northern Ireland as well as competition and the economic depression. Northern Ireland's electricity is produced by high-cost oil-fired power stations and there is no link with the British natural gas supply grid which would offer cheaper energy. The high transport costs caused by the need to import and export most products makes high-bulk industries uncompetitive. When ICI closed its Carrickfergus plant, it switched polyester production to Pontypool in Wales.

Food, drink and tobacco: 20 000 people work in food, drink and tobacco industries, many based on local

Fig. C Harland and Wolff shipyard

farm products: bacon-curing, meat and fruit canning, biscuits and milk products. Grain-milling and tobacco production are based on imported materials.

Engineering

The most important manufacturing industry in Northern Ireland is engineering. A wide range of engineering products is made, including textile machinery, turbines, machine tools, telephone equip-

Manufacturing sector	Total employees (thousands)	% of total in manufacturing
Engineering	39	30
Food, drink and tobacco	20	15
Textiles	19	15
Clothing and footwear	15	11
Man-made fibres	2.5	2
Other manufacturing	35	27
Total	130.5	100

Fig. D

Fig. E Short Brothers' aircraft factory, Belfast

ment and car components. The two most important branches of engineering are shipbuilding and aircraft manufacture.

Harland & Wolff's shipyard at Belfast is one of the largest in Britain. An extensive modernisation programme has given it the capacity to build ships of up to one-million tonnes in a dock over half a kilometre long. Steel is imported from Scotland. Oil tankers, bulk carriers and car ferries are built here, and marine diesel engines and generators are manufactured. Ship-repairing is carried out at the many dry docks at the yard.

Short Brothers employ over 6000 people at Belfast manufacturing aircraft, missiles and components. Shorts specialise in building small commuter airliners such as the Short 360. The US-owned Learavia company build the Learfan executive aircraft at Aldergrove near Belfast.

QUESTIONS

A1 Describe Northern Ireland's agriculture. What factors influence the types of farming?
2 Why did the textile industry develop in Northern Ireland?
3 What changes have occurred in the region's textile industry?
4 List Northern Ireland's engineering industries.
5 What are the two most important branches of engineering in the region?
B1 (a) Construct a pie graph from Fig A.
   (b) How do these figures compare with the figures for employment in the UK as a whole?
2 What problems does Northern Ireland's economy face?
3 Describe and account for the growth and decline of Northern Ireland's man-made fibres industry.
4 What are the problems of such a narrow range of manufacturing industry in a region (Fig D)?

215

12.9 NORTHERN IRELAND: PROSPECTS

"At the east end of town
At the foot of the hill
There's a chimney so tall
This is Belfast Mill.

But there's no smoke at all
Coming out of the stack
For the mill has shut down
And she's never coming back.

There's no children playing
In the dark, narrow streets
And the loom has shut down
It's so quiet I can't sleep.

Now I'm too old to work
And I'm too young to die
Tell me where will we go now,
My family and I?"

Fig. A

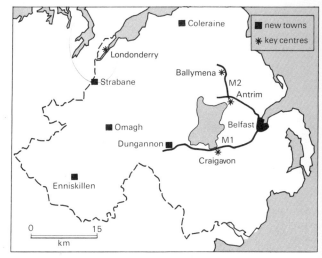

Fig. C Urban development policy

People are leaving Northern Ireland at a rate of nearly ten thousand a year. Between 1971 and 1981, over 130 000 emigrated. Northern Ireland's unemployment is the worst in the UK and among the worst in Europe. In some towns, the unemployment rate exceeded 45 per cent by 1983. Some of the causes are the continuing violence, the limited resource base, the small market and the peripheral location. Northern Ireland's manufacturing sector is based on too narrow a range of industries, most of which have declined since the 1970s:

1 Employment in Harland & Wolff's shipyard fell from 25 000 in 1970 to 6000 in 1983.

2 Employment in man-made fibres fell from 10 000 in 1970 to 2500 in 1983.

3 In 1981 alone, 22 000 jobs in manufacturing were lost.

	Available in Northern Ireland
Building grants	30–50%
Machinery grants	30–50%
Grants towards start-up costs	Negotiable
Factory rents	Rent-free for 5 years
Loans	Government loans available
Help for transferred workers	Full fares and removal costs paid, plus grants for settling in
Training grants	40% or more
Tax allowances	100% of machinery costs 79% of construction costs
Research and development	Grants of 40–50%

Fig. B Incentives to industry in Northern Ireland

4 Companies like BP, Michelin and ICI have pulled out of Northern Ireland.

5 Total manufacturing employment in Northern Ireland declined by 35 per cent between 1980 and 1983.

Northern Ireland receives financial assistance from the British government and the European Regional Development Fund. The whole of the region qualifies for the maximum incentives under the Assisted Areas policy (Fig B). Some notable successes have been achieved under this policy (General Motors and Learavia), but many other firms have collapsed (de Lorean Motor Company).

Another problem is the geography of employment and population in Northern Ireland. Forty per cent of the region's people live in and around Belfast, and manufacturing is concentrated in Belfast and Londonderry. Much of the region suffers from limited alternative employment to agriculture. The population of the more remote rural areas is declining rapidly, and the areas suffer all the problems of rural decline: an ageing population, low incomes and decreasing services.

Belfast has some of the worst housing problems in Europe. The rapid growth of the city during the nineteenth century has left areas of barrack-style terraced housing running right into the city centre. A survey in 1974 found that half of Belfast's houses lacked proper sanitation. Much of the inner-city area needs redevelopment. Housing estates have been built on the outskirts of the city and the houses have been allocated on a sectarian basis, thus carrying the religious segregation of the inner areas into suburbs

Fig. D (i) The mountains of Mourne (ii) Annalong Harbour, County Down

such as Andersonstown.

The government has set up new towns around Belfast at Ballymena, Antrim and Craigavon. Craigavon is sited beside the M1 motorway and has attracted several new factories making:

rubber products	forklift trucks
printed circuit boards	generators
steel wire products	pottery
electrical equipment	grinding machinery
plastic pipes	paper tubes
carpet tiles	

Government policy for dealing with the rural decline has been similar to that adopted in Mid Wales. In 1976, the Northern Ireland Development Agency was established. The agency provides advice, finance and administration for industrial develop-

	Percentage of workforce unemployed
Strabane	38
Omagh	22
Dungannon	35
Enniskillen	25
Coleraine	23
Londonderry	28
Ballymena	22
Craigavon	19
Newry	32
Armagh	21
Belfast	17

Fig. E

ment. A number of growth poles called Key Centres have been set up in the west of the region. Success has been limited, as shown by the unemployment rates of the mid-1980s (Fig E).

People have not been keen to leave Belfast, partly for social reasons but mainly because of the costs involved: the new housing is expensive. Out-migration continues, however. The emigration rate, 8000 a year by the mid-1980s, remains very high, but is offset by the region's high birth rate (18.5 births per thousand of population against the UK average of 13.5 per thousand).

Standards of living in Northern Ireland are among the lowest in Europe. The traditional industries continue to decline and new industry is not attracted to the region in sufficient amounts. The guerrilla war continues. There is hope for greater stability, but prospects are not good.

QUESTIONS

A1 Why does Northern Ireland suffer from a high rate of unemployment?

2 What incentives are there for new industry in Northern Ireland?

3 What problems do the more remote rural areas of the region face?

4 Name (i) the new towns and (ii) the key centres in Northern Ireland.

B1 Discuss the government's policy for regional development in Northern Ireland.

2 On an outline map of Northern Ireland, draw pie graphs to illustrate the unemployment rates of the towns shown in Fig E.

13.1 A THREATENED ENVIRONMENT

As the year 2000 approaches, the environment, both urban and rural, is changing faster than ever before. Civil engineering projects are consuming tens of thousands of hectares of land every year. Around many towns and villages, new housing estates spread into the countryside. Large areas are *blighted* by speculation. Inner urban areas are allowed to decay or are demolished and replaced by offices and apartment blocks. In the countryside, modern farming methods are changing the landscape. Farm buildings are large and obtrusive. Livestock has been withdrawn from fields and placed in giant sheds. Hedges have been destroyed and huge prairie-style fields have been created. As leisure activities have increased and people have become more mobile threats to the environment have grown. Mountain areas, the coasts and inland water sites are visited by more and more people, and erosion and pollution follow. Special arrangements have been made to cater for visitors, but there is concern about damage to Britain's natural and historic landscape.

Conservation

Since World War II, the government has introduced measures to assist conservation. Among the most important is the 1968 Civil Amenities Act which introduced Conservation Areas in England and Wales. Scotland adopted the idea in 1974. Conservation areas have been designated for a variety of sites: village centres, historic buildings, canal warehouses, factories. The designation allows some control over the development of an area but it cannot prevent change.

At the local level, new ideas on urban renewal have assisted conservation in towns and cities. During the 1950s and 1960s, inner-city housing was demolished on a vast scale and often replaced with high-rise tower blocks. Since the early 1970s, many old houses have been renovated rather than destroyed. In Birmingham, for example, a policy of 'enveloping' has been introduced in which areas comprising about 200 old terraced houses are renovated. Chimneys, roofs, windows, doors and brickwork are repaired and replaced, and pavements and roads are improved. The houses are transformed at a cost of about £5000 each compared with between £20 000 and £30 000 for rehousing each family.

Conservation in Sheffield: The first and most important act in the conservation of Sheffield was to remove the dark and dirty skies, a legacy from the industrial revolution. Smoke, soot, ash and cinders were pumped into the air from steelworks, forges, brickworks and houses. Sheffield was one of the dirtiest cities in Britain. Efforts to clear the polluted air began in 1959, following the government's Clean Air Act of 1956 which gave Sheffield City Council the power it needed. The city was divided into areas. Council officials went from door to door telling people what they had to do to make their fires and boilers smokeless. By starting in the south-west of the city, the heavy industries, mainly in the north-east, were given time to comply with the smokeless zone rules. It cost as much as £100 000 for a single piece of smoke control equipment in a large factory. Faced with any resistance to smoke control, the council used their powers under the Clean Air Act to force companies to comply.

The campaign took thirteen years and its success allows Sheffield to claim that it is now the cleanest industrial city in Europe:

Fig. A Paradise Square, Sheffield

	1959	1972
	(microgrammes per m³)	
smoke	255	48
sulphur	215	134

Fig. B Abbeydale Industrial Hamlet

The cleaner air has made it possible to clean old buildings. In the city centre, a number of important and attractive historic buildings have been conserved, including the Cutler's Hall, the Victorian Town Hall, the fifteenth-century cathedral and the Georgian terraces of Paradise Square. The old canal basin is being renovated for leisure uses. On the outskirts, the Abbeydale Industrial Hamlet, an open-air museum, exhibits Sheffield's industrial heritage. The site contains an eighteenth-century crucible furnace, a water-drive forge and grindstone, workshops, warehouses and cottages. Sheffield has thus taken care to preserve some parts of its past, but elsewhere has 'improved' the city by the construction of high-rise blocks, so that offices crowd around the cathedral and tower over Paradise Square.

Among the many groups concerned with conservation are the National Trust, the Council for the Preservation of Rural England, and Friends of the Earth. You can join these organisations and local societies. You can be informed about plans for your area, visit exhibitions and public enquiries, write to your councillor and MP and read about conservation issues.

Attacks on Britain's landscape and heritage will succeed if people are ill-informed and apathetic. The interest of young people is an important force in the fight for sensible conservation measures and planned progress.

QUESTIONS

A1 What major changes have affected the landscape of the area where you live over the past five years? Are efforts being made to conserve the heritage of your area? What more could be done?

2 (a) What are 'conservation areas'?
  (b) When were they first introduced?

3 What is meant by the policy of 'enveloping' in Birmingham? What advantages does enveloping have over rehousing?

4 How did Sheffield transform itself into 'the cleanest industrial city in Europe'?

B1 Study the table below:

	Smoke		Sulphur dioxide	
	1969	1979	1969	1979
Northern England	111	25	101	49
Yorkshire and Humberside	98	35	144	74
East Anglia	51	20	87	49
Greater London	46	24	152	82
South-east England	39	17	81	51
South-west England	35	16	59	43
East Midlands	80	30	106	69
West Midlands	63	28	119	70
United Kingdom	74	26	118	62

(All figures are taken in towns and are in microgrammes/m^3)

(a) Construct a bar graph to illustrate these statistics.
(b) Account for the general decline in the average daily concentrations.
(c) Attempt to explain the regional variations in 1979.

2 Find out the conservation areas in your area. Comment on local conservation issues.

13.2 THE FUTURE

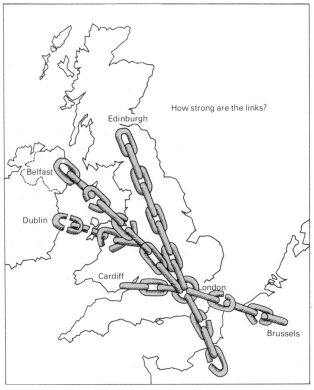

Fig. A

The 56 million people living in the United Kingdom are not evenly distributed. England contains over 80 per cent of the total population, much of which is in urban areas at a density which is one of the highest in Europe (335 persons per square kilometre). A large proportion of highland Britain is thinly peopled and predominantly rural. Density is 3–10 persons per square kilometre. The distribution of population will not change much in the future.

Two nations: north and south

North and south Britain contrast in many ways apart from the differences in physical geography. The standard of living in northern Britain and Northern Ireland lags behind the more wealthy south. Unemployment is higher in northern regions, income per head is lower and households generally have fewer consumer goods such as cars, telephones, video recorders and caravans. People tend to be more healthy in the south, and they live longer.

The nation can be divided by politics. The south is mainly Conservative and the north mainly Labour.

Distance from London is another dividing factor. The country is governed from London and the major financial institutions and commercial firms operate from the capital. People living in the peripheral areas of Britain may feel a sense of remoteness. Look at television news and note how London dominates the bulletin. Listen to the national radio programmes and note how often London is mentioned.

There is further evidence of two nations in Britain's largest urban settlements. The inner-city areas suffer a range of problems. The areas are deprived, they lack jobs and investment, housing and education standards often fall short of those in the outer suburbs and surrounding areas.

Is there a future for a more 'united' Britain, where wealth is shared more equally? At the present time, the deprived areas of Britain are caught in a 'vicious circle' of decline. The problem is to break the circle and improve the quality of life.

Multi-racial Britain

Britain's ethnic minority population has grown since the end of World War II. In 1951, there were 200 000 black people in Britain, mainly from the New Commonwealth and Pakistan. By the early 1980s there were about 2 million (4 per cent of total population). About 40 per cent of black people were born in Britain and by the year 2000 about 70 per cent of all black people will be British by birth.

Immigration is now tightly controlled, and in 1982 only 2000 people settled in Britain from the Caribbean. More than 2000 people emigrated from Britain to the Caribbean. In 1982, the EEC countries supplied the largest numbers of immigrants to Britain —

Fig. B The Notting Hill carnival

Fig. C

	UK	India
birth rate	11.8	35.2
death rate	11.7	15.9
infant mortality	14.0	122.0
life expectancy	73 yrs.	51 yrs.
GNP* per head in US dollars	6320	190
% employed in agriculture	3	80
population per doctor	1 for 800	1 for 4000

*GNP = Gross National Product (figures at 1980)

Fig. D

41 000. All too often, immigrant people find it difficult to be accepted in Britain, and many have the feeling that they are second-class citizens.

Britain's ethnic minority population is not evenly distributed. It is concentrated in the major towns and cities, especially in inner city areas. In some inner city wards, concentration is such that over 30% of the resident population were born outside the UK (1981 census: Moss Side (Manchester) 31.3%; Spitalfields (Tower Hamlets, London) 51%; Sparkhill (Birmingham) 43.7%). The majority of these people originated from Asian countries and the West Indies, but in some parts of London, Chinese people live in the same areas; in other towns and cities there are well-established Irish, Greek and Polish communities.

A report on the Brixton (London) riots in 1981 identified serious *racial disadvantage* for black people in employment, housing and education. In 1981, 53 per cent of black people under nineteen were unemployed; they were three times more likely to be unemployed than young white people.

Britain is a multi-racial country. Can the minority communities look forward to improved opportunities in the future?

The future economy

This book has described a group of countries experiencing decline in traditional industries. There is a prosperous agricultural sector and a growing tertiary economy. Britain appears to be moving into a post-industrial economy. Living in such an economy, where information industries provide more jobs than manufacturing, will mean a change for most people. Whether or not Britain can cope with a life-style in which many people cannot have work depends upon the adaptability of individuals. There is no guarantee that standards of living will be maintained.

It is essential to remember that whatever the current problems are in Britain, the country has a highly developed economy. It is part of the rich *industrial world*. Most people enjoy a high standard of living. There is an advanced system of communications, services are well developed and most people have spare cash for leisure and recreation. A comparison with any Third World country illustrates the great gap between its quality and life and that of Britain. Whatever economic changes may occur, Britain will remain one of the richest countries in the world.

QUESTIONS

A1 What do you understand by 'north and south contrasts' in Britain?

2 In what ways does London dominate the life of the country? Why might people who live a long way from London feel a sense of remoteness?

3 How many black people are there and what percentage is this of the total population?

4 What do you understand by racial disadvantage?

B1 Why do you think the ethnic minority population has suffered racial disadvantage? What hope is there that Britain can become a successful multi-racial society?

2 What do you understand by the phrase 'a country experiencing industrial decline'?

3 Figure D compares the United Kingdom with India. In what ways will the United Kingdom remain a rich country compared with India? Could the gap ever be closed?

4 What do you think will be the most significant changes in Britain in the future?

THEME INDEX

PLACE INDEX